Date Due

A
Century
of
Oil and Gas
in
Books

A
Century
of
Oil and Gas
in
Books

A Descriptive Bibliography

Compiled by
E. B. SWANSON

APPLETON-CENTURY-CROFTS, INC.

NEW YORK

Foreword

When the American Petroleum Institute agreed to sponsor the publication of this bibliography, it did so with full knowledge and appreciation of the author's qualifications. On the other hand, until Mr. Swanson completed his manuscript, we had no conception of what a monumental job of scholarly research it would turn out to be.

Mr. Swanson is a career civil servant, having headed the first Division of Petroleum Economics of the United States Department of the Interior. Prior to his retirement in 1954, he had built up a large library of oil and gas books, pamphlets, and other literature. Upon his retirement, he sold this library to the Venezuelan government's Ministry of Hydrocarbons.

It soon became apparent that Mr. Swanson's collection had been a valuable adjunct to the Interior Department. As a result, several public-spirited oilmen donated funds to purchase another library. Mr. Swanson set to work, and in time amassed an even larger library than before, equalling, if not surpassing, the famous DeGolyer collection.

As Mr. Swanson states in his introduction, he has personally examined virtually every item which appears in this book. He enjoys a personal acquaintanceship with many of the authors whose works are listed here. The Institute is proud to have played a part in this truly splendid contribution to the literature of the petroleum industry.

Frank M. Porter

President
American Petroleum Institute

Introduction

The year 1959 marked the centennial of the oil industry—the passing of one hundred years since the Drake Well was completed near Titusville, Pennsylvania, in late August, 1859. More important, perhaps, it marked also the beginning of the second century of oil. This descriptive bibliography is presented as a century-end stocktaking of the books which have been written in the English language on matters pertaining to oil and gas.

Even as books reflect the learning and experience of their authors, so a list of books represents a summation of that learning and experience. When one deals with books about oil and gas, the list becomes a record, not of the books alone, but of the achievements and accomplishments of a great industry as seen by hundreds of writers in many fields.

The objective of this bibliography was to include all items published commercially or privately in English, which had to do directly or essentially with some aspect of petroleum. Attempt was made to list all available material known to the compiler up to the month of August, 1959.

Fiction was not included, nor has there been any listing of items covering broad fields of chemistry, geology, or other material not written with specific application to some aspect of petroleum. Promotional material lacking essential educational application or historic interest, and books dealing with equipment for utilizing petroleum products have been eliminated.

No attempt was made to list reprints of articles which appeared originally in periodicals generally available to the oil industry or which were published subsequently in proceedings of meetings which are accessible to persons in the oil and gas industries. Publications of the Federal Government have been included when the item was thought to have some standing in oil history and affairs.

Reports issued by Federal agencies with established responsibilities for oil and gas matters were not listed. Such agencies will supply, on request, lists of their publications. Certain Congressional documents, especially those of earlier days, have been included. No attempt was made to list proceedings and reports resulting from the large number of investigations and inquiries conducted by Congressional committees, particularly during the last thirty years.

Reports of state governments dealing with specific local areas, or covering activities of a single year or so, were not included, except in the case of outstandingly historical oil fields. On the other hand, an effort was made to include representative reports on oil and gas prospects and developments for as many states as possible.

Further limitation was imposed by the requirement that each item would need to be seen and examined prior to its entry, or failing that, verification of the book, its author and title. Very few items were included without having been seen or examined.

With the passage of time, early books on oil and gas have become increasingly difficult to find and acquire. It would seem appropriate that efforts be made to establish oil and gas libraries while the search for these books may still succeed and while the current publications, possibly destined to be scarce in the future, are still available.

Despite many efforts to assemble a complete collection of books on oil and gas, there is at present no single library which has such a collection. There are many libraries, however, in several sections of the United States which have collections ranging from reasonably good to superb.

The several libraries in Washington, D.C., including the Library of Congress, the Central Library of the Department of the Interior, Geological Survey, Patent Office, and Interstate Commerce Commission can provide access to most of the books on oil and gas.

The Drake Memorial Library at Titusville, Pennsylvania, is a repository for much scarce and valuable material on the early Pennsylvania oil industry. The public library at Warren, Pennsylvania, has a special collection on the history of oil. The public library in New York City is well provided with early oil books, as are many of the public and university libraries in New England. The American Petroleum Institute Library in New York City has a good collection.

In the Southwest, Southern Methodist University at Dallas, Texas, houses the DeGolyer collection, assembled over a period of more than four decades. The University of Oklahoma, Norman, Oklahoma, has the DeGolyer collection on the history of science and technology. The public library in Tulsa, Oklahoma, has a noteworthy oil collection. Others are in public libraries in Dallas, Fort Worth, and Houston, and at the University of Texas, Rice Institute, Agricultural and Mechanical College of Texas, and Louisiana State University.

In the Rocky Mountain area, the University of Wyoming at Laramie is building a library to specialize in the oil history of Wyoming and other Rocky Mountain states. There are numerous oil collections in California; the State Library in Sacramento, the Kern County Free Library at Bakersfield, the University of California at Berkeley, the Henry E. Huntington Library at San Marino, and public libraries in Los Angeles, San Diego, and other California communities.

Many oil company and other libraries are associated with the Petroleum Section, Special Libraries Association. Most of these libraries participate in a procedure whereby, except for rare books, books on oil and gas are loaned by one library to another.

In compiling the material for this bibliography, the Central Library of the

Department of the Interior was especially helpful, particularly the Librarian, Paul Howard, and Mrs. Janet B. Talbot, who worked diligently and capably to arrange loans of books from other libraries. The Library of Congress provided study desk facilities from August through December, 1958, and its staff, including the Law Library, was most courteous and helpful.

The library work was supplemented by hundreds of inquiries to authors, publishers, and others. Of the many who were particularly helpful, special credit should go to Ernest C. Miller of Warren, Pennsylvania; Paul S. Allen, Librarian, Standard Oil Company (New Jersey); Mrs. Margaret M. Rocq, Librarian, Standard Oil Company of California; and Miss Patricia Moran, Universal Oil Products Company. Also to Robert E. Friedman for help on early oil matters in Southern California; Robert E. Hardwicke, attorney of Fort Worth, who pioneered with his oil bibliography two decades ago; and Paul Pearlman of Washington, D.C., who has a knack for turning up the unexpected in oil literature. The Tulsa Public Library was also most cooperative.

The creation and publication of this bibliography was made possible through the financial support of the American Petroleum Institute. The compiler appreciates the personal interest of Kendall F. Beaton of the Shell Oil Company who was outstandingly helpful through reviewing and editing the original manuscript material and helping to prepare it for publication.

However, the compiler willingly assumes full responsibility for selecting the material, describing the items, and for the errors which will certainly be brought to light. The work is not that of a bibliographer—amateur or professional—but of one who has had a long-time personal interest in the literature and an equally long association with members of the petroleum industry. The listings were prepared from the viewpoint of one long experienced in collecting and reading books on oil and gas.

Because of the limitations involved, significant items may well have been overlooked. Notice of such omissions, and of errors which may be noted, will be gratefully received, and appropriate revisions will be made if there is to be a subsequent publication.

E. B. Swanson

Washington, D.C., January, 1960

Contents

A
Century
of
Oil and Gas
in
Books

I.

The Origin and Finding
of Oil

A. INTRODUCTORY

James Irving Crump, *Our Oil Hunters,* New York, Dodd, Mead & Co., 1948, pp. 210.
The work of men who hunt oil in many parts of the world.

Rufus Rockwell Wilson, *A Noble Company* of Adventurers, New York, B. W. Dodge & Co., 1908, pp. 219.
Chapter, "The Men Who Hunt For Oil," deals with drilling for oil in Pennsylvania, oil scouting, oil finding.

B. GEOLOGY AND GEOPHYSICS

Agricultural and Mechanical College of Texas, *Well Logging Methods Conference,* College Station, Tex., the College (Bulletin No. 93), 1946, pp. 171.
Papers covering methods of well logging.

Milton A. Allen, *Oil and Its Geology,* Tucson, Ariz., University of Arizona Bureau of Mines, 1917, pp. 32.
Properties and origin of oil, concentration, geology, structures and movement; possible petroleum and gas-bearing rocks of Arizona.

Milton A. Allen, *Prospecting for Oil,* Tucson, Ariz., University of Arizona Bureau of Mines, 1917, pp. 18.
Surface indications of oil, geology, well sites, etc.

Richard Ambronn, *Elements of Geophysics as Applied to Exploration for Minerals, Oil and Gas,* trans. from German by Margaret C. Cobb, New York, McGraw-Hill Book Co., 1928, pp. xi + 372.
Geophysical methods used in prospecting: gravitational, magnetic, electrical, seismic, and other geophysical equipment.

American Association of Petroleum Geologists, *Report of a Conference on the Origin of Oil,* Tulsa, the Association, 1941, pp. 81.
Views of 37 participants in conference on theories on origin of petroleum and application to commercial geology, with bibliography on theories on origin of petroleum.

American Association of Petroleum Geologists, *Report of a Conference on Sedimentation,* Tulsa, the Association, 1942, pp. 68.
Views of 27 participants on sedimentation and stratigraphy.

American Association of Petroleum Geologists, *A Symposium on Petroleum Discovery Methods,* Tulsa, the Association, 1942, pp. 164.
Discussion of methods with greatest promise of maintaining adequate oil and gas discovery rate, best approach to problem of oil and gas discovery.

American Association of Petroleum Geologists, *Geology of Salt Dome Oil Fields. A Symposium on the Origin, Structure, and*

1

General Geology of Salt Domes, Tulsa, the Association, 1926, pp. xix + 797.
Information accumulated during 20 years of oil exploration in salt dome region of Gulf Coast, with descriptions of known salt domes, articles on geologic origin of salt domes, descriptions of salt dome oil fields in Europe; 35 papers by 30 authors. Has been described as memorial marking end of era of Gulf Coast production from shallow salt domes.

American Association of Petroleum Geologists, Gulf Coast Oil Fields, Tulsa, the Association, 1936, pp. xxii + 1070.
Symposium by 52 authors supplementing earlier volume on salt dome fields. Records progress of geophysical discovery of salt domes, deeper drilling, introduction of electric well logging.

American Association of Petroleum Geologists, Habitat of Oil, Tulsa, the Association, 1958, pp. viii + 1384.
Fifty-five papers on habitat of oil in North and South America, Europe, Middle and Far East.

American Association of Petroleum Geologists, Problems of Petroleum Geology: A Sequel to Structure of Typical American Oil Fields, Tulsa, the Association, 1934, pp. xii + 1073.
Progress report by 47 authors on theories of origin, migration, and accumulation of oil and relations to structure, porosity, permeability, compaction, oil field waters, and subsurface temperature gradients.

American Association of Petroleum Geologists, Stratigraphic Type Oil Fields, Tulsa, the Association, 1941, pp. xii + 902.
Papers on stratigraphic type oil fields in 13 states, with bibliography of articles describing such fields.

American Association of Petroleum Geologists, Structure of Typical American Oil Fields. A Symposium on the Relation of Oil Accumulation to Structure, Tulsa, the Association, 1929, 2 vols., pp. xl + 1290.
Vol. I: Presents authoritative descriptions of structure of typical oil fields in United States, with emphasis on fields other than salt domes; 30 papers on fields in 13 states.

Vol. II: Presents 40 papers on fields in 13 states, with summary of role of geologic structure in accumulation of petroleum.

American Association of Petroleum Geologists, Structure of Typical American Oil Fields, etc., Tulsa, the Association, 1948, Vol. III, pp. x + 516.
Papers on 24 fields in 12 states and Canada. Considered fifth volume in series of oil field descriptions, which include the two volumes on salt dome fields.

American Institute of Mining and Metallurgical Engineers, Seventy-Five Years of Progress in the Mineral Industry, 1871–1946, New York, the Institute, 1947, pp. xii + 817.
Thirteen articles covering technological progress in major branches of mineral industry. Includes history of Institute.

American Institute of Mining and Metallurgical Engineers, Geophysical Prospecting, Transactions, New York, the Institute, Vol. 81, 1929, pp. 676; Vol. 97, 1932, pp. 510; Vol. 110, 1934, pp. 583; Vol. 138, 1940, pp. 489; Vol. 164, 1945, pp. 426.
Papers and discussions at Institute annual meetings dealing with principles underlying geophysical prospecting methods, current practice and results, criticism and discussion.

American Petroleum Institute, Fundamental Research on Occurrence and Recovery of Petroleum, New York, the Institute, 1944–1947, 7 vols., pp. 1850.
Reports on the progress of API's petroleum research projects.

Ardmore Geological Society, Petroleum Geology of Southern Oklahoma: A Symposium, Tulsa, American Association of Petroleum Geologists, 1959, pp. v + 341.
Seventeen papers on petroleum geology of southern Oklahoma.

William M. Barret, Mapping Geologic Structure with the Magnetometric Methods, Shreveport, La., the author, 1927, pp. 23.
Principles of operation of magnetometric methods of mapping, with report of results obtained by surveys in 10 areas.

Robert Latimer Bates, Focus on Oil, Columbus, Ohio Dept. of Natural Resources, Div. of Geological Survey, and Ohio

State University Geological Museum, 1954, pp. 9.
Review of origin, accumulation, and distribution of oil, methods and prospects of finding, and production in Ohio.

Ernest Beerstecher, Jr., *Petroleum Microbiology,* Houston and New York, Elsevier Press, 1954, pp. xv + 375.
Theory and practice of employment of naturally occurring catalysts in petroleum industry; role of microorganisms in geological processes and in synthesis of petroleum, their use in petroleum exploration and drilling muds, and their role in corrosion.

Anthony Blum, *Petroleum: Where and How to Find It,* Chicago, Modern Mining Books Publishing Co., 1922, pp. 367.
Practical aspects of oil business from oil finding to marketing.

Eli Bowen, *Coal and Coal Oil,* Philadelphia, T. B. Peterson & Bros., 1865, pp. iv + 494.
Revised edition of *Physical History of the Earth,* Philadelphia, W. S. Laird & Co., 1861, pp. 480.

Henry Gould Busk, *Earth Flexures,* Cambridge (England), Cambridge University Press, 1929, pp. vi + 106.
Geological processes, geometrical construction of earth flexures in geological sections, flexures of Tertiary age in petroliferous rocks of several oil areas.

Colorado School of Mines, *Quarterly,* Vol. 45 No. 4A, *Geophysics,* Golden, Colo., Colorado School of Mines, 1950, pp. vii + 103.
Six papers on seismic research and exploration, electrical logging, interpretation of geophysical data at conference on geophysics.

Colorado School of Mines, *Quarterly,* Vol. 44, No. 3, *Subsurface Geologic Methods, A Symposium,* Golden, Colo., Colorado School of Mines, 1949, pp. 826. 2nd Ed. 1950, pp. 1156.
Papers on subjects related to subsurface geologic techniques, including subsurface logging methods, directional drilling, oil well surveying, casing.

Colorado School of Mines, *Subsurface Geology in Petroleum Exploration, A Symposium,* Golden, Colo., Colorado School of Mines, 1958, pp. 887.
Outgrowth of two preceding editions of Subsurface Geologic Methods; 41 papers by 47 authors deal with tools and techniques used in search for oil and gas. Analysis of well cuttings, cores, and fluids; well-logging methods and interpretation; subsurface stratigraphical and structural interpretation; geophysical and geochemical prospecting; drilling, formation testing, and well completion, subsurface reports, and exploration planning, with brief biographical sketches and photographs of authors.

Thomas P. Converse, *Oil and How to Find It,* Amarillo, Texas, Russell & Cockrell, 1920, pp. 44.
Simplified petroleum geology and drilling.

Eugene Coste, *The Volcanic Origin of Natural Gas and Petroleum,* Ottawa, Canadian Mining Institute, 1903, pp. 50.
Volcanic origin of oil and gas, illustrations from several localities; comments on views and writings of others.

G. H. Cox, C. L. Dake, and G. A. Muilenburg, *Field Methods in Petroleum Geology,* New York, McGraw-Hill Book Co., 1921, pp. xiv + 305.
Field procedure in engineering geology, instruments and methods used, geologic criteria in correlating beds and identifying structures, map preparation.

Edward Hubert Cunningham-Craig, *Oil Finding,* London, Edward Arnold, 1912, pp. xi + 195. 2nd Ed. 1920, pp. xi + 324.
Authoritative early work. Origin of petroleum, its formation, accumulation; structures, indications, stratigraphy, field work. Second Edition adds natural gas and shale.

Samuel Harries Daddow and Benjamin Bannan, *Coal, Iron, and Oil; or The Practical American Miner,* Pottsville, Penna., Benjamin Bannan, 1866, pp. 808.
Mainly about coal and iron mining, with one chapter on geology and distribution of petroleum, plus statistics.

E. DeGolyer, *The Development of the Art of Prospecting,* Princeton, N.J., Princeton University Press, 1940, pp. 38.
History of prospecting techniques in pe-

troleum industry; theories, methods, physical devices, persons associated with technological advances.

E. DeGolyer, Ed., *Elements of the Petroleum Industry,* New York, American Institute of Mining and Metallurgical Engineers, 1940, pp. vii + 519.
Papers by 20 authoritative authors describing techniques current in American petroleum industry, all branches; review of technical literature by DeGolyer.

C. Hewitt Dix, *Seismic Prospecting for Oil,* New York, Harper & Bros., 1952, pp. xx + 414.
Summary of methods commonly used, tools employed, interpretation of data.

Milton Burnett Dobrin, *Introduction to Geophysical Prospecting,* New York, McGraw-Hill Book Co., 1952, pp. xi + 435.
Geophysical methods in current use with emphasis on gravity, magnetic, and seismic techniques. Less detailed treatment of electrical and radioactivity prospecting, geophysical well logging, physical principles, instrumentation, field techniques, data interpretation.

Armand John Eardley, *Structural Geology of North America,* New York, Harper & Bros., 1951, pp. xiv + 624.
Said to be first book to describe in detail structural evolution of area as large as continent; formation and constitution of mountain systems, basins, arches, and volcanic archipelagos; leveling of highland and filling of basins.

William Harvey Emmons, *Geology of Petroleum,* New York, McGraw-Hill Book Co., 1921, pp. xiv + 610. 2nd Ed. 1931, pp. xi + 736.
Origin of oil, surface indications, properties, reservoir rocks, structural features, behavior of wells and rock pressure, with description of oil fields in United States and elsewhere.

Gideon Frost, *A New Exposition of the Leading Facts of Geology,* New York, Trow & Smith Book Mfg. Co., 1869, pp. 80.
Origin and formation of petroleum and coal, rejecting vegetable origin, supports theory of chemical union of carbon and hydrogen to form petroleum.

Dorsey Hager, *Practical Oil Geology,* New York, McGraw-Hill Book Co., 1915, pp. xii + 149. 2nd Ed. 1916, pp. xiv + 187. 3rd Ed. 1919, pp. xiv + 253. 4th Ed. 1926, pp. xii + 309. 5th Ed. 1938, pp. xix + 466. 6th Ed. 1951, pp. xxi + 589.
Handbook on oil geology, with emphasis on American methods. Later editions include geophysics, historical geology, improved well logging and sampling, subsurface mapping.

Carl August Heiland, *Geophysical Exploration,* New York, Prentice-Hall, 1940, pp. xiii + 1013.
Surveys entire field of geophysical exploration, including geophysical methods in oil exploration, well testing, etc.

Edward Allison Hill, *Geological Notes on Oil Structures,* San Francisco, Hall-Gutstadt Co., 1922, pp. 85.
Determination of better known types of oil structures; possibility of discovering additional oil-bearing areas.

G. D. Hobson, *Some Fundamentals of Petroleum Geology,* London, Oxford University Press, 1954, pp. x + 139.
Fundamentals of petroleum geology: oil accumulation, composition and properties of reservoir fluids, origin, migration, and accumulation of petroleum, reservoir pressure.

G. D. Hobson, *The Geology of Petroleum,* London, International Geological Congress, 1950, pp. 99.
Part VI: Proceedings of Section E, 18th International Geological Congress, London, 1948. Papers on structure and stratigraphy of Middle East, Colombia, Peru, Pakistan, and other oil fields, petroleum migration and other geological aspects.

T. Sterry Hunt, *Notes on the History of Petroleum or Rock Oil,* Washington, Smithsonian Institution, 1862.
Annual Report of the Board of Regents, 1861, pp. 319–329. Geological aspects of oil production, followed by report on Explosibility of Coal Oils, by T. Allen.

Jay John Jakosky, *Exploration Geophysics,* Los Angeles, the author, 1940, pp. xii + 786. 2nd Ed., Los Angeles, Trija

Publishing Co., 1950, pp. xvi + 1195.
Theories, equipment, and field techniques of recognized exploratory geophysical methods; problems of economic geology, including oil exploration.

A. Kartsev, Z. A. Tabasaranski, M. I. Subbota, G. A. Mogilevski, *Geochemical Methods of Prospecting and Exploration for Petroleum and Natural Gas* (translated from Russian edition of 1954 by Paul A. Witherspoon and William D. Romey), Berkeley, Cal., University of California Press, 1959, pp. xxiii + 349.
Geochemical methods in use for prospecting in Russia.

acob Garrett Kemp, *Lecture Notes on Practical Petroleum Geophysics*, College Station, Tex., Texas Agricultural and Mechanical College (Bulletin No. 50), 1940, pp. 65.
Geophysical methods: gravimeter and torsion balance, magnetometer, electrical.

Frederic Henry Lahee, *Field Geology*, New York, McGraw-Hill Book Co., 1916, pp. xxiv + 508. 2nd Ed. 1923, pp. xxviii + 651. 3rd Ed. 1931, pp. xxxi + 789. 4th Ed. 1941, pp. xxxii + 853. 5th Ed. 1952, pp. xxx + 883.
Recognition and interpretation of geologic structures and topographic forms, geologic surveying; making of maps, sections, block diagrams; geophysical surveying in later editions.

Cecil G. Lalicker, *Principles of Petroleum Geology*, New York, Appleton-Century-Crofts, 1949, pp. xii + 377.
Principles of petroleum geology, chemical and physical properties of petroleum, its origin, migration, and accumulation, reservoir rocks, classification of oil and gas pools, origin of structures, details on various types of fields, petroleum discovery methods, geological considerations in recovery methods, and valuation of oil and gas properties.

Kenneth Knight Landes, *Petroleum Geology*, New York, John Wiley & Sons, 1951, pp. xi + 660. 2nd Ed. 1959, pp. xi + 443.
Origin, migration, and accumulation of natural hydrocarbons, distribution of

oil and gas fields around the world; methods of searching for and finding oil and gas deposits; future oil supplies, including synthetic fuels. Second edition outlines modern theories of origin and accumulation of oil and gas, technical aspects of oil finding, and geologic occurrence of petroleum, particularly manner in which commercial deposits have been trapped.

William Clement Leonard, *Applied Geophysics in the Location of Oil*, Amarillo, Texas, Geophysical Corp., 1929, pp. 8.
Geophysical methods and apparatus; possibilities of oil finding through advancements in geophysics.

Leslie Walter LeRoy and Julian William Low, *Graphic Problems in Petroleum Geology*, New York, Harper & Bros., 1954, pp. ix + 238.
Manual on problems and exercises in structural and stratigraphic geology.

A. I. Levorsen, *Geology of Petroleum*, San Francisco, W. H. Freeman & Co., 1954, pp. x + 703.
Reservoir rock, pore space, traps, salt domes and reservoir conditions; temperature and pressure of fluids; origin, migration, and accumulation of petroleum; application of foregoing in study of subsurface geology and discovery of new oil pools and provinces.

Ernest Raymond Lilley, *The Geology of Petroleum and Natural Gas*, D. Van Nostrand Co., 1928, pp. x + 524.
Petroleum and related bitumens: their fundamental geologic conditions, reservoir rocks; concentration of oil and gas; structures; factors controlling accumulations; exploration of new areas.

John Muirhead MacFarlane, *Fishes, The Source of Petroleum*, New York, Macmillan Co., 1923, pp. 451.
Biology and chemistry of fishes in relation to petroleum in various geologic periods; also relation of fishes to bituminous shales, coals, and allied minerals.

John Muirhead MacFarlane, *The Quantity and Sources of Our Petroleum Supplies*, Philadelphia, Noel Printing Co., 1931, pp. 250.
Relationship of fish life to petroleum;

Mowry shales of Middle West, Green River shales of Wyoming, Utah, and Colorado, and Miocene shales of Southern California.

R. I. Martin, *Fundamentals of Electric Logging,* Tulsa, Petroleum Publishing Co., 1955, pp. 68.
Articles on electric logging reprinted from *Oil and Gas Journal.*

William Pitt Mayer, *Popular Oil Geology,* Chicago, the author, 1917, pp. 15.
Description of oil geology, particular attention to evidences of oil and gas in Mobile County, Alabama.

E. G. McKinney, *Seismographing for Oil,* Oklahoma City, Okla., Times-Journal Publishing Co., 1935, pp. vi + 38.
Describes methods used in seismograph operations in search for oil, including equipment and its use, interpretation, etc.

Henry Brewer Milner, *Sedimentary Petrography,* London, Thos. Murby & Co., 1st Ed.: *An Introduction to Sedimentary Petrography,* 1922, pp. 125. Supplement, 1926, pp. 156. 2nd Ed.: *Sedimentary Petrography,* 1929, pp. xxi + 514. 3rd Ed. 1940, pp. xxiii + 666. Reprinted 1952, pp. xix + 666.
Microscopic examination of sediments in modern oil-land development, with reference to oil sands in specific fields. Author was lecturer in petroleum technology, Imperial College of Science and Technology, London.

Ludger Mintrop, *On the History of the Seismic Method for the Investigation of Underground Formations and Mineral Deposits,* Hanover, Germany, Seismos G. m. b. H., 1930, pp. 128.
Account of development of seismic method by its chief inventor and pioneer, Baron Mintrop.

Lewis Lomax Nettleton, *Geophysical Prospecting for Oil,* New York, McGraw-Hill Book Co., 1940, pp. 444.
Principles and practice of modern oil prospecting.

University of Oklahoma, *A Symposium on Subsurface Logging Techniques,* Norman, Okla., University of Oklahoma Book Exchange, 1949, pp. 113; 2nd Symposium, 1951, pp. 143; 3rd Symposium, 1954, pp. 94; 4th Symposium, 1955, pp. 115; 5th Symposium, 1958, pp. 167.
Papers delivered at symposia on subsurface logging and geology.

Louis S. Panyity, *Prospecting for Oil and Gas,* New York, John Wiley & Sons, 1920, pp. xvii + 249.
Tools and methods of the scientific oil and gas prospector.

Erich Pautsch, *Methods of Applied Geophysics,* Houston, the author, 1927, pp. 82.
Results of theoretical and experimental research in applied geophysics, with discussion of gravitational, seismic, acoustic, magnetic, electric, and radioactive methods.

Peter Henry Pearson, *Surface Marks of Oil Deposits,* Washington, the author, 1920, pp. 74.
For the layman who wishes to know surface indications of oil and gas.

Alfred Peterson, *Oil and Gas, Be Your Own Geologist,* Kansas City, Mo., Franklin Hudson Publishing Co., 1921, pp. iv + 162.
Author's system of "oilology," purporting to show that petroleum deposits are most likely found in natural living and gathering places of marine animal life, located by reference to course of ocean currents.

William Plotts, *Origin of Petroleum, Coal, etc.,* Whittier, Cal., the author, 1905, pp. 29.
Author, a driller, presents his views concerning origin and occurrence of carbonaceous products.

William Plotts, *Isogeotherm Hypothesis of Mineral Occurrence and Origin, etc.,* Whittier, Cal., Will A. Smith's Print Shop, 1911, pp. 68.
Further refinements of theses advanced in earlier pamphlet.

William Woods Porter, II, *The Practical Geology of Oil,* Houston, Gulf Publishing Co., 1938, pp. vi + 142. 2nd Ed., retitled *Basic Oil Geology,* 1954, pp. vi + 142.

Basic principles of oil geology, geophysics, sedimentation, structural geology, oil accumulation, drilling.

Wallace E. Pratt, *Oil in the Earth,* Lawrence, Kansas, University of Kansas Press, 1942, pp. 110. Revised and reprinted 1943.
Four lectures delivered to geology students.

E. E. Rosaire, *The Handbook of Geochemical Prospecting,* Houston, the author, 1939, pp. iii + 113.
Theory, classification, analytical procedure and halo formation in geochemical prospecting for petroleum; data on field procedure and costs; geochemical well logging, recognition of geochemical anomalies.

William Low Russell, *Principles of Petroleum Geology,* New York, McGraw-Hill Book Co., 1951, pp. xi + 508.
Basic principles of petroleum geology, methods and techniques.

William Low Russell, *Structural Geology for Petroleum Geologists,* New York, McGraw-Hill Book Co., 1955, pp. x + 427.
Structural geology as it pertains to finding of oil. Maps, cross sections, folds, faults, joints and fractures; continental shelves, classification of traps.

17th International Geological Congress, *Proceedings: The Petroleum Problem and the Petroleum Resources of the World,* 17th Cong., Moscow, 1937.
Vol. I, pp. 177–188: General article, "World Petroleum Reserves," deals largely with estimates of Russian petroleum reserves.
Vol. IV, pp. 1–526: Twenty-five articles and abstracts on geology, geophysical methods, oil resources, oil and gas fields in various areas of U.S.S.R.

Francis Parker Shepard, *Submarine Geology,* New York, Harper & Bros., 1948, pp. xvi + 348.
Pioneer textbook on methods of exploring ocean floor, waves and currents, origin, history, topography, and sediments of continental shelves, continental slopes, submarine canyons, coral reefs, and floor of deep oceans; oil possibilities and mapping oil structures of continental shelves.

George A. Shufeldt, Jr., *History of the Chicago Artesian Well: A Demonstration of the Truth of the Spiritual Philosophy,* Chicago, Religio-Philosophical Publishing Assn., 1866, pp. 49.
Boring for water and oil in Chicago, 1863–64, in site "revealed" by spiritualism.

Frederick H. Smith, *Revised Pocket Geologist and Mineralogist, etc.,* Baltimore, the author, 1890, pp. 208. Revision and combination of *Pocket Geologist,* published 1877, and *Rocks, Minerals and Stocks,* pp. vii + 234, published 1882 by The Railway Review, Chicago, Ill., by same author.
Contains chapter, pp. 76–81, on oil and gas. Discusses oil- and gas-bearing strata, oilbreaks, oil and gas springs and prospects.

Lawrence Wesley Smith, Ed., *The Origin of Petroleum,* Azusa, Cal., Annular World Association, 1942, pp. 51.
"Petroleum on the Planets" and "The Future of Petroleum," by Donald Lee Cyr; "The Origin of Petroleum," "Trenton Petroleum in Ohio," and "Oil in California," by Isaac Newton Vail. Item of eccentric interest.

Society of Exploration Geophysicists, *Early Geophysical Papers,* Tulsa, the Society, 1947, var. pag.
Reprint of geophysical papers delivered or published between establishment of Society of Exploration Geophysicists in 1930 and start of its journal, *Geophysics,* in 1936. Papers contain much early history and technical fundamentals of present geophysical exploration industry.

Society of Exploration Geophysicists, *Geophysical Case Histories,* Tulsa, the Society, 1949. *Vol. I.—1948,* pp. xii + 671.
Collection of 60 papers by 61 authors, presenting material by which geophysical surveys can be judged and interpreted; salt dome, Mid-Continent, Rocky Mountain, California, and foreign case histories. *Geophysical Case Histories, Vol. II.—1956,* pp. xiv + 676.
Collection of 53 papers by 75 authors,

presenting salt dome, reef, anticline, and stratigraphic trap case histories.

Percy Edwin Spielmann, *The Genesis of Petroleum,* London, Ernest Benn, 1923, pp. 72. French Ed., 1926.
Survey of articles in scientific periodicals dealing with origin of petroleum.

Ivan Ascanio Stigand, *Outlines of the Occurrence and Geology of Petroleum,* London, Charles Griffin & Co., 1925, pp. x + 246.
Handbook of petroleum geology, with field examples. Appendix on geophysical methods.

Murray Stuart, *The Geology of Oil, Oil-Shale, and Coal,* London, Mining Publications, 1926, pp. viii + 104.
Origin and accumulation of oil deposits, oil shales, and bituminous coal.

Forest John Swears Sur, *Oil Prospecting, Drilling and Extraction,* San Francisco, A. Carlisle & Co., 1914, pp. 64.
How oil is found, discussion of geological formations, and methods used in development and extraction.

Eric Neshan Tiratsoo, *Petroleum Geology,* London, Methuen & Co., 1951, pp. xix + 449.
Text for students at Royal School of Mines.

Edgar Tobin, *Aerial Maps and Oil Geology,* San Antonio, Edgar Tobin Aerial Surveys, 1932, pp. 16.
Aerial mapping in oil geology, scale of map, mapping methods.

Parker Davies Trask, *Recent Marine Sediments,* Tulsa, American Association of Petroleum Geologists, 1939, pp. vi + 736.
Symposium on recent sediments and phenomena associated with deposition, conditions of formation of marine deposits, methods of studying sediments.

Parker Davies Trask and H. Whitman Patnode, *Source Beds of Petroleum,* Tulsa, American Association of Petroleum Geologists, 1942, pp. xiv: + 566.
Investigation of ancient deposits, with main object of determining diagnostic criteria to recognize source beds.

Parker Davies Trask, *Origin and Environment of Source Sediments of Petroleum,* Houston, Gulf Publishing Co., 1932, pp. xv + 323.
Analysis of coastal sediments and deposits from continental slopes; some 2,000 samples were obtained from 1,580 localities in 150 regions.

Loyal Wingate Trumbull, *Petroleum in Granite,* Cheyenne, S. A. Bristol Co., 1916, pp. 27.
Geologic possibilities of oil occurrence in granite in Wyoming; migration and separation of hydrocarbons in Wyoming light oil fields.

Francis Maurice Van Tuyl, *Elements of Petroleum Geology,* Denver, Petroleum Publishing Co. of Colorado, 1924, pp. 275.
Popular lectures on oil geology.

F. M. Van Tuyl, Ben H. Parker, and W. W. Skeeters, *The Migration and Accumulation of Petroleum and Natural Gas,* Golden, Colo., Colorado School of Mines, Vol. 40, No. 1 of *Quarterly,* 1945, pp. 111.
Deals with nature, mode, and theories of migration and location of accumulation of oil and gas.

F. M. Van Tuyl and Ben H. Parker, *The Time of Origin and Accumulation of Petroleum,* Golden, Colo., Colorado School of Mines, Vol. 36, No. 2 of *Quarterly,* 1941, pp. 180.
Views regarding source of oil and gas, time and conditions of generation, and mode and time of accumulation into commercial pools, based on responses to inquiries sent to 181 petroleum geologists in United States and 77 in foreign countries and to questionnaires including 24 specific questions on occurrence of oil and gas, bearing on problem of origin and accumulation.

F. M. Van Tuyl and Truman H. Kuhn, *Applied Geology,* Golden, Colo., Colorado School of Mines, Vol. 45, No. 1B of *Quarterly,* 1950, pp. iv + 343.
Contains 10 papers and discussion presented Sept. 30–Oct. 1, 1949, at Conference on Applied Geology, including *Petroleum Geology of Colorado,* by Carroll E. Dobbin, and *Modern Meth-*

ods in Petroleum Exploration, by Godfrey F. Kaufmann.

Walter August Ver Wiebe, *How Oil Is Found,* Wichita, Kan., University of Wichita, 1951, pp. iv + 247.
Oil seepages, oil rocks, time and place of rock formation, structures, oil formation, movement underground, accumulation and oil finding.

Charles Albert Warner, *Field Mapping for the Oil Geologist,* New York, John Wiley & Sons, 1921, pp. x + 145.
Handbook of field mapping methods.

Lewis George Weeks, *Principles of Basin Development, Sedimentation, and Oil Occurrence,* New York, Standard Oil Development Co., 1948, pp. xvii + 230.
Dynamics of crustal framework of earth which control development, growth, and architecture of basins; factors directly controlling oil occurrence, its migration and accumulation; habitat and identification of source beds.

William Cook Welles, *The True Origin of Coal and Petroleum,* Parkersburg, West Va., the author, 1902, pp. 56.
Author's theories on origin of coal and petroleum.

Luther Melville Wilson, *Petroleum and Natural Gas,* Houston, the author, 1916, pp. 64.
Origin, distribution, accumulation, surface signs; oil wells and fields, especially those of the Gulf Coast country.

Alexander Winchell, *Walks and Talks in the Geological Field,* Meadville, Penna., Chautauqua-Century Press, 1894, pp. vi + 353.
Author had been professor of geology and paleontology at University of Michigan. Book contains chapter on petroleum, "Liquid Sunlight," and on natural gas, "Gaseous Sunlight."

J. C. Yancey, *Why and Where Oil Is Found,* New York, the author, 1919, pp. 23.
Geology and oil prospects of North Central Texas, with maps.

Victor Ziegler, *Popular Oil Geology,* Golden, Colo., C. H. Merrifield, 1918, pp. 149. 2nd Ed., New York, John Wiley & Sons, 1920, pp. 171.
Fundamental principles of oil geology.

II.

Drilling and Production

A. DRILLING

Agricultural and Mechanical College of Texas, *Drilling Fluids Conference,* College Station, A. & M. College of Texas (Bulletin No. 96, Texas Engineering Experiment Station), 1946, pp. vi + 93.
Papers on functions and properties of drilling fluids, chemistry, testing, oil base and silicate base fluids, field applications, etc.

Milton A. Allen, *Drilling for Oil,* Tucson, Ariz., University of Arizona Bureau of Mines, 1918, pp. 8.
Drilling systems, difficulties, costs.

American Association of Oilwell Drilling Contractors, *Tool Pusher's Manual,* Dallas, the Association, 1955, pp. 500, loose-leaf. 2nd Ed. 1955. 3rd Ed. 1956. 4th Ed. 1958, with additions and revisions in 3rd and 4th.
Twenty-two indexed sections answer technical questions on oil well drilling: bits, pipe, cementing, tanks, safety, mud fluids, etc.

American Petroleum Institute, *Drilling and Production Practice, 1958,* New York, the Institute, 1959, pp. 212.
Twenty-fifth in annual series started with *Drilling and Production Practice, 1934,* with corresponding volumes for each succeeding year. Papers on drilling and production practice.

American Society of Mechanical Engineers, *Report of Tests on Steam Equipment for Drilling Rotary-Drilled Oil Wells,* New York, the Society, 1932, pp. 42.
Observations of typical steam equipment used in drilling deep well in Oklahoma City to determine fuel, water, and steam consumption, efficiency.

American Society of Mechanical Engineers, *Report of Tests on Electrical Equipment for Drilling Rotary-Drilled Oil Wells,* New York, the Society, 1933, pp. 16.
Second report of Special A.S.M.E. organized 1931 to obtain engineering and cost data on alternative sources of drilling power.

R. R. Angel, *Volume Requirements for Air & Gas Drilling,* Houston, Gulf Publishing Co., 1958, pp. 89.
Circulation rates required for air and gas drilling.

Earl L. Beard, Jr., *The Rotary-Drilling Contracting Industry in the Mid-Continent Area and Related Bank Financing,* Tulsa, National Bank of Tulsa, 1954, pp. xiv + 134.
Characteristics of rotary-drilling contracting industry, tools and equipment, problems and hazards; drilling contracts; bank loans to drilling contractors; glossary.

Roy A. Bobo, Robert S. Hoch, George S. Boudreaux, and R. R. Angel, *Keys to Successful Competitive Drilling,* Houston, Gulf Publishing Co., 1958, pp. ix + 133.
Treatise on rotary drilling: rock-bit design, size, and weight; circulation systems, drilling fluids, hydraulics; reduced pressure drilling.

John Edward Brantly, *Rotary Drilling Handbook,* New York, Russell Palmer, 1936, pp. 304. 2nd Ed. 1938, pp. 350. 3rd Ed. 1942, pp. 420. 4th Ed. 1948, pp. 568. 5th Ed. 1952, pp. 702.

Practical handbook for "man on the rig."

eorge E. Burton, *Methods of Exploring for Oil and Gas,* Norman, Okla., Oklahoma Geological Survey (Circular No. 8), 1917, pp. 20.
Existing exploration methods, including diamond drilling; compilation of drilling costs in Texas and Oklahoma.

irnegie Steel Company, *Steel Derricks and Drilling Rigs for Oil, Gas, Salt and Other Wells,* Pittsburgh, the Company, 1913, 4th Ed. pp. 104. 5th Ed. 1918, pp. 96. 6th Ed. 1921, pp. 86.
Plans and types of drilling rigs, dimensions, design, equipment, specifications.

A. Crumley, R. H. Edele, and D. H. Harnish, Jr., *Fishing Tools,* Morgantown, W. Va., West Virginia University (Engineering Experiment Station Technical Bulletin No. 35), 1953, pp. 36.
Guide to tools suited to retrieval of lost tools, tubing, or casing.

A. Crumley, R. H. Edele, and D. H. Harnish, Jr., *Well Packers,* Morgantown, W. Va., West Virginia University (Engineering Experiment Station Technical Bulletin No. 38), 1954, pp. 50.
Types of packers employed in oil wells.

ames D. Cumming, *Diamond Drill Handbook,* Toronto, J. K. Smit & Sons of Canada, 1951, pp. xxiii + 501. 2nd Ed. 1956, pp. xxx + 655.
History, mechanical features, diamonds, bits; chapter on diamond coring in oil fields. Glossary and bibliography.

. Evans and A. Reid, *Drilling Mud: Its Manufacture and Testing,* Calcutta, Transactions of the Mining and Geological Institute of India, 1936, Vol. XXXII, pp. xxx + 263.
Based partly on laboratory and field experimental work of Burmah Oil Co., deals with mixing, maintenance, reconditioning and testing of drilling mud.

Hubert Guyod, *Electrical Well Logging,* Duncan, Okla., the author, 1944, pp. 103.
Sixteen articles published in *The Oil Weekly,* on well-logging methods.

Hubert Guyod, *Electrical Well Logging Fundamentals,* Houston, the author, 1952, pp. 164.
Includes 16 articles published in 1944 plus 9 additional articles on methods and interpretation; bibliography.

Hubert Guyod, *Temperature Well Logging,* Houston, Well Instrument Developing Co., 1954, pp. 47.
Series of 7 articles on heat conduction, salt intrusions, temperature distribution, and thermal equilibrium in temperature well logging.

Hubert Guyod, *Resistivity Determination from Electric Logs,* Houston, the author, 1957, var. pag.
Procedures of determining and interpreting resistivity of reservoir rock from electric logs.

Marshall Henry Haddock, *Deep Borehole Surveys and Problems,* New York, McGraw-Hill Book Co., 1931, pp. vii + 296.
Borehole surveying devices; problems of strata location and orientation; deviation and its causes; core orientation; fluid, compass, plumb-bob, pendulum, photographic, gyroscopic-compass, and geophysical methods of surveying boreholes.

C. Isler, *Well-boring for Water, Brine and Oil,* London, E. & F. N. Spon, 1902, pp. ix + 195. 2nd Ed. 1911, pp. ix + 269. 3rd Ed. 1921, pp. vii + 259.
Methods of digging and drilling wells, including cable-tool method; chapter on rotary drilling in 3rd Ed.

Walter Henry Jeffery, *Deep Well Drilling,* Houston, Gulf Publishing Co., 1921, pp. 531. 2nd Ed. 1925, pp. 662. 3rd Ed. 1931, pp. viii + 816.
Operating handbook of deep well drilling by cable-tool and rotary methods.

University of Kansas, *Fundamentals of Logging,* Lawrence, University of Kansas, n.d., pp. 172.
Papers on electric, resistivity, and radiation logging.

Emory N. Kemler, *Rotary-Percussion Drilling,* Spring Park, Minn., the author, 1954, pp. 139.

Patent abstracts and technical literature on rotary-percussion drilling tools and techniques.

Robert Kittle, *The History and Science of Irrigation, Artesian and Petroleum and Deep Well Drilling,* Fremont, Neb., the author, 1895, pp. 49.
Four chapters on oil and gas wells.

Arthur W. McCray and Frank W. Cole, *Oil Well Drilling Technology,* Norman, Okla., University of Oklahoma Press, 1959, pp. xi + 492.
Geological and geophysical principles governing oil accumulation; seismic and radioactive prospecting; various drilling methods and tools; cementing; drilling economics.

McMurry College, School of Business Administration, *First Annual Petroleum Conference on Logging,* Abilene, Tex., the School, 1956, var. pag. 2nd Conference, 1957. 3rd Conference, 1958.
Papers on application, analysis, and interpretation of well logging.

National Lumber Manufacturers Association, *Lumber for Oil Industry Purposes,* n.p., the Association, 1930, pp. 52.
Includes plans and specifications for wooden derricks.

Organisation for European Economic Co-Operation, *Production of Drilling and Refining Oil Equipment in the U.S.A.,* Paris, the Organization, 1953, pp. 130.
Drilling and refining equipment; design and equipment of refineries.

Robert Cecil Paget, *Rigbuilding,* London, Williams & Norgate, 1935, pp. xii + 104.
Detailed handbook of wood derrick building.

The Petroleum Engineer, Comp., *Fundamentals of Rotary Drilling,* Dallas, The Petroleum Engineer, 1958, pp. 152.
Handbook of rotary drilling technology.

Walter Francis Rogers, *Composition and Properties of Oil Well Drilling Fluids,* Houston, Gulf Publishing Co., 1948, pp. vii + 525. 2nd Ed. 1953, pp. x + 676.
Specifications, testing, composition, properties, and use of drilling fluids; calcium treated and oil-emulsion muds;

thinning agents, fluid-loss reducing agents.

R. R. Sanderson, *Drill Work, Methods and Costs,* Orrville, Ohio, Cyclone Drill Co., 1911, pp. 350.
Drilling wells with cable and hollow rod tools; tables.

Society of Petroleum Engineers of A.I.M.E., *Well Logging,* Dallas, the Society, 1959, pp. 168.
Papers on electric, gamma-ray-neutron and dipmeter logging, selected from Petroleum Transactions of A.I.M.E.; bibliography.

Sullivan Machinery Company, *Diamond Drilling for Oil,* Chicago, the Company, 1925, pp. 78.
History and application of diamond core drilling for oil.

University of Texas Extension Service, Industrial and Business Training Bureau, *A Primer of Oil Well Drilling,* Austin, the Bureau, 1951, pp. vi + 90. Issued in cooperation with American Association of Oilwell Drilling Contractors.
Practices, procedures, and terminology of drilling; contract drilling; costs; rigs; offshore techniques.

University of Texas, Petroleum Extension Service, *Principles of Drilling Mud Control,* Austin, the Service, March, 1946. 2nd Ed. June, 1946. 3rd Ed. Sept., 1946. 4th Ed. March, 1947. 5th Ed. March, 1948. 6th Ed. July, 1948. 7th Ed. July, 1950. 8th Ed. August, 1951. 9th Ed. August, 1952, pp. 122. 10th Ed. 1955, pp. 131.
Functions, composition, tests, and conditioning of drilling muds; drilling mud practice in principal producing regions of United States and Canada.

Union Tool Company, *Petroleum Well Drilling Methods of the United States and Their Adaptability to the Fields of Argentina,* Torrance, Cal., the Company, 1922, pp. 167.
Evolution of United States drilling methods, feasibility of adapting these methods to Argentina.

United States Steel Corporation, *Offshore Drilling in the Gulf of Mexico, A Forecast of Future Steel Requirements,*

Pittsburgh, the Corporation, 1957, pp. 27.
Steel requirements for offshore drilling, 1957–1970.

Ialcolm Robert Jesse Wyllie, *The Fundamentals of Electric Log Interpretation,* New York, Academic Press, pp. x + 126. 2nd Ed. 1957, pp. 176.

Basic principles, theory, and practice of electric log interpretation.

Victor Ziegler, *Oil Well Drilling Methods,* New York, John Wiley & Sons, 1923, pp. xii + 257.
Handbook of oil well drilling methods and tools.

B. PRODUCTION PRACTICE

Iorace Dewey Allen, Comp., *Allen's Superintendents Hand Book,* Los Angeles, Allen Publications, 1924. 2nd Ed., Philadelphia, Chilton Class Journal Co., 1929, pp. 454.
Articles on cable tool and rotary well drilling, cementing, pumping, etc.

American Institute of Mining, Metallurgical, and Petroleum Engineers, *Transactions,* AIMME, Dallas, 1921 to date.
Early volumes entitled *Petroleum and Natural Gas* (1921–23), *Production of Petroleum in 1923,* and *Production of Petroleum in 1924.* Title since 1925: *Petroleum Development and Technology.* Society's name has included words "and Petroleum" since 1956. Annual volumes of technical papers on exploration and production techniques presented at AIMME meetings.

American Petroleum Institute, *Finding and Producing Oil,* New York, the Institute, 1939, pp. 338.
Oil exploration and drilling; sampling, coring, and borehole surveying; vocational and scholastic training; oil and gas conservation laws; lists of associations, producers, suppliers, drilling contractors.

American Petroleum Institute, *Primer of Oil and Gas Production,* New York, the Institute, 1954, pp. 73.
Normal operations in oil and gas production; glossary.

American Petroleum Institute, Committee on Drilling and Production Practice and Division of Production, *Oil-Well Cementing Practice in the United States,* New York, the Institute, 1959, pp. 297.
History of oil well cementing, chemis-

try of cements, effects of temperature and additives, planning and conducting casing-cementing jobs, other procedures.

American Society of Mechanical Engineers, *Proceedings of the 1946 National Conference on Petroleum Mechanical Engineering,* New York, the Society, 1947, pp. 220.
Papers on equipment, operational problems, performance in petroleum production, refining, transportation.

Mark Edwin Andrews, *Wildcatter's Handbook,* Houston, the author, 1952, Vol. 1, pp. xi + 47.
Terminology and techniques of well drilling, coring, logging and completion.

Alfred Hannam Bell, *Brine Disposal in Illinois Oil Fields,* Urbana, Ill., Illinois State Geological Survey, 1957, pp. 12.
Illinois portion of brine disposal study prepared for Interstate Oil Compact Commission.

Bethlehem Steel Company, *Sucker Rod Handbook,* Bethlehem, Penna., the Company, 1950, pp. 213.
Technical data for selecting sucker rods and design of sucker rod strings; brief history of pumping.

Emil J. Burcik, *Properties of Petroleum Reservoir Fluids,* New York, John Wiley & Sons, 1957, pp. ix + 190.
Petroleum deposits, behavior of gases and liquids, reservoir fluid characteristics.

John C. Calhoun, *Fundamentals of Reservoir Engineering,* Norman, Okla., University of Oklahoma Press, 1953, pp. xvi + 417.

Reservoir fluids, rocks, rock fluid systems, and principles; gas flow, drainage, water influx; well-performance application.

John C. Calhoun, *Notes on the Engineering Analysis of Petroleum Reservoirs,* State College, Penna., the author, 1953, var. pag.
Material-balance equation, solution gas drive, fluid injection, etc.

California State Department of Education, *Technical Practices in Petroleum Production,* Sacramento, Bureau of Trade and Industrial Education, 1945, pp. 19.
Vocational class instruction in petroleum production.

Alfred Chatenever, *Microscopic Behavior of Fluids in Porous Systems,* New York, American Petroleum Institute, 1957, pp. 12.
Photographic data on mechanisms of fluid flow.

James Mansfield Cleary, *Hydraulic Fracture Theory. Part I. Mechanics of Materials,* Urbana, Ill., Illinois State Geological Survey, 1958, pp. 24. *Part II. Fracture Orientation and Possibility of Fracture Control,* 1958, pp. 19.
Problems of hydraulic fracture.

Wilbur F. Cloud, *Petroleum Production,* Norman, Okla., University of Oklahoma Press, 1937, pp. x + 613.
Oil and gas production equipment, methods, fundamentals; legal considerations; flowing and pumping wells; cleaning and reconditioning; air-gas lift; repressuring; gathering, gauging, shipping. Geology and drilling not discussed, except as related to well completion and operation.

Colorado School of Mines, *Petroleum Engineering,* Golden, Colo., Colorado School of Mines, *Quarterly* (Vol. 45, No. 3B), 1950, pp. xi + 51.
Papers on gas condensate fields; valuation of oil properties for secondary recovery; conservation and other laws.

Benjamin Cole Craft and Murray F. Hawkins, *Applied Petroleum Reservoir Engineering,* Englewood Cliffs, N.J., Prentice-Hall, Inc., 1959, pp. ix + 437.

Application of reservoir engineering calculation of reservoir contents, recovery potentials; analysis and prediction of reservoir performance.

East Texas Salt Water Disposal Company, *Salt Water Disposal, East Texas Field,* Austin, Petroleum Extension Service, University of Texas, 1953, pp. 116.
Short history of East Texas field 1942, when East Texas Salt Water Disposal Company was formed. Design, operation, equipment, construction, treatment of salt water; accounting, regulations.

Harold Coulter George, *Oil Well Completion and Operation,* Norman, Okla., University of Oklahoma Press, 1931, pp. 234.
Cooperative report of United States Bureau of Mines and State of Oklahoma. Well equipment, methods for completing oil wells, producing practices.

Dorsey Hager, *Oil-Field Practice,* New York, McGraw-Hill Book Co., 1921, pp. ix + 310.
American methods of oil field development. Glossary.

William Frederick Heisler, *Elementary Science Applied to Petroleum Production and Refining,* Stillwater, Oklahoma, A. & M. College Bookstore, 1934, pp. 125. 2nd Ed. 1944, pp. 189.
A.P.I. training course covering principles of science and mathematics for oil industry employees.

Stanley Carrollton Herold, *Analytical Principles of the Production of Oil, Gas and Water from Wells,* Menlo Park, Stanford University Press, 1928, pp. xviii + 659.
Described as first attempt to set down natural laws governing fluid delivery from oil and gas wells.

Stanley Carrollton Herold, *Oil Well Drainage,* Menlo Park, Stanford University Press, 1941, pp. xiv + 407.
Artificial and natural reservoirs; reservoir energy, function of gas, radius, area, drainage, multiple zones; injection of gas, water, or oil; reserves; proration, conservation.

ames Herman Highsmith, *Appraisal of Oil Production,* Greenfield, Ill., Mitchell Printing Co., 1922, pp. 132.
Methods commonly in use for appraisal of oil properties. Tables for determining monthly depletion of flow.

Iouston Geological Society, *The Problem of Well Spacing,* Houston, the Society, 1940, pp. 24.
Physical and economic aspects of well spacing; bibliography on reservoir behavior, 1931–1939.

Ingersoll-Rand Company, *Oil Well Blowing Handbook,* New York, the Company, 1927, pp. 128.
Pioneer paper on air- and gas-lift practice.

Interstate Oil Compact Commission, Engineering Committee, *Oil and Gas Production,* Norman, Okla., University of Oklahoma Press, 1951, pp. xv + 128.
Nature of oil and gas reservoirs; secondary recovery methods and principles.

Roswell H. Johnson and L. G. Huntley, *Principles of Oil and Gas Production,* New York, John Wiley & Sons, 1916, pp. 371.
General treatise on American oil and gas production practices.

Ogden Sherman Jones, *Disposition of Oil Field Brines,* Lawrence, University of Kansas Publications, 1945, pp. 192.
Salt water problems, brine disposal, its use in secondary recovery.

Ogden Sherman Jones, *Fresh Water Protection from Pollution Arising in the Oil Fields,* Lawrence, University of Kansas Publications, 1950, pp. 132.
Control and abatement of pollution originating in oil fields.

Ogden Sherman Jones, *A Review of Lease Housekeeping Practices,* Lawrence, University of Kansas, n.d., pp. 15.
Subsurface contamination of fresh water; protective methods against pollution.

Ogden Sherman Jones, *The State's Responsibility in Oil and Brine Pollution Originating in Oil Fields,* Lawrence, University of Kansas, n.d., pp. 20.

Examination of pollution control, with suggestions for regulation.

Park J. Jones, *Petroleum Production,* New York, Reinhold Publishing Co., 1946–1948, 5 vols., pp. xxx + 1304.
Vol. I: *Mechanics of Production*—Oil Condensate, Natural Gas, 1946; II: *The Optimum Rate of Production,* 1946; III: *Oil Production by Water,* 1947; IV: *Condensate Production and Cycling,* 1948; V: *Oil Production by Gas and Flooding,* 1948.

Donald La Verne Katz, *Phase Relationships in Oil and Gas Reservoirs,* College Station, A. & M. College of Texas (Bulletin No. 114, Texas Engineering Experiment Station), 1949, pp. v + 63.
Behavior of reservoir fluids, vapor-liquid equilibria, phase densities, water-hydrocarbon phase relations, surface tension, viscosity.

Emory N. Kemler and Edward W. Rosencrants, *Offshore Summary,* Spring Park, Minn., Summary Reports, 1954, pp. 403.
Brings together references in fields of meteorology, oceanography, fluid mechanics, soil mechanics, marine engineering, structures, and petroleum engineering as applied to offshore oil development.

Oscar E. Kiessling (and others), *Technology, Employment, and Output per Man in Petroleum and Natural-Gas Production,* Philadelphia, Works Projects Administration, 1939, pp. xxvii + 346.
Long-time trends in production, employment, and output per man.

Benson M. Kingston, *Acidizing Hand Book,* Houston, Gulf Publishing Co., 1936, pp. 78. 2nd Ed. 1947, pp. 116.
Acid treatment of oil and gas wells; chemistry, geology, preparation, mechanics, producing after treatment.

R. L. Martin, *Mathematics for Oil Field Workers,* Austin, University of Texas, 1934, pp. 84.
Course for oil field workers under sponsorship of American Petroleum Institute.

William McGraw and E. H. Adams, *A Treatise on Oil and Gas Separation,* Los

Angeles, Trumble Gas Trap Co., 1930, pp. 31.
Construction, installation, and operation of oil and gas separators.

R. P. McLaughlin, *Oil Land Development and Valuation,* New York, McGraw-Hill Book Co., 1921, pp. viii + 196.
Steps necessary for full and proper development of oil lands; principles of oil land valuation. Author was California State Supervisor of Oil and Gas.

V. H. McNutt and Conrad Lambert, *First Principles of the Oil Business,* Kansas City, Mo., McKinley Publishing Co., 1924, pp. 196.
Finding, developing, producing oil; establishing a sound producing business.

Harold C. Miller, *Function of Natural Gas in the Production of Oil,* New York, American Petroleum Institute, 1929, pp. xiii + 267.
Regarded as outstanding contribution to petroleum engineering. Joint report of Bureau of Mines and Division of Development and Production Engineering of American Petroleum Institute. Importance of natural gas in recovery of oil; methods for controlling gas and oil production to gain greatest ultimate recovery; conclusions concerning behavior of oil and gas mixtures in underground formations.

Morris Muskat, *The Flow of Homogenous Fluids Through Porous Media,* New York, McGraw-Hill Book Co., 1937, pp. xix + 763.
Fundamental laws of flow of homogenous fluids through porous media; natural water drive, water flooding, gas-oil ratios, gas flow.

Morris Muskat, *Physical Principles of Oil Production,* New York, McGraw-Hill Book Co., 1949, pp. xv + 922.
Principles underlying mechanics of oil production; physical properties of petroleum fluids and oil-bearing rocks; hydrodynamics of flow through porous media.

National Gasoline Association of America, Condensate Well Corrosion Committee, *Condensate Well Corrosion,* Tulsa, the Association, 1953, pp. vii + 203.
Papers on corrosion in gas condensate wells, causative conditions, metallurgical factors, effects of flow rate and temperature, inhibitors, laboratory studies; field histories and history of Committee.

Maurice Edward Nicklin, *Something About Gas Lift,* Waukesha, Wis., Waukesha Motor Co., 1928, pp. 140.
Gas lift using natural gas under pressure as lifting medium; practices, economics.

Oil and Gas Journal, *Engineering Fundamentals on Petroleum Reservoirs,* Tulsa, the Journal, 1946, pp. 116.
Reservoir measurements, core analysis, acidizing, oil field waters, salt water disposal, etc.

University of Oklahoma, *Petroleum Engineering-Management Conference,* Norman, Okla., the University, 1952, pp. 77.
Papers on problems of management in petroleum industry, need for technicians in management.

Wentworth H. Osgood, *Increasing the Recovery of Petroleum,* New York, McGraw-Hill Book Co., 1930, 2 vols., pp. xi + 858.
Nature of oil and gas reservoirs; theory of normal production; methods of increasing recovery.

Paul Paine and Benjamin Stroud, *Oil Production Methods,* San Francisco, Western Engineering Publishing Co., 1913, pp. 239.
How wells are drilled and oil produced, with emphasis on California practice; chapter on accounting systems.

Pennsylvania State University Staff Members, *Notes for Reservoir Engineering Seminar,* University Park, Penna., 1957, var. pag.
Guidebook to study of reservoir engineering.

Robert William Phelps and Francis Wilbur Lake, *Petroleum Engineering,* Houston, Gulf Publishing Co., 1924, pp. xi + 574. 2nd Ed. 1927, pp. xii + 637.
Basic theories of geology and petroleum geology; occurrence and extraction of petroleum; operating technology; economics.

Sylvain J. Pirson, *Elements of Oil Reservoir Engineering,* New York, McGraw-Hill Book Co., 1950, pp. vii + 441.
Reservoir rocks and structures, fluids, forces, equations; Magnolia field, Arkansas, used as example.

Sylvain J. Pirson, *Oil Reservoir Engineering,* New York, McGraw-Hill Book Co., 1958, pp. x + 735.
Fundamental principles by which oil recovered from reservoir rocks; evaluation of oil originally in place; forecasts and control of reservoir performance.

Portland Cement Association, *Concrete in the Petroleum Industry,* Chicago, the Association, n.d., pp. 46.
Cement and its use in oil fields; in cementing for reservoirs and tanks; at refineries. Specifications.

Walter Deane Rose, *Fluid Flow in Petroleum Reservoirs, Part I. The Kozeny Paradox,* Illinois State Geological Survey, 1957, pp. 8. *Part II. Predicted Effects of Sand Consolidation,* 1957, pp. 14.
Fluid flow in porous media.

Adrian E. Scheidegger, *The Physics of Flow Through Porous Media,* New York, Macmillan Co., 1957, pp. xii + 236.
Homogenous single phase fluids and multiple phase flow through porous media.

Silas Frederick Shaw, *Gas-Lift Principles and Practices,* Houston, Gulf Publishing Co., 1939, pp. 156.
Compressed air and gas in lifting water, oil, and other fluids; principles controlling gas-lift operations; patents; equipment, methods.

Silas Frederick Shaw, *Flow Characteristics of Gas Life in Oil Production,* College Station, A. & M. College of Texas (Bulletin No. 113, Texas Engineering Experiment Station), 1949, pp. v + 90.
Flow characteristics of air life in oil production; bibliography.

Lee Francis Smith, *General Information on Recovery of Oil by Air and Gas Lift,* 216.
Recovery of oil by air and gas lift, soda ash, putting pressure on sand; information on compressors and engines.

Standard Oil Development Company, *Joint Progress Report on Reservoir Efficiency and Well Spacing,* n.p., the Company, 1943, pp. xix + 77.
Study, 1939–1941, of oil recovery efficiency and influence thereon of well spacing.

Marshall Burton Standing, *Volumetric and Phase Behavior of Oil Field Hydrocarbon Systems,* New York, Reinhold Publishing Corp., 1952, pp. vii + 123.
Pressure-production characteristics of oil and gas reservoirs, phase behavior and fluid flow concepts; sampling; material balance calculations, with specific treatment of behavior of gases, liquids, and gas-condensates.

Maynard M. Stephens, *Petroleum and Natural Gas Engineering,* University Park, Penna., Pennsylvania State College, Vol. I, 1940, pp. viii + 533. Rev. Ed., *Petroleum Engineering Fundamentals,* by Stephens and Oscar Fritzland Spencer, 1952, pp. 486. Vol. II, marked *Second Edition,* by Maynard M. Stephens, 1938, pp. ix + 483. Revised Edition: by Maynard M. Stephens and Oscar Fritzland Spencer, 1946, pp. x + 517. Third Edition: *Petroleum and Natural Gas Production,* 1957, pp. x + 604.
General preparatory textbook for extension course.

Robert Stirling, *The Gas Air-Lift Pocket Book,* London, E. & F. N. Spon, 1929, pp. 95.
Theory and working of air lift, its application to oil wells, with brief account of history of its application.

John R. Suman, *Petroleum Production Methods,* Houston, Gulf Publishing Co., 1921, pp. viii + 558. 2nd Ed. 1922, pp. viii + 558. 3rd Ed. 1923, pp. 652.
Problems arising from drilling wells, producing and handling oil.

University of Texas, *Vapor and Gravity Control in Crude Oil Production,* Austin, Petroleum Extension Service, the University, 1956, pp. 62.
Practices for elimination of vapor loss.

University of Texas, *Treating Oil Field Emulsions,* Austin, Petroleum Extension

Service, the University, 1949. 2nd Ed. 1955, pp. xx + 99.
Principal methods of treating emulsions.

University of Texas, *Casing Information,* Austin, Petroleum Extension Service, the University, 1952. 2nd Ed. 1956, pp. 75.
Casing, running, landing, and cementing techniques; installation of wellhead fittings.

University of Texas, *Applied Mathematics for the Petroleum Industry,* Austin, Petroleum Extension Service, the University, 1948, pp. 193.
Oil industry mathematical problems.

University of Texas, *Care and Operation of Pumping Engines and Units,* Austin, Petroleum Extension Service, the University, 1949, pp. 96.
Operation and maintenance of internal combustion engines.

University of Texas, *Basic Instrumentation,* Austin, Petroleum Extension Service, the University, 1948, pp. 224.
Instruments for control of production and manufacturing processes.

University of Texas, *A Primer of Oilwell Service and Workover,* Austin, the University, 1954, pp. 88.
Well servicing and maintenance. Glossary.

A. Beeby Thompson, *Petroleum Mining and Oil-Field Development,* London, Crosby Lockwood & Son, 1910, pp. xx + 362.
Treatise on exploration and development of oil fields.

A. Beeby Thompson, *Oil-Field Development and Petroleum Mining,* London, Crosby Lockwood & Son, 1916, pp. xix + 648.
Practical guide to exploration, petroleum engineering problems, legislation, and customs.

A. Beeby Thompson, *Oil Field Exploration and Development,* London, Crosby Lockwood & Son, 1925, 2 vols. 2nd Ed., London, Technical Press, 1950, 2 vols., pp. cxx + 1241.
Accounts of principal oil fields, with maps; leasing; petroleum legislation,

customs, usages; principles of refining properties of crude oil and products engineering problems; oil field equipment. Author is well-known British petroleum consultant.

L. C. Uren, *A Textbook of Petroleum Production Engineering,* New York, McGraw-Hill Book Co., 1924, pp. vii + 657. Subsequent editions broken into sections: "Petroleum Production Engineering: Oil Field Development," 1934 (2nd Ed.), pp. x + 531; 3rd Ed., 1946, pp. xiii + 764; 4th Ed., 1956, pp. xii + 792. "Petroleum Production Engineering: Oil Field Exploitation," 1939 (2nd Ed.), pp. ix + 756; 3rd Ed., 1953, pp. xiii + 807. "Petroleum Production Engineering: Production Economics," 1950, pp. xiii + 639.
Widely used standard text series by acknowledged authority.

Harold Vance, *Elements of Petroleum Subsurface Engineering,* St. Louis, Mo., Educational Publishers, 1950, pp. vi + 168.
For senior students in geology and petroleum engineering; determination of size, shape, and content of petroleum reservoirs.

John W. Waitz, *Flowing Oil Wells With Compressed Air,* New York, the author, 1909, pp. 20.
Describes performance of author's patented device.

World Petroleum Publishing Company, *Petroleum Engineering Hand Book,* Los Angeles, the Company, 1930, pp. 496, 2nd Ed. 1931, pp. 461.
Technical developments in California petroleum industry, including well completion, cementing, casing, pumping, repressuring, natural gasoline, storage.

Joseph Zaba and Wilfred Thomas Doherty, *Practical Petroleum Engineers' Handbook,* Houston, Gulf Publishing Co., 1937, pp. vi + 401. 2nd Ed. 1939, pp. viii + 492. 3rd Ed. 1949, pp. xiv + 654. 4th Ed. 1956, pp. 818.
Handbook of drilling and production methods. General engineering, power transmission, compressors, tubular goods, drilling, production, transportation.

C. SECONDARY RECOVERY OF PETROLEUM

American Petroleum Institute, *Secondary Recovery of Oil in the United States,* New York, the Institute, 1942, pp. viii + 259. Second Printing, with supplement, 1946. 2nd Ed. 1950, pp. xii + 838.
Papers describing methods to maintain or increase production of oil from underground reservoirs by air and gas injection or water flooding; data on porosity, permeability, thickness and area of oil-producing reservoirs, with review of data on amounts of oil, either recovered or susceptible of possible recovery, by secondary methods, in United States. Supplement and 2nd Ed. have bibliography.

American Petroleum Institute, *Water Flooding,* Norman, Okla., University of Oklahoma, 1956, pp. x + 74.
American Petroleum Institute training manual for oil industry employees.

ay Edgar Billingsley and Robert L. Alkire, *An Introduction to the Problems of Increasing Recovery of Oil and Gas in West Virginia,* Morgantown, W. Va., West Virginia University (Engineering Experiment Station Bulletin No. 21, Part 1), 1947, pp. 38.
Experimentation on gas wells, pumps, and compressors used in secondary oil recovery.

Robert S. Bossler, *Oil Fields Rejuvenated,* Harrisburg, Pennsylvania Bureau of Topographic and Geologic Survey (Bulletin No. 56), 1922, pp. 14.
Economics of water flooding; compressed air process; estimates.

George Homer Fancher and Donald Kenneth MacKay, *Secondary Recovery of Petroleum in Arkansas,* El Dorado, Ark., Arkansas Oil and Gas Commission, 1946, pp. ix + 264.
Prospects for secondary recovery in oil fields of South Arkansas.

Illinois Geological Survey, *Papers on Improved Methods of Exploring For and Recovering Petroleum in Illinois,* Urbana, State of Illinois, 1934, pp. 74.
Papers on improved methods of recovering oil, air repressuring, water flooding, acid treatment.

Illinois Geological Survey, *Symposium on Waterflooding,* Urbana, the Survey, published in 4 parts, 1956–1958, pp. 239.
Eleven papers on various aspects of water flooding.

Kentucky Oil & Gas Association, *Technical Session Papers,* Frankfort, Kentucky Geological Survey, 1953, pp. 64; 1954, pp. 96; 1955, pp. 76; 1956, pp. 83; 1957, pp. 75; 1958, pp. 84.
Technical session papers, chiefly on water flooding and other secondary recovery methods. Includes some papers on other related exploration and production matters.

William S. Lytle, *Crude Oil Reserves of Pennsylvania,* Harrisburg, Topographic and Geologic Survey of State of Pennsylvania, 1950, pp. iv + 256.
Reports on stripper well oil reserves of Pennsylvania covering, by counties, all 164 oil fields, with summary of secondary recovery operation, as of Jan. 1, 1950.

William S. Lytle, *Secondary Recovery Operations in Pennsylvania to Jan. 1, 1954,* Harrisburg, Topographic and Geologic Survey, 1955, pp. 23.
Summary to Jan. 1, 1954.

University of Missouri, School of Mines and Metallurgy, *A Symposium on Water Flooding of Oil Reservoirs,* Rolla, Mo., the School, 1952, pp. 55.
Five papers on history and theory of water flooding.

Oscar Fritzland Spencer, *Secondary Recovery of Oil,* State College, Penna., Pennsylvania State College, 1949, pp. vii + 438. Reprinted 1954, pp. 441.
Textbook for extension course.

Frederick Squires and Alfred Hannam Bell, *Water Flooding of Oil Sands in Illinois,* Urbana, Illinois State Geological Survey, 1943, pp. 101.
Geologic description of producing sands in old Illinois fields; natural, accidental, and applied floods.

University of Texas, Department of Petroleum Engineering, *Improving Oil Re-*

covery, Bradford, Penna., Producers Publishing Co., 1959, pp. 226.
Sixteen lectures on oil recovery, with emphasis on fluid injection, significance of secondary recovery and pressure maintenance, new techniques for improving recovery.

III.

Oil and Gas Law

A. GENERAL
(See also "Conservation")

Milton Arthur Allen, *Laws Pertaining to Oil,* Tucson, Ariz., University of Arizona, 1918, pp. 12.
Federal oil and gas statutes.

John Burton Amsbary and Jonah Jones, Jr., *Oil and Gas Law of California,* Los Angeles, Parker, Stone & Baird Co., 1932, pp. xv + 367. Rev. Ed. 1936, pp. xiv + 425.
Appellate decisions, oil and gas; nature and rights; leases, royalties, fixtures, drilling equipment; briefs of 200 California cases, forms; statutory regulation; case index.

Rachel B. Archer, *Archer's Law and Practice in Oil and Gas Cases,* Cincinnati, W. H. Anderson Co., 1911, pp. 1x + 1060.
Important cases in States producing oil and gas; Federal courts, analyses, practice, table of cases analyzed and cited.

Ernest R. Bartley, *The Tidelands Oil Controversy,* Austin, University of Texas Press, 1953, pp. 312.
Legal and historical analysis of dispute between Federal and State governments on control and ownership of offshore lands of Texas, Louisiana, and California, concluding with enactment in 1953 of quitclaim deed, by House of Representatives.

Richard Leroy Benoit, *Cyclopedia of Oil and Gas Forms,* St. Louis, Mo., Thomas Law Book Co., 1928, pp. viii + 634. (See *Benoit's Oil and Gas Forms,* by Curtis M. Oakes.)
Forms in current use in industry, from acquisition of unproven leasehold to consumption of product.

Earl A. Brown, *The Law of Oil and Gas Leases, with Forms and Special Purposes Clauses,* Albany, Matthew Bender & Co., 1958, pp. 681.
Legal guide covering conditions, problems of clauses and principles of leases, implied covenants of development, conservation laws.

George Bryan, *The Law of Petroleum and Natural Gas, with Forms,* Philadelphia, George T. Bisel, 1898, pp. xvi + 521.
Earliest book on oil and gas law; study of leading cases from several courts.

George Charles Felix Butte, *A Model Oil and Gas Contract,* Austin, University of Texas (Bulletin No. 1923, April 20, 1919), 1919, pp. 8.
Form of oil and gas contract for use by landowners in undeveloped territory.

R. W. Byram and Company, *Texas Oil and Gas Handbook. Procedures and Forms Required for Operation under Provisions of the Rules and Regulations of the Texas Railroad Commission,* Austin, the Company, 1958, pp. 111.

Continental Oil Company, *Landman's Legal Handbook. A Practical Guide in Leasing for Oil and Gas,* Denver, F. H. Gower, 1957, pp. 194. (Prepared by Denver Legal Staff of the Company.)
Describes land, legal work, preparation of documents for drilling; leases on fee and Federal lands; examination of records, unit agreements, lease and other forms.

Clay Cooke and W. W. Hubbard, *Texas Oil Laws Related to Public Lands and*

Reserved Minerals, n.p., n. pub., 1919, pp. 59.
Mineral reservation law; legislative history from law of 1837; mineral laws of oil and gas; forms; leases.

Harriet Spiller Daggett, *Mineral Rights in Louisiana,* Baton Rouge, Louisiana State University Press, 1939, pp. xxxv + 427. Rev. Ed. 1949, pp. xxi + 616.
Civil Code in relation to oil and gas development, leasing, royalty, etc.; tables of cases; appendices contain Louisiana statutes, forms.

George G. Dimick, *Louisiana Law of Oil and Gas: Jurisprudence, State and Federal; Statutes; Forms; Rules of the Department of Conservation Complete,* New Orleans, F. F. Hansell & Bro., 1922, pp. xi + 387.
Statement of oil and gas law; principles announced in decisions; statutes; rules of Louisiana Department of Conservation.

Daniel Douglas Donahue, *A Treatise on Petroleum and Natural and Manufactured Gases,* Bloomington, Ill., Pantagraph Printing & Stationery Co., 1902, pp. 461.
Principles of law in discovery, development, transportation, and use.

Robert Tucker Donley, *The Law of Coal, Oil and Gas in West Virginia and Virginia, with Forms,* Charlottesville, Va., Michie Co., 1951, pp. xiii + 454.
Reasons and theories supporting West Virginia and Virginia laws pertaining to subsurface minerals, partition, conveyance and leasing, duties and covenants under leases, assignments and surrender, rents, royalties, transportation, etc.

Sheridan Downey, *Truth About the Tidelands,* San Francisco, the author, 1948, pp. v + 74.
Written by a United States Senator from California, deals with controversy over submerged lands of California seacoast, including opinions of Supreme Court of United States, and review of hearings of Congressional committees in so-called "Tidelands Fight."

Federal Oil Conservation Board, *State and Federal Conservation Laws and Regulations Relating to the Production of Oil and Gas,* Washington, Government Printing Office, 1931, pp. 298.
Oil and gas conservation laws of States and United States, compiled by Technical and Advisory Committee of Federal Oil Conservation Board.

Gaughan and Sifford, Streett and Streett. and L. P. Brooks, *Mid-Continent Oil and Gas Forms,* Dallas, Post Publishing Co., 1926, pp. 352.
Forms most frequently used in oil and gas operations, statutory forms, forms in use by oil companies.

Samuel H. Glassmire, *Law of Oil and Gas Leases and Royalties. A Practical Legal Treatise on Petroleum Rights Accruing by Virtue of Mineral Deeds and Oil and Gas Leases,* St. Louis, Mo., Thomas Law Book Co., 1935, pp. 400. 2nd Ed 1938, pp. ix + 467. Cumulative pocket supplement.
Oil fields and production methods, new conception of production, evolution of lease, royalties, estates, law of leases, legal incidents of leases and royalties.

Frank Herbert Gower, *Forms and Land Decisions Relating to Oil and Gas Leasing and Unitization, Including Federal Forms Prescribed by the Department of Interior and Typical, Related, but no Prescribed Forms,* Denver, the author, 1948, var. pag.
Sections deal with leases, unitization operations.

Frank Herbert Gower, *Oil and Gas Leasing Laws, Including Sections of The Act of February 25, 1920, with Amendments and Supplements Thereto Relating to Oil and Gas Rights Owned by United States,* Denver, the author, 1952 (Rev.), var. pag.
Part I: Law.
Part II: Regulations.

Frank Herbert Gower, *Outer Continental Shelf Lands,* Denver, the author, 1954 var. pag.
Law and regulations.

D. H. Gregg, *Short Summary of Texas Law Relating to Oil and Gas,* Houston South Texas College of Law, 1946, pp xviii + 139.
Summary of casebook course on oil and gas law, as taught by author.

Marvin Andrew Harder, *The Tidelands Controversy*, Wichita, Kan., Municipal University of Wichita, 1949, pp. 35.
Chronology of principal events, 1937–49, oil exploration in tidelands, litigation, and positions of State and Federal governments and oil companies.

Robert E. Hardwicke, *Innocent Purchaser of Oil and Gas Lease*, Dallas, Oil and Gas Legal Service, Martin Stationery Co., 1921, pp. 112.
Discusses estate created by oil and gas lease.

Lyndsay D. Hawkins, *A Digest and Brief Book of Texas Oil and Gas Decisions*, Austin, Gammel's Book Store, 1922, pp. 141.
Accurate and pointed citations to recent leading cases decided in courts of Texas.

G. Hazel, *Public Lands of Texas. An Examination of the History of the Public Domain of This State, with the Constitutional and Statutory Provisions, and Leading Cases, Governing Its Use and Disposition*, Austin, Gammel's Book Store, 1938, pp. viii + 121.
Nature of oil and gas mineral reservations, prospects, river-bed and other leases, leasing.

Lewis Edwin Hoffman, *Oil and Gas Leasing on the Public Domain*, Denver, F. H. Gower, 1951, pp. xviii + 429. 2nd Ed. 1957, pp. x + 597.
Comprehensive outline of procedure for prospecting, leasing, and producing on public domain.

Carus S. Icenogle, *Handbook of Illinois Oil and Gas Law*, Mattoon, Ill., Midcontinent Map Co., 1938, pp. 71.
Compilation of Illinois cases and statutes; oil and gas leases, other agreements; statutory provisions; forms.

James Manford Kerr, *Mining and Water Cases Annotated; A Collection of Leading American, Canadian and English Cases on Topics of Irrigation, Drainage, Reclamation, Mining, Oil, Gas, and Related Subjects, with Annotations, Indexes, and Forms*, Vol. I, Chicago, Callaghan & Co., 1912, pp. xii + 856. (No further volumes published.)
Series of annotated cases, current and

important decisions, of wide range; includes cases involving oil companies; laws.

Victor Henry Kulp, *Cases on the Law of Oil and Gas*, Norman, Okla, the author, 1922, 3 parts, pp. 345.
Emphasis on Oklahoma decisions; property rights in oil and gas, leases, development assignment, rights, liabilities, with forms. Compiled as aid in presentation of law of oil and gas at law school of University of Oklahoma.

Victor Henry Kulp, *Digest of Oil and Gas Decisions*, Dallas, Oil and Gas Legal Service, 1928, pp. xiii + 486.
Oklahoma cases, including Federal from Oklahoma; cases from other states and Federal courts; Oct. 1922 to Dec. 1927, covering Martin's Oil and Gas Legal Service, Vol. V through VIII. (See Digest by Smedley.)

Victor Henry Kulp, *Cases on Oil and Gas, Selected from Decisions of American Courts*, St. Paul, Minn., West Publishing Co., 1924, pp. xix + 512. 2nd Ed. 1935, pp. xiv + 663. 3rd Ed. 1947, pp. xxxiv + 910, *Supplement*, 1953, pp. ix + 94.
Nature of landowner's rights in oil and gas, interference, oil and gas lease, drilling, use, taxation, rights on public lands, government control.

Victor Henry Kulp, *Oil and Gas Rights*, (Reprinted from *American Law of Property*, Part 10), Boston, Little, Brown & Co., 1954, pp. xiii + 506–916. Supplement in pocket.
History, nature of landowner's rights to oil and gas in place, interference, oil and gas lease, joint ventures, government control of production, conservation, drilling, storage and use, transportation, taxation, oil and gas rights on public land.

David Levine, *The Petroleum Industry. A Study of its Interstate Aspect*, New York, Works Progress Administration, 1938, pp. 92.
Interstate aspects of integrated oil operations.

Curtis Holbrook Lindley, *A Treatise on the American Law Relating to Mines and Mineral Lands Within the Public Land*

States and Territories, and Governing the Acquisition and Enjoyment of Mining Rights in Lands of the Public Domain, San Francisco, Bancroft-Whitney Co., 1897, 2 vols. 2nd Ed. 1903, 2 vols. pp. cli + 2150. 3rd Ed. 3 vols. pp. cclii + 2813.
Government as proprietor holding paramount title to public domain; right of disposal.

Martin Stationery Company, *Oil and Gas Laws of Texas, 1921,* Dallas, the Company, 1921, pp. 223. (Also used title, *Oil and Gas Legal Service.*)
Copies of Texas laws of oil and gas; forms. Valuable section "Oil and Gas Rights in State Lands" by Graham Best Smedley, who later became Judge of Supreme Court of Texas. First published 1919.

Alfred E. McLane, *Oil and Gas Leasing on Indian Lands,* Denver, F. H. Gower, and Albany, Matthew Bender Co., 1955, pp. viii + 407.
Documented material on status of Indians, their lands, procedures on leasing Indian land, statutes and regulations, data on leases, production, etc.

Maurice Hitchcock Merrill, *The Law Relating to Covenants Implied in Oil and Gas Leases,* St. Louis, Mo., Thomas Law Book Co., 1926, pp. 303. 2nd Ed. 1940, pp. 517.
Lessee's duty to explore, develop, and operate leased premises in light of court decisions; principles behind cases.

John Lawrence Mills and James Cook Willingham, *The Law of Oil and Gas,* Chicago, Callaghan & Co., 1926, pp. xv + 791.
Federal leasing act; rules governing leasing of public lands; restrictions on Indian lands; forms of leases.

Montana Bar Association, *Oil and Gas Law Institute Proceedings,* Helena, the Association, 1949, pp. 83.
Eight papers: unitization; oil and gas leases; essentials of petroleum geology of Montana.

W. C. Montgomery, Ed., *Lectures on Texas Oil and Gas Law,* Midland, Tex., the editor, 1954, pp. 98.
Eight lectures by different authors on oil and gas leases, mineral interests, covenants, state regulation, etc.

Robert Stewart Morrison and Emilio Dominguez De Soto, *Oil and Gas Rights on the Public Domain and Private Lands, etc.,* San Francisco, Bender-Moss Co., 1920, pp. xv + 1115.
Book suggested by enactment of Oil and Gas Leasing Act, Feb. 25, 1920; analysis, comments; lands not affected by Act; pipe lines on public domain; interstate commerce, etc.

Curtis M. Oakes, *Benoit's Oil and Gas Forms,* St. Louis, Mo., Thomas Law Book Co., 1939, pp. 686.
Comprehensive list of forms in common use by oil and gas industry.

Curtis M. Oakes, *Standard Oil and Gas Forms,* St. Louis, Mo., Thomas Law Book Co., 1952, pp. 611.
Comprehensive list of forms in common use by oil and gas industry.

Stephen R. Pratt, *Pratt's Mining Laws of Colorado and Locators' Manual,* Denver, Pratt Mercantile & Publishing Co., 1900, pp. 163. Supplement: 1902, contains changes to Feb. 1902, pp. xxxii.
Supplement contains oil laws, relating to oil locations on United States, State, and private lands; statutes; forms.

Benjamin Franklin Rice and Thomas Daniel Lyons, *The Oil Operator in Oklahoma. The Law of Oil and Gas. The Law of Corporations,* New York, Dispatch Press, 1918, pp. 628.
Discusses legal matters; waste of oil and gas. "True conservation," possibly first published use of phrase, as contrasted with "commercial conservation," used to describe "attempted economic regulation."

John S. Roberts, *Primer of Oil and Gas Law of Texas,* Bellaire, Tex., Belltex Publishing Co., 1955, pp. 56.
Written for the layman; discusses nature and type of ownership in oil and gas properties; basic contracts; unitization and joint operation; conservation; taxation.

Rocky Mountain Mineral Law Institute *Proceedings,* Albany, Matthew Bender & Co.

First Annual Meeting, 1955, pp. 554. 19 papers: case, statute, and substantive indexes; land acquisition, exploration, development, public lands, operations. *Second Annual Meeting,* 1956, pp. xi + 509. 17 papers: problems of oil and gas conservation, valuation, taxation of production. *Third Annual Meeting,* 1957, pp. xii + 806. 22 papers. *Fourth Annual Meeting,* 1958, pp. xi + 703. Problems in acquisition of oil and gas interests, exploration and development, administration, government control.

Milan C. Rowald, *Handbook for Landmen,* Houston, the author, 1952, pp. 209.
Aid in handling land and title matters in oil and gas transactions; sections on Alabama, California, Florida, Georgia, Louisiana, Mississippi, New Mexico, Texas.

G. B. Smedley, *Digest of Oil and Gas Decisions,* Dallas, Martin Stationery Co., 1923, pp. 293.
Texas decisions on law of oil and gas; includes decisions from nearby states. Covers *Oil and Gas Legal Service,* Vol. I through IV, No. 2. (See Digest by Kulp.)

South Texas College of Law, *Oil and Gas Law. Special Series of 16 Lectures,* Houston, the College, 1954, pp. 211.
Petroleum geology for lawyers; history; rules and regulations of Railroad Commission of Texas; government regulation of production; problems of leasing, pipe lines, taxation.

Southwestern Legal Foundation, *Oil and Gas Reporter,* Vol. I, No. 1, Albany, Matthew Bender & Co., 1952. (Foundation in Dallas.)
Selected cases, statutes, administrative rulings; cases arranged geographically by states. Sections on substantive law, taxation cases, statutes and administrative rulings, Canadian law, special articles and reviews.
Intended as quarterly, 4 issues of Vol. I published 1952 and 1953. Beginning with Vol. II, 1953, issued as monthly releases including current cases and decision notes; cumulative case table, index, annual binder. Vol. VIII issued

1958. 4 issues, Vol. I reprinted with binder.

Robert E. Sullivan, *Handbook of Oil and Gas Law,* New York, Prentice-Hall, 1955, pp. xix + 556. 2nd Ed. Englewood Cliffs, N.J., Parker Publishing Co., 1958.
Basic principles of oil and gas law, reasons, applications in present-day operations. Covers landowner's interest, leases, obligations, assignments, government regulation, cooperative development, transportation, taxation, financing.

Walter Lee Summers, *The Law of Oil and Gas. A Treatise Covering the Law Relating to the Production of Oil and Gas from Public and Private Lands and Transportation Thereof, with Statutes and Regulations, Forms,* (first published in single volume as *A Treatise on the Law of Oil and Gas*), Kansas City, Mo., Vernon Law Book Co., 1927, pp. xviii + 863, 12 vols. (9 numbered, Vols. 1, 3, and 5 in 2 parts), 1938–1939. Rev. Eds.: Vol. 6, 1950; Vols. 5 and 5a, 1951; Vols. 1 and 1a, 1954; Vols. 8 and 9, 1955, Vols. 3 and 3a, 1958. With current pocket supplement.
Landowner's rights and duties, leases, liabilities and performance, statutes of States, Federal Government, Canadian Provinces; forms; table of cases.

Walter Lee Summers, *Cases and Materials on Oil and Gas,* St. Paul, Minn., West Publishing Co., 1952, pp. xxviii + 781.
Selected cases and materials on production, conservation, nature of landowner's interest, relations of landowner and lessee, assignment of lessee's interest, payment, transfer and apportionment of rents and royalties, table of cases.

Texas Law Review, *Oil and Gas Law, with Articles Pertaining to Sulphur, Taxation, Tidelands, etc.,* Austin, *Texas Law Review,* 1951, pp. xix + 1736.
All articles, comments, case notes, book reviews in field of oil and gas law, and related topics which have been published in *Texas Law Review* since its original issue in 1922; arranged in order of appearance; index and table of cases. Covers Vol. 1–29. *Supplement to Oil*

and Gas Law, with Articles Pertaining to Sulphur, Taxation, Tidelands, Etc., 1955, Reprinted from Vol. 30, 31, 32 of *Texas Law Review*, 1951–54, pp. ix + 439.
Covers three additional years, new page numbers continue paging of Vol. 1. *Supplement*, 1959, pp. xii + 967.

William Wheeler Thornton, *The Law Relating to Oil and Gas, etc.,* Cincinnati, The W. H. Anderson Co., 1904, pp. 918. 2nd Ed. 1912, pp. 1184. 3rd Ed. 1918, 2 vols., pp. 1639. 4th Ed. 1925, 2 vols., pp. 2947. 5th Ed., rev. by Simeon S. Willis: *The Law of Oil and Gas, including Forms of Oil and Gas Leases, Contracts, Etc., Together with Annotated Statutes and Regulations Pertaining to Natural Gas and Oil,* 1932–1934, 6 vols., pp. 3275. Vol. 7 with Oil and Gas Statutes, 1933–1939, added 1939. Replacement Vols. 4 and 5 compiled and edited by Charles L. Cole, 1946.
Collates and discusses cases involving petroleum and natural gas, rights and liabilities of production, sale, transportation; with statutes and forms.

Andrew Joseph Thuss, *Texas Oil and Gas. A Treatise on the Law, Etc.,* Kansas City, Mo., Vernon Law Book Co., 1929, pp. 633. 2nd Ed. 1925, pp. v + 680.
Legal considerations in leasing oil and gas lands, royalties, implied covenants, contracts, public lands, pipe lines, gas utilities, taxation.

Tulane University, *Legal Problems in the Tidelands,* Baton Rouge, The Offshore Co., 1959, var. pag.
Ten papers presented Nov. 21–22, 1958, at 3rd Symposium on Legal Problems in the Tidelands, by Professional Study Program of School of Law, Tulane University. Symposium initiated 1956.

James A. Veasey, *Inquiries Looking to a Change in One Element of the Rule of Capture as it Now Obtains at Common Law to the End that the Rights of Operators to Produce Oil and Gas Shall be Determined Upon the Relativity of Reservoir Conditions Between and Among the Separate Properties in a Reservoir,* Ann Arbor, Mich., the author, 1941, pp. 213.

Discusses Rule of Capture as interpreted in various decisions and from various statutes.

Marlin M. Volz and Leo H. Whinery, *Lectures on Oil and Gas Law,* Kansas City, Mo., University of Kansas City School of Law, 1954, var. pag.
Fourteen papers presented by various authors at lecture series, 1953. Covers functional phases of industry, related legal aspects and problems.

John Mort Walker, Jr., *Cases and Materials on Oil, Gas and Minerals,* New Orleans, the author, 1938, pp. 321.
Fundamental principles of oil, gas and mineral law in Louisiana, for use in School of Law, Loyola University. Part I: Nature of rights in oil, gas, other minerals; their sale and reservation. Part II: Mineral leases.

Lewis A. Wallace, *Oklahoma Oil and Gas Laws,* St. Louis, Mo., Thomas Law Book Co., 1922, pp. 266.
Laws, decisions citing and construing laws, digest of cases decided by Supreme Court of Oklahoma; Oklahoma cases decided by Federal courts; rules and regulations of Oklahoma Corporation Commission; forms.

Alfred Ernest Wilkinson and Julian Andrew Richardson, *Law of Oil and Natural Gas. A Hand Book of the Statutes of Texas and the Decisions of Courts Relating to Oil and Natural Gas Organization and Operation of Oil and Gas Companies, and Ownership and Transfer of Mineral Rights,* Austin, E. L. Steck, 1915, pp. 162.
Corporation and mining laws of Texas, franchise tax, oil and gas wells, blue sky laws, mineral and mining rights, statutes and rulings.

Howard Russell Williams, Richard C. Maxwell, and Charles J. Meyers, *Cases and Materials on the Law of Oil and Gas,* Brooklyn, N.Y., Foundation Press, 1956, pp. xlv + 790.
For use of advanced students; materials on cases involving problems unique to oil and gas; includes review and discussion of conservation, well spacing, proration, unitization, taxation.

B. WORLD PETROLEUM

Gordon H. Barrows, *World Petroleum Legislation,* New York, Mona Palmer Corporation, 1956, 1957, 2 vols. (Looseleaf, revised currently.) Var. pag.
Legal and fiscal legislation of petroleum industry in 49 countries, Alaska, and United States.

Marion Clawson and Burnell Held, *The Federal Lands, Their Use and Management,* Baltimore, Johns Hopkins Press, 1957, pp. xxi + 501.
Leasing of Federal lands for oil and gas, production, bonus bids, royalties and revenues derived, submerged lands, wild life reservations.

M. W. Mouton, *The Continental Shelf,* The Hague, Martinus Nijhoff, 1952, pp. xi + 367.
Critical analysis of legal documents defining continental shelf; discusses proclamations, declarations, decrees concerning jurisdiction over mineral resources; offshore drilling techniques and problems.

Kenneth Redden and John Huston, *The Petroleum Law of Turkey,* Istanbul, Fakulteler Matbaasi, 1956, pp. x + 322.
Text, legislative history, administrative interpretation of Turkish Petroleum Law, March 16, 1954, amended May 21, 1955; 7 sets of regulations. Ankara University Faculty of Law—New York University Graduate School of Public Administration and Social Service, Joint Publication Series, No. 4.

Max Weston Thornburg, *Report on Proposed Petroleum Legislation for Guatemala,* Washington, Inter-American Development Commission, 1946, pp. 82.
Prepared to assist Guatemalan Government in drafting petroleum legislation, reviews objectives which a nation should seek in petroleum legislation, factors which would make such legislation effective.

IV.

Oil Fields and Areas
of Western Hemisphere

Independent Petroleum Association of America, *Petroleum in the Western Hemisphere,* Washington, the Association, 1952, pp. viii + 183.
Data on oil production, productive capacity, reserves, expected future availability of petroleum in Western Hemisphere through 1960; historical data on supply and demand and expected situation in 1955; oil country tubular goods and requirements; governmental stability, land ownership and petroleum laws, producing and non-producing countries.

James Trumbull, John Lyman, James F. Pepper, and Edwin M. Thomasson, *An Introduction to the Geology and Mineral Resources of the Continental Shelves of the Americas,* Washington, Geological Survey Bulletin No. 1067, Government Printing Office, 1958, pp. vii + 92, with chart.
Potential mineral resources, including oil and gas, in the Continental shelves and slopes from Alaska to Argentina; problems of petroleum development on the Continental shelf of the Gulf of Mexico.

A. NORTH AMERICA

American Association of Petroleum Geologists, *Possible Future Oil Provinces of the United States and Canada,* Tulsa, the Association, 1941, pp. 154.
Possible oil provinces of Alaska, Canada, and United States.

American Association of Petroleum Geologists, *Possible Future Petroleum Provinces of North America,* Tulsa, the Association, 1951, pp. xiii + 358.
Undiscovered oil resources of Mexico, United States, Canada, Alaska, and continental shelf.

Walter August Ver Wiebe, *Oil Fields in North America,* Ann Arbor, Mich., Edwards Bros., 1949, pp. 251.
(See below)

Walter August Ver Wiebe, *North American and Middle East Oil Fields,* Wichita,

Kan., the author, 1950, pp. iv + 259.
(See below)

Walter August Ver Wiebe, *North American Petroleum,* Wichita, Kan., the author, 1952, pp. iv + 459. Also published 1957.
These three books discuss origin and occurrence of oil and gas; describe oil fields in United States by geological province; oil fields in Alaska, Canada, Mexico, and Middle East.

Western Oil Men's Association, Bureau of Publicity, *Oil Development of the United States and Canada,* Toledo, Ohio, the Bureau, 1903, pages unnumbered.
Reviews oil production and development in various sections of United States, Canada, and elsewhere, with history of association.

B. CANADA

Province of Alberta, Royal Commission, *Alberta's Oil Industry. The Report of a Royal Commission Appointed by the*

Government of the Province of Alberta under the Public Inquiries Act to Inquire into Matters Connected with

Petroleum and Petroleum Products, Toronto, Imperial Oil Co., 1940, pp. 278.
Review of testimony presented to Commission inquiring into production, refining, transportation, and marketing of petroleum and petroleum products in the Province of Alberta, costs, prices, with view to reducing consumer price or governmental participation in marketing.

American Association of Petroleum Geologists, *Western Canada Sedimentary Basin*, Tulsa, the Association, 1954, pp. x + 521.
Papers on general geology, stratigraphy, structures, oil and gas development in western Canada.

Floyd K. Beach and John Langhorne Irwin, *The History of Alberta Oil*, Edmonton, Alberta, Issued by Dept. of Lands and Mines, published by Publicity and Travel Bureau, 1940, pp. 62.
History of Alberta's oil and gas development; bituminous sands; oil production in 1939.

Borden Commission, *Royal Commission on Energy, First Report*, Ottawa, Queen's Printer, 1958, pp. xiv + 98.
Report of investigatory body set up by Canadian Parliament in 1957 under chairmanship of Henry Borden to study Canada's energy resources and needs, and recommend on national policy. Important recommendations on the future of Canadian oil industry.

H. Peareth H. Brumell, *Report on Natural Gas and Petroleum in Ontario prior to 1891*, Ottawa, Geological Survey of Canada, 1892, pp. 94.
Early history of oil and gas drilling; details of wells drilled in Ontario through 1890.

Canada. Department of the Interior, Natural Resources Intelligence Branch, *Oil and Gas in Western Canada*, Dept. of Interior, Canada, 1920, pp. 27.
Topography, transportation, general development of western Canada's oil and gas fields.

Howard McDougall Chantler, P. B. Seely, and F. E. Goodspeed, *Analyses of Canadian Crude Oils*, Ottawa, Mines Branch, Dept. of Mines and Technical Surveys (Report No. 832), 1951, pp. 90.
Analyses of 88 representative samples of Canadian crude oil received at Fuel Research Laboratories from 1931 to 1950.

Howard McDougall Chantler, Pearce Victor Rosewarne, and Aylmer Aberffrau Swinnerton, *Analyses of Canadian Crude Oils, Napthas, Shale Oil and Bitumen*, Ottawa, Dept. of Mines (Report No. 765), 1936, pp. vi + 21.

Edward John Chapman, *A Popular and Practical Exposition of the Minerals and Geology of Canada*, Toronto, W. C. Chewett & Co., 1864, pp. xii + 236.
Short summary of early oil developments in Canada and more extended discussion of prevailing view on origin of petroleum.

Frederick G. Clapp (and others), *Petroleum and Natural Gas Resources of Canada*, Ottawa, Government Printing Bureau, 1914, 2 vols., pp. xxvi + 782.
Vol. I: Reviews history, geographical occurrence and production of petroleum, developments by countries, geology, properties of oil and gas, storage, transportation, utilization, and conservation. Vol. II: Presents detailed description of Canadian oil and gas fields, showing, for each province, geology, history of drilling operations, possibilities of oil and gas, and oil shale.

Donaldson Bogart Dowling, S. E. Slipper, and F. H. McLearn, *Investigations in the Gas and Oil Fields of Alberta, Saskatchewan, and Manitoba*, Ottawa, Canadian Dept. of Mines, Geological Survey (Memoir No. 116), 1919, pp. ii + 89.
Structure and correlation of underground formations of Alberta, Saskatchewan, and Manitoba, geology of southern and central Alberta, and Cretaceous of Peace and Athabaska Valleys; records of selected wells.

The Financial Post, *Survey of Canadian Oils*, Toronto, MacLean-Hunter Publishing Co., Vols. I to XVI, 1929 to 1958, pp. 4040.
Reviews of Canadian oil and gas com-

panies, drilling, royalties, prices, refineries, and statistics.

Eric J. Hanson, *Dynamic Decade,* Toronto, McClelland & Stewart, 1958, pp. 314.
Changes in economy of Alberta from dormant economic society into rapidly expanding, vigorous society, 1946–1956, following discovery of oil at Leduc; earlier and later discoveries and developments, companies involved, and problems created.

George Sherwood Hume, *Petroleum Geology of Canada,* Ottawa, Geological Survey of Canada (Economic Geology Series No. 14), 1944, pp. 64.
Geology of various areas of Canada, account of oil developments.

George Sherwood Hume. *Oil and Gas in Eastern Canada,* Ottawa, Geological Survey of Canada, 1932, pp. vii + 187.
Geology of areas in eastern Canada, descriptions of oil and gas fields, and history of oil developments, including early drilling.

George Sherwood Hume, *Oil and Gas in Western Canada,* Ottawa, Geological Survey of Canada, 1928, pp. v + 152. 2nd Ed. 1933, pp. v + 359.
Origin and accumulation of oil and gas, geophysical exploration, geology of Great Plains, descriptions of oil and gas fields.

George Sherwood Hume and A. Ignatieff, *Natural Gas Reserves of Prairie Provinces,* Ottawa, Geological Survey of Canada, 1948, pp. 244.
Appraisal and calculation of gas reserves; areas of proven, probable, and potential reserves; with 45 appendices, each dealing with specific field or area, accompanied by map. Peace River area of Alberta and foothills and plains of northeastern British Columbia not included.

Imperial Oil Ltd., *A Canadian Achievement, Delivery of Alberta Crude Oil at Sarnia, Ontario, Apr. 24, 1951,* Toronto, Imperial Oil Ltd., 1951, pp. 15.
Souvenir booklet outlining oil development in Alberta, pipe line to Superior, Wis., and movement of oil by tankers to Sarnia.

Imperial Oil Ltd., *Facts and Figures About Canadian Oil,* Toronto, Imperial Oil Ltd., 1952, pp. 15.
Data on Canadian oil development up to midsummer 1952, with map.

Wyatt Malcolm, *Oil and Gas Prospects of the Northwest Provinces of Canada,* Ottawa, Canadian Dept. of Mines, Geological Survey (Memoir No. 29–E) 1913, pp. vi + 99.
Geological conditions, oil and gas possibilities of northwestern provinces of Canada; logs of wells.

Wyatt Malcolm, *The Oil and Gas Fields of Ontario and Quebec,* Ottawa, Government Printing Bureau (Canadian Dept. of Mines, Geological Survey, Memoir 81, Geological Series No. 67), 1915, pp. ii + 248.
Geology of Ontario and Quebec; history and description, by counties, of oil and gas fields; logs of wells; analyses of oil; production.

C. V. Myers, *The Oil Investor,* Calgary, Alberta, the author, 1945, pp. 90.
General background on oil geology, origin, accumulation, distribution of petroleum, producing and potential oil areas of Canada.

Carl Olaf Nickle, *The Valley of Wonders,* Calgary, Alberta, Oil Bulletin, 1941, pp. 40.
Turner Valley field; geology, production, conservation, prices, royalties, record of wells, accumulative production to October 1941.

Joseph E. Pogue, *Oil in Canada,* New York, Chase National Bank, 1949, pp. 16.
Potential resources, exploration effort, exchange problems, capital formation, hemispheric considerations, tar sands, natural gas.

Victor Ross, *Petroleum in Canada,* Toronto, printed by Southern Press Limited, 1917, pp. 109.
Nontechnical commercial account of Canadian oil development, with map of Ontario fields.

Saskatchewan Dept. of Mineral Resources, *Oil in Saskatchewan,* Regina, the Department, 1956, pp. 72.

History of oil in Saskatchewan, including provisions of land tenure.

oronto Globe, *The Petroleum District of Canada West,* Toronto, Rollo & Adam, 1865, pp. 49.
Early account of Ontario oil fields.

John F. Tyrrell, *The Oil Districts of Canada,* New York, American News Co., 1865, pp. 40.
Early account of Ontario fields. Describes Shaw well, Jan. 16, 1862, as first flowing well in Canada.

C. UNITED STATES

(For works of primarily historical interest, see also Section XIV)

1. GENERAL

Ralph Arnold and William Kemnitzer, *Petroleum in the United States and Possessions,* New York, Harper & Bros., 1931, pp. 1052.
Excellent survey of development of United States oil fields and areas, with detail not found elsewhere, with maps.

William J. Buck, *Early Accounts of Petroleum in the United States,* Titusville, Penna., Bloss & Cogswell, 1876, pp. 12.
Early accounts of presence of petroleum, by various travellers in New York, Pennsylvania, Ohio and West Virginia.

Leonard M. Fanning, *The Rise of American Oil,* New York, Harper & Bros., 1936, pp. ix + 221. 2nd Ed. 1948, pp. xii + 178.
Oil history and achievement of oil industry in meeting needs of advancing civilization. Revised 2nd Ed. also covers secondary recovery, wartime oil products, synthetics, agriculture.

Leonard M. Fanning, Ed., *Our Oil Resources,* New York, McGraw-Hill Book Co., 1945, pp. viii + 331. 2nd Ed. 1950, pp. x + 420.
Papers by oil industry leaders, edited, reviewing oil and natural gas reserves, oil from shale and coal, role of private enterprise in development of oil resources, operations abroad, and role of technology, with list of "oil-shortage scares."

Independent Petroleum Association of America, *The Oil-Producing Industry in Your State,* Tulsa, the Association, 1959, pp. 96.
General review, with charts, of oil-producing industry in the United States, with maps showing counties with oil and gas production, and historical and statistical data for each of 31 states. Present series started with 1950 edition, pp. 61, covering 26 states, with subsequent edition each two years. Series preceded by *The Oil Industry in Your State,* Tulsa, the Association, 1940, pp. 42, and 1941, pp. 26, covering 19 states.

Juanita Morris Kreps, Ed., *Our Natural Resources, Their Development and Use,* New York, H. W. Wilson Co., 1955, pp. 189.
Reviews Tidelands oil controversy, discusses Submerged Lands Act, May 22, 1953; extracts, with comments, from other writings on subject.

Max Miller, *Speak to the Earth,* New York, Appleton-Century-Crofts, 1955, pp. 310.
An "oil tour" through the United States, California to Williston Basin to Appalachian oil region, back through Ohio to Southwest, including offshore operations; popular, generalized treatment.

National Oil Scouts and Landmen's Association, *Oil and Gas Field Development in United States and Canada, 1958,* Austin, Tex., 1959, pp. 1136.
Geological and geophysical prospecting, land and leasing activities, exploration, proven field development, oil and gas production, pipe line and refinery statistics. First published in 1931, with review of 1930, and annually for each succeeding year. Canada added to title in 1951. Detailed field statistics make this series valuable reference work.

National Petroleum Council, *Petroleum Productive Capacity,* Washington, the Council, 1952, pp. xvi + 102.

Report to National Petroleum Council prepared by Committee on Oil and Gas Availability; summarizes results of study by oil industry experts on future supplies.

Bruce Carlton Netschert, *The Future Supply of Oil and Gas,* Baltimore, Johns Hopkins Press, 1958, pp. xiv + 134.
Investigation of resources for the future; indicated total availability of crude oil in United States, 1975.

Jacob Harris Patton, *Natural Resources of the United States,* New York, D. Appleton & Co., 1888. 2nd Ed. 1894. 3rd Ed. 1899, pp. xv + 526.
Petroleum and natural gas, origins and localities where found.

Sir Morton Peto, *The Resources and Prospects of America,* London, Alexander Strahan, 1866, pp. xv + 428.
Chapter on petroleum deals generally with American oil industry.

Mark L. Requa, *Petroleum Resources of the United States,* Washington, Government Printing Office (Senate Document No. 363, 64th Congress, 1st Session), 1916, pp. 18.
Article on exhaustion of petroleum resources of United States showing supply and demand of oil and production of principal fields, with recommendation for conservation by coordinating drilling to market requirements. Requa was a leader in early attempts at conservation.

Luther Crocker Snider and Benjamin T. Brooks, *Petroleum Shortage and Its Alleviation,* New York, Chemical Foundation, 1935, pp. 38.
Considers possibility of petroleum shortage in United States, and changes likely in oil industry.

Walter August Ver Wiebe, *Oil Fields in the United States,* New York, McGraw-Hill Book Co., 1930, pp. x + 629.
Occurrence of oil in United States, with large structural features, or tectonic elements, grouped into petroliferous provinces; stratigraphy of each province, and structural conditions which have controlled accumulation of oil and gas.

2. EASTERN STATES

a. New York

John P. Herrick, *Bolivar, New York Pioneer Oil Town,* Los Angeles, Ward Ritchie Press, 1952, pp. x + 150.
Reviews early oil discoveries and developments and resulting boom, in and around Bolivar, as well as later and more lasting prosperity resulting from secondary recovery oil operations, with sketches of oil and gas pioneers and sidelights on earlier oil activities.

Edward Orton, *Petroleum and Natural Gas in New York,* Albany, University of the State of New York (Bulletin of New York State Museum), 1899, pp. 397–526, Vol. 6, No. 30.
Geologic structure, theories of origin and accumulation of oil and gas, geologic scale in New York as related to oil and gas, production of gas from lower formations and from gas belt bordering Lake Erie.

b. Pennsylvania

Charles A. Ashburner, *The Product and Exhaustion of the Oil Regions of Pennsylvania and New York,* n.p., n. pub., 1885, pp. 10, 2 charts, and map of oil regions. (Reprint of paper read before American Institute of Mining Engineers, Halifax.)
Describes oil-producing regions of Pennsylvania and New York, with comment on possibilities of other areas.

George Hall Ashley and J. French Robinson, *The Oil and Gas Fields of Pennsylvania,* Harrisburg, Bureau of Topographic and Geological Survey, 4th series, Bulletin M-1, 1922, pp. 78.
Short description of Pennsylvania oil pools by counties.

F. W. Beers, *Atlas of the Oil Regions of Pennsylvania,* New York, Beers, Ellis & Soule, 1865, pp. 48.
First collection of oilfield maps in book form; also article "Petroleum: Historically, Scientifically, and Commercially Reviewed," by Ivan C. Michaels.

John Herbert A. Bone, *Petroleum and Petroleum Wells,* New York, American

News Co., and Philadelphia, J. B. Lippincott & Co., 1865, pp. 94. 2nd Ed. Ed. 1866, pp. vi + 153.
Early history of petroleum in United States, methods employed, description of oil regions. Advertisement of Weikel Run and McElhinny Oil Co., Venango County in 1st Ed., lists J. D. Rockefeller among directors. 2nd Ed. includes Kentucky in subtitle.

John F. Carll, *Report of Progress in the Venango County District,* Harrisburg, Pennsylvania Board of Commissioners, 2nd Geological Survey, 1875, pp. 127.
Landmark report of early geological and production practice by famous early geologist; shows maps of contour lines of upper and under surfaces of First and Third Oil Sand formations.

John F. Carll, *Oil Well Records and Levels,* Harrisburg, Pennsylvania Board of Commissioners for Geological Survey, 1877, pp. xiv +398.
Well log records of about 2,000 oil wells drilled in Pennsylvania, as kept by well owners, representing about 10 per cent of total Pennsylvania wells.

John F. Carll, *The Geology of the Oil Regions of Warren, Venango, Clarion, and Butler Counties; Descriptions of Oil Well Rig and Tools.* Harrisburg, Pennsylvania Board of Commissioners, 2nd Geological Survey, 1880, pp. xxiv + 482.
Discussion of oil geology and development; chapters describing oil well rig, drilling, pumping, use of torpedo, and other production methods, including function of gas and water in oil production. Described as "foundation of both petroleum geology and engineering."
Atlas of Oil Regions. Contains maps and plates to accompany Carll's 1880 report. Sectional drawings of 3 oil wells, showing successive variations in style of drill hole, drive pipe, seed bag, tubing and casing in 1861, 1868, and 1875, drawings which were widely copied by succeeding writers.

John F. Carll, *Report on the Oil and Gas Regions,* Harrisburg, Pennsylvania Board of Commissioners for Geological Survey, Annual Report, 1887, Part II, pp. viii + 575–918.
History of oil and gas development in Pennsylvania and New York; discussion of geography, topography and geological structures; developments during 1886; natural gas wells and pipe line in vicinity of Pittsburgh prior to 1885; well records.

Andrew Carnegie, *The Empire of Business,* New York, Doubleday, Page & Co., 1922, pp. 356.
Chapter on oil and gas wells of western Pennsylvania, which briefly reviews oil history of region, devoted largely to gas wells and gas-producing area adjacent to Pittsburgh. Carnegie was successful participant in early oil ventures before he entered steel business.

Denslow & Bush, *Petroleum: What It Is and Where to Get It; With Sketches of the Oil Regions of Pennsylvania,* New York, Denslow & Bush, 1876, pp. 16.
Early oil development in Pennsylvania; lithographs of field scenes, sketches of tools.

Charles R. Fettke, *The Bradford Oil Field, Pennsylvania and New York,* Harrisburg, Topographic and Geologic Survey (Pennsylvania Geological Survey, 4th series, Bulletin M–21), 1938, pp. xvii + 454.
History, development, stratigraphic and structural geology, reservoir rocks, individual pools, oil production, water flooding, reserves, anticipated future of Bradford oil field.

Charles R. Fettke, *Summarized Record of Deep Wells in Pennsylvania,* Harrisburg, Topographic and Geologic Survey (Pennsylvania Geological Survey Bulletin M–31), 1950, pp. iii + 148.
Deep-sand exploration in Pennsylvania, with comparable data for New York, Ohio, West Virginia, and Maryland.

Charles R. Fettke, *Summarized Records of Deep Wells in Pennsylvania, 1950 to 1954,* Harrisburg, Topographic and Geologic Survey (Pennsylvania Geological Survey Bulletin M–39), 1956, pp. 114.
Supplement to Bulletin M–31 above.

F. M. L. Gillelen, *The Oil Regions of Pennsylvania, with Maps and Charts of Oil Creek, the Allegheny River, etc.,* Pittsburgh, John P. Hunt, 1864, pp. 67.

Prepared to give accurate account of oil regions, with maps strictly drawn; 16 charts of Allegheny River and one regional chart; lithographs of refineries.

Charles H. Harris (Oof T. Goof), *History of the Venango Oil Regions: Showing Where Petroleum is Found,* Buffalo, N.Y., 1866, pp. 108.
Accounts of original oil properties and companies, statistics of production, sketches of towns and cities in oil regions, leaders of the industry.

Elmer W. Hickman and Roy Minet, *Titusville. Birthplace of the Petroleum Industry,* Titusville, Penna., Canadohta Chapter, Daughters of the American Revolution and General Committee, Diamond Jubilee of Oil, 1935, pp. 93.
Produced in commemoration of 75th anniversary of the drilling of first oil well, Titusville, Pennsylvania, August 27, 1859.

Ernest C. Miller, *Oily Daze at Cherry Grove,* Warren, Penna., the author, 1942, pp. 21.
Account of "646 Mystery Well," discovery well at Cherry Grove and field developments of 1882, with account of boom, frantic drilling, and speculation.

Alexander von Millern, *All About Petroleum, and the Great Oil Districts of Pennsylvania, West Virginia, Ohio, etc.,* New York, American News Co., 1864, pp. 89.
The petroleum belts of Ohio and West Virginia.

Alexander von Millern, *All About Petroleum, and the Great Oil Districts of Crawford and Venango Counties, Pa.,* New York, American News Co., 1865, pp. 88.
Similar to previous title, both of which were published for sale to rail travellers by "news butchers."

Edmund Morris, *Derrick and Drill; or, An Insight Into the Discovery, Development, and Present Condition and Future Prospects of Petroleum, in New York, Pennsylvania, Ohio, West Virginia, etc.,* New York, James Miller, 2nd Ed. 1865, pp. 277.
A compilation from magazine and news-paper articles of fact and opinion on oil development.

J. H. Newton, Ed., *History of Venango County, Pennsylvania,* Columbus, Ohio, J. A. Caldwell, 1879, pp. 651.
History of county containing Drake well, chapter devoted to history of petroleum, including Silliman Report: excerpts relating to drilling, production, refining, with lists of wells and refineries.

M. P. Sargent, *Pioneer Sketches: Scenes and Incidents of Former Days, etc.,* Erie, Penna., Herald Printing and Publishing Co., 1891, pp. 512.
Author engaged in coal and lumber business in Oil City and Titusville, dealt in oil leases and drilled for oil. Several chapters on early oil developments, Colonel Drake, towns and farms in oil region.

H. H. Simmons, *The Oil Region of America,* New York, the author, 1866, pp. 28.
History, facilities, and communities served by Atlantic and Great Western Railway; developments following Drake discovery, transportation, exports.

James Donaldson Sisler, George Hall Ashley, Forrest Theodore Moyer, and William Orville Hickok, *Contributions to Oil and Gas Geology of Western Pennsylvania,* Harrisburg, Pennsylvania Topographic and Geologic Survey (Pennsylvania Geological Survey Bulletin M–19), 1933, pp. iv + 94.
Stratigraphy of oil and gas fields, correlation of oil and gas sands, production statistics.

J. E. Hilary Skinner, *After The Storm: or Jonathan and His Neighbors in 1865–6,* London, R. Bentley, 1866, 2 vols.
Chapters on visits to Oil Regions of Pennsylvania, particularly Pithole: description of drilling operations; Enniskillen field in Canada.

Rufus Barrett Stone, *McKean: The Governor's County,* New York, Lewis Historical Publishing Co., 1926, pp. 315.
History of Pennsylvania county in which Bradford field discovered 1876; incidents of petroleum discovery; natural gas utilization.

S. H. Sweet, *Special Report on Coal, Showing Its Distribution, Classification and Cost Delivered Over Different Routes to Various Points,* New York, D. Van Nostrand, 1865, pp. 94.
New York Senate Report No. 71, March 18, 1865. Contains appendix on petroleum, map of oil regions of Pennsylvania and West Virginia.

William Wright, *The Oil Regions of Pennsylvania. Showing Where Petroleum is Found.* New York, Harper & Bros., 1865, pp. 275.
Author made extensive tour of Oil Regions early in 1865 as correspondent for *New York Times.* Book widely read and highly regarded.

Henry E. Wrigley, *Special Report on the Petroleum of Pennsylvania, its Production, Transportation, Manufacture and Statistics,* Harrisburg, Board of Commissioners for the 2nd Geological Survey of Pennsylvania, 1875, pp. vii + 122.
American oil production; theories of origin of petroleum, source, "belt" lines; foreign fields; description of oil regions; horizons of oil-bearing formations; statistics; methods of drilling and pumping; pipelines; refining; safety measures; tests; uses of petroleum. Maps various oil regions.

c. West Virginia

American News Company, *The Oil-Dorado of West Virginia; A Full Description of the Great Mineral Resources of West Virginia, Kanawha Valley, etc.,* New York, the Company, 1865, pp. 86.
Oil belts of Ohio and West Virginia; rock oil; coal oil; account of visit to oil regions of West Virginia.

J. R. Dodge, *West Virginia: Its Farms and Forests, Mines and Oil-Wells,* Philadelphia, J. B. Lippincott & Co., 1865, pp. 276.
Eleven chapters dealing with petroleum, its discovery in West Virginia, drilling and distillation; description of oil fields of West Virginia; list of companies; discussion of prospects. Describes early dug wells.

Oscar L. Haught, *Oil and Gas in West Virginia,* Morgantown, W. Va., West Virginia Geological and Economic Survey, 1956, pp. i + 31.
Geology of oil and gas in West Virginia, production, and history of development.

M. F. Maury and William M. Fontaine, *Resources of West Virginia,* Wheeling, W. Va., Register Co., 1876, pp. x + 430.
Chapter on "Salt and Petroleum" refers to well-drilling methods, development of "slips" or "jars," distillation of cannel coal for illuminating oils and lubricants.

George W. Summers, *The Mountain State: A Description of the Natural Resources of West Virginia,* Charleston, W. Va., Moses W. Donnally, 1893, pp. 259.
Chapter on oil and gas which reviews early oil history and developments of West Virginia, describes Sisterville field as "the greatest producing oil field in the world."

R. C. Tucker, *Deep Well Records,* Morgantown, W. Va., West Virginia Geological Survey, 1936, Vol. VII, pp. xvi + 560.
Records of over 500 deep wells drilled up to July, 1936, in West Virginia and bordering states.

R. C. Tucker, *Summarized Record of Deep Wells,* Morgantown, W. Va., West Virginia Geological Survey, 1943, Vol. XVI, pp. xv + 938.
Records of 1350 deep wells in West Virginia and 250 in bordering states.

I. C. White, *Discussion of the Records of Some Very Deep Wells in the Appalachian Oil Fields of Pennsylvania and West Virginia,* Morgantown, W. Va., West Virginia Geological Survey, 1918, pp. 79.
Well records of 13 deep wells in Pennsylvania, West Virginia, and Ohio.

I. C. White, *Petroleum and Natural Gas. Precise Levels,* Morgantown, W. Va., West Virginia Geological Survey, 1904, Vol. I A, pp. xi + 625.
Historical sketch and geological review of oil and gas in West Virginia, with oil and gas records.

John Russell Young, *A Visit to the Oil Regions of West Virginia, Ohio, and Pennsylvania,* Forney's *Philadelphia Press,* Philadelphia, 1864, pp. 16.

Author was correspondent for *Philadelphia Press*, later ambassador to China and Librarian of Congress.

d. Georgia

Thomas Mann Prettyman and H. S. Cave, *Petroleum and Natural Gas Possibilities in Georgia*, Atlanta, Byrd Printing Co. (Geological Survey of Georgia, Bulletin No. 40), 1923, pp. viii + 164.
Based on 1921–1922 field trip, mainly in Coastal Plain area. History of oil prospecting in Georgia, geology and structural conditions of Coastal Plain, oil seeps and petroleum possibilities.

e. Florida

William Gregg Blanchard, *What Do You Really Know of Florida's Petroleum Possibilities?*, Miami, the author, 1934, pp. 22. 2nd Ed. 1935.
Geology of Florida and possibilities of finding oil.

Herman Gunter, *Exploration for Oil and Gas in Florida,* Tallahassee, Florida Geological Survey, 1948, pp. 9, plus appendix. Rev. Ed. 1949, pp. iii + 108. Annual Supplements.
Data on oil exploration in Florida from earliest drilling to Jan. 1, 1949. Continued by means of annual supplements (1957 Supplement, pp. 16, published 1958). Tabulations by counties of wells drilled.

Elias Howard Sellards and Herman Gunter, *On the Petroleum Possibilities of Florida,* Tallahassee, 14th Annual Report, Florida Geological Survey, 1922, pp. 33–135.
Geologic formations and structural features of Florida, by areas; review, by counties, including logs of wells drilled, oil possibilities.

3. GULF COAST AND SOUTHWEST

a. General

Charles B. Eliot, *Petroleum Industry of the Gulf Southwest,* Washington, Government Printing Office (Domestic Commerce Series No. 44, Part II of The Commercial Survey of the Gulf Southwest. Bureau of Foreign and Domestic Commerce), 1931, pp. vi + 252.
Statistical summary of production and consumption of petroleum, natural gas, natural gasoline, and refined petroleum products in Gulf Southwest; proration, unit development, code of ethics for gasoline marketers.

Shreveport Geological Society, *Reference Report on Certain Oil and Gas Fields of North Louisiana, South Arkansas, Mississippi, and Alabama,* Shreveport, La., the Society, 1946 to 1959, 4 vols., pp. xii + 839.
Vol. 1: Geology, discovery, and development of 60 fields, with 3 stratigraphic sections.
Vol. II: Comparable data on 25 fields, 9 stratigraphical sections, and paper on stratigraphy of Cretaceous in area.
Vol. III and IV: Further data on fields and stratigraphy.

Shreveport Geological Society, *Penetration Charts and Reservoir Data,* Shreveport, La., the Society, 1953, var. pag.
Data for 527 reservoirs in 250 oil and gas fields.

b. Alabama

Edgar Oliver Bowles, *Well Logs of Alabama,* University, Ala., Geological Survey of Alabama (Bulletin No. 50), 1941, pp. 357.
Logs, by counties, of 270 oil and gas wells; oil prospects in 8 geological provinces; oil and gas conservation laws of Alabama; rules and regulations of State Oil and Gas Board; forms.

Douglas Ramsay Semmes, *Oil and Gas In Alabama,* University, Ala., Geological Survey of Alabama (Spec. Report 15), 1929, pp. xv + 408.
Surface indications of oil in Alabama; stratigraphy; depth of oil and gas horizons; structural features; favorable areas; list of wells in Alabama; description of areas and counties.

Eugene Allen Smith, *Concerning Oil and Gas in Alabama,* University, Ala., Geo-

logical Survey of Alabama (Circular No. 3), 1917, pp. 18.
Prepared following discovery of oil at Cordova, Ala., in 1916, to review available data on oil and gas in Alabama.

Eugene Allen Smith, *Petroleum Possibilities of Alabama,* University, Ala., Geological Survey of Alabama (Bulletin No. 22), 1920, pp. 230.
Stratigraphy; oil and gas horizons; descriptions by counties of geology, structure, and development; oil possibilities of Coastal Plain.

Lyman D. Toulmin, *Well Logs of Alabama, 1940–1945,* University, Ala., Geological Survey of Alabama (Bulletin No. 57), 1945, pp. 177.
Logs, by counties, of 83 wells.

c. Mississippi

Ralph E. Grim, *Recent Oil and Gas Prospecting in Mississippi,* University, Miss., Mississippi State Geological Survey (Bulletin No. 21), 1928, pp. 98.
Subsurface geology; logs, by counties, of wells drilled in Mississippi.

Ephraim Noble Lowe, *Oil and Gas Prospecting in Mississippi,* University, Miss., Mississippi State Geological Survey (Bulletin No. 15), 1919, pp. 78.
Structures favorable for oil and gas prospecting by counties.

Mississippi Geological Society, *Wilcox Oil Fields, Southern Mississippi and Adjacent Areas,* Jackson, the Society, 1952, pp. 164.
Data on 33 Wilcox oil fields in Mississippi and Louisiana, as of July 1, 1952, with interpretation of electrical logging.

d. Louisiana

Louisiana Department of Conservation, *Development of Louisiana's Offshore Oil and Gas Reserves,* Baton Rouge, Engineering Division, the Department, 1955, pp. 87.
Data on wells completed in offshore producing areas; producing history and characteristics of each of 14 Louisiana offshore areas.

Arthur Troutman, *The Oil and Gas Fields of Southwest Louisiana,* Houston, Five Star Oil Report, 1955, pp. xiii + 376.
Detailed data on location, discovery, structure, productive zones, production, and other information on oil and gas fields in 16 parishes of southwest Louisiana.

Arthur Troutman, *The Oil and Gas Fields of Southeast Louisiana,* Houston, Five Star Oil Report, 1956, pp. xi + 342.
Data on oil and gas fields in 22 parishes of southeast Louisiana.

e. Arkansas

George C. Branner, *An Outline of the Petroleum and Natural Gas Resources of Arkansas,* Little Rock, Arkansas Geological Survey, 1927, pp. 47.
Oil and gas possibilities of Arkansas by areas; data on producing fields.

William M. Caplan, *Subsurface Geology and Related Oil and Gas Possibilities of Northeastern Arkansas,* Little Rock, Arkansas Resources and Development Commission, Division of Geology (Bulletin No. 20), 1954, pp. 124.
Structures and stratigraphy of northeastern Arkansas; discussion of possibilities.

Alec M. Crowell, *A Survey of the Oil and Gas Industry of Arkansas,* El Dorado, Ark., Arkansas Oil and Gas Commission, 1940, pp. viii + 87.
Oil and gas development in Arkansas; geology, stratigraphy; list of oil fields; drilling, production, proration; performance record of prorated fields.

Charles Albert Renfroe, *Petroleum Exploration in Eastern Arkansas,* Little Rock, Arkansas Resources and Development Commission, Division of Geology (Bulletin 14), 1949, pp. 159.
Selected well logs, by counties, with discussion of possibilities of eastern Arkansas.

William C. Spooner, *Oil and Gas Geology of the Gulf Coastal Plain in Arkansas,* Little Rock, Parke-Harper Printing Co. (Arkansas Geological Survey, Bulletin 2), 1935, pp. xxxii + 516.
Stratigraphy and structure of south-

western and eastern Arkansas; historical, geological, production, and other
data, by counties; list of wells drilled.

f. Texas

1. General

**George H. Fancher, Robert L. Whiting, and
James H. Cretsinger,** *The Oil Resources
of Texas,* Austin, Texas Petroleum Research Committee, 1954 and 1955, pp.
xi + 358.
Part 1: History, statistics, bibliography.
Part 2: History, production, and reserves, divided according to 11 Railroad
Commission Districts; maps, geological
sections, productive oil acreage; original
oil in place, ultimate primary reserves,
production, secondary reserves. Object
was to determine secondary recovery
reserves of Texas.

William Battle Phillips, *Texas Petroleum,*
Austin, University of Texas, 1901, pp.
viii + 102.
Historical sketch; discusses nature and
origin of petroleum, oil- and gas-bearing formations, use of oil as fuel in
early industrial and railroad applications in Texas.

Texas Legislative Council, *The Texas Petroleum Industry and State Finances,*
Austin, the Council, 1950, pp. iv + 91.
Prepared for information of Texas
Legislature; reviews revenue from petroleum, its disbursement, reasonable
market demand, inventories, impact of
foreign oil imports, relationship of oil
revenues to welfare of state.

**Texas Mid-Continent Oil and Gas As-
sociation,** *Texas Oil and Gas,* Dallas,
the Association, 1956, pp. 47.
Oil and gas production statistics, drilling, reserves, transportation, refining,
petrochemicals, taxation, conservation;
review of Texas oil history. Oil production by counties; operating refineries;
annual crude oil production, 1896–1955.
Earlier editions of *Texas Oil and Gas*
issued 1954, 1951, 1948, 1947.
Series initiated with *Important Facts
About Texas Oil,* published 1937, followed by Supplement No. 1, 1937, 3rd
Ed. 1939. 4th Ed. 1940. 5th Ed. 1943.
6th Ed. (Silver Anniversary) 1944. 7th

Ed.: *Important Facts About Texas Oil*
and Gas, 1946.

2. Spindletop and Beaumont

E. DeGolyer, *Spindletop, 1901–1951,* Dallas, DeGolyer & McNaughton, 1951,
pp. 8.
Commemorative address reviewing circumstances surrounding completion of
Lucas gusher.

Thelma Johnson, et al., *The Spindle Top Oil*
Field: A History of Its Discovery and
Development, Beaumont, Tex., the
authors, 1927, pp. 63.
Written as English project at Beaumont
High School; extracts from newspaper
and magazine accounts; biographies of
local oilmen.

Reid Sayers McBeth, *Pioneering the Gulf*
Coast, New York, the author, 1918, pp.
80.
Life and work of Captain Anthony F.
Lucas, discoverer of Spindletop field;
use of rotary drill; development of back-
pressure valve; addition of mud to drilling fluid.

Spencer W. Robinson, Ed., *Spindletop,*
Where Oil Became an Industry, Beau-
mont, Tex., 1951, pp. vii + 201.
Official proceedings of program con-
ducted by Spindletop 50th Anniversary
Commission.

John S. Spratt, *The Road to Spindletop:*
Economic Change in Texas, 1875–1901,
Dallas, Southern Methodist University
Press, 1955, pp. xxix + 337.
Economic trends in development of
Texas during last quarter of 19th cen-
tury; tremendous changes sparked by
oil discovery at Spindletop.

3. East Texas

James A. Clark, *East Texas Oil Field. The*
First 25 Years, Dallas, Texas Mid-Continent Oil and Gas Association, 1955,
pp. 21.
Brief account of early exploration for
oil in East Texas and activities of Columbus Marion ("Dad") Joiner, who drilled
discovery well; review of events which
followed, including salt water disposal.

East Texas Chamber of Commerce, *A Book of Facts: Martial Law in East Texas, etc.,* Longview, Tex., Longview Chamber of Commerce, 1932, pp. 60. Brief history of chaotic drilling and production practices which led to declaration of martial law in East Texas field by Gov. Ross Sterling, Aug. 16, 1931; copies of petitions, resolutions, newspaper accounts, editorials, letters and other communications to Gov. Sterling.

Harry Harter, *East Texas Oil Parade,* San Antonio, Naylor Co., 1934, pp. 220. East Texas land titles, early oil promotions, discovery well, activities and developments which followed, overproduction, proration, martial law, action of Federal Government; royalties, future of field.

Ruel Robly McDaniel, *Some Ran Hot,* Dallas, Regional Press, 1939, pp. 252. "What transpired in East Texas from date of discovery to frenzied days of trading, fighting, hot-oil running and martial law; of days of chaos and five-cent oil and coming of regulation in world's greatest oil field."

University of Texas, Bureau of Economic Geology, *Occurrence of Oil and Gas in Northeast Texas,* Austin, the University, 1951, pp. xiv + 449. Papers by 69 authors dealing with commercial occurrences of oil or gas in northeast Texas up to 1950. Geology, methods of exploration, discovery wells, history and production data, maps and geological sections.

Dabney White and T. C. Richardson, *East Texas, Its History and Its Makers,* New York, Lewis Historical Publishing Co., 1940, 3 vols., pp. 1466. County sketches contain many oil references; also history of East Texas field.

4. Other Oil Areas in Texas

Abner Davis, *The Stream of Liquid Gold in Flowing Reality vs. the Pot of Gold at the Rainbow's End: The Famed Burkburnett Gusher Oil Pool,* Fort Worth, the author, 1919, no pag. Contemporary account, with pictures, of wide-open oil boom town, Burkburnett.

Frank J. Gardner, *Reference Report on Oil and Gas Fields of the Texas Lower Gulf Coast,* Dallas, Five Star Oil Report, 1951, pp. 240. Data on oil and gas fields in 10 counties in Texas Lower Gulf Coast. (Texas Railroad Commission District No. 2.)

Frank J. Gardner, *Reference Report on the Oil and Gas Fields of the Texas Upper Gulf Coast,* Houston, Five Star Oil Report, 1952, pp. 484. Data for 427 oil and gas fields in 29 counties of Texas Upper Gulf Coast, including location, discovery, structure, productive formations, wells, production. (Texas Railroad Commission District No. 3.)

Frank J. Gardner and Robert L. Phifer, *The Oil and Gas Fields of West Texas,* Houston, Five Star Oil Report, 1953, pp. 304. Comparable data on oil and gas fields *in 14 counties of West Texas.* (Texas Railroad Commission District No. 7–c.)

James Levi Horlacher, *A Year in the Oil Fields,* Lexington, Ky., *Kentucky Kernel,* 1929, pp. 68. Account of 1926–1927, working in oil fields near Pampa, Texas, published in University of Kentucky student newspaper; operations and activities described, with comments on experiences, labor, and social problems.

Boyce House, *Were You In Ranger?* Dallas, Tardy Publishing Co., 1935, pp. xxii + 210. Discovery of oil on John McCleskey farm, south of Ranger, Oct. 22, 1917, and boom which followed.

Boyce House, *Oil Boom. The Story of Spindletop, Burkburnett, Mexia, Smackover, Desdemona, and Ranger,* Caldwell, Idaho, Caxton Printers, 1941, pp. 194. Events and persons involved in a half dozen famous oil booms.

Boyce House, *Roaring Ranger. The World's Biggest Boom,* San Antonio, Naylor Co., 1951, pp. vii + 122. The Ranger oil field.

Boyce House, *Oil Field Fury,* San Antonio, Naylor Co., 1954, pp. 142.
Oil field experiences of author, largely Eastland, Tex.

John P. Jones, *Borger. The Little Oklahoma,* n.p., the author, 1927, pp. 171.
Author's experiences in oil fields in Borger (Tex.) area.

John P. Jones, *Ten Years in the Oil Fields,* El Dorado, Ark., n.pub., 1926.
Included in previous title, also published separately. Author's experiences, 1915–25, in oil fields of Oklahoma, Texas, Arkansas.

George Parker (George Parker Stoker), *Oil Field Medico,* Dallas, Banks Upshaw & Co., 1948, pp. 139.
Practicing medicine in early Texas oil fields.

Rinehart Oil News Company, *The Wilcox in Texas: A Study of the Wilcox Sand Trend in Texas Coastal Fields,* Houston, the Company, 1942, pp. 82.
Data, by counties, on 342 wells drilled, up to June 15, 1952, in the Wilcox Sand in Texas.

Martin W. Schwettmann, *Santa Rita, The University of Texas Oil Discovery,* Austin, Texas State Historical Association, 1943, pp. xix + 43.
Story of discovery well at Big Lake, Reagan County, second producing field in West Texas; well marked beginning of oil development on lands set aside for University of Texas.

Southwest Texas Oil Scouts Association, *Oil and Gas Development in Southwest Texas,* San Antonio, the Association, 1930, pp. 84.
Describes producing fields, pipe lines, refineries, geophysical activities, geology, production and development activities in Southwest Texas, with special articles.

University of Texas, Bureau of Economic Geology, *Occurrence of Oil and Gas in West Texas,* Austin, the University (Publication No. 5716), 1957, pp. xvi + 442.
Papers by 104 authors provide examples of significant conditions associated with occurrence of oil and gas.

Arthur Troutman, *The Oil and Gas Fields of West Texas,* Houston, Five Star Oil Report, 1954, 2 vols. pp. xlii + 701.
Vol. I: Data on oil and gas fields in 17 counties of West Texas. (Texas Railroad Commission District No. 8.)
Vol. II: Data on 24 counties of West Texas. (Texas Railroad Commission District No. 8.)

Arthur Troutman, *The Oil and Gas Fields of Southwest Texas,* Houston, Five Star Oil Report, 1955, pp. xxiv + 365.
Data on oil and gas fields in 33 counties of Southwest Texas. (Texas Railroad Commission District No. 1.)

Arthur Troutman, *The Oil and Gas Fields of the Rio Grande Valley,* Houston, Five Star Oil Report, 1956, pp. xiii + 264.
Data on oil and gas fields in 6 counties of southern Texas. (Texas Railroad Commission District No. 4.)

Arthur Troutman, *The Oil and Gas Fields of the Laredo Area,* Austin, Oil Frontiers Publishing Co., 1957, pp. vi + 300.
Data on oil and gas fields in 4 counties of southern Texas. (Texas Railroad Commission District No. 4.)

West Texas Geological Society, *Introduction to the Petroleum Geology of the Permian Basin of West Texas and Southeastern New Mexico,* Midland, Tex., the Society, 1951, pp. 51.
General and historical geology of Permian Basin; oil and gas development in West Texas and southeastern New Mexico.

g. New Mexico

Robert L. Bates, *The Oil and Gas Resources of New Mexico,* Socorro, N. Mex., New Mexico School of Mines (Bulletin 18), 1942, pp. 320.
General discussion of oil in New Mexico, bringing up to date earlier publication by Dean E. Winchester (q.v.).

University of New Mexico, *Papers Presented at New Mexico Oil Conference,* Albuquerque, University of New Mexico Press (Bulletin No. 343), 1939, pp. 128.

Papers on oil and gas development in New Mexico, conservation, proration.

obert L. Phifer, *Petroleum Review, Lea County, New Mexico,* Houston, Phifer Petroleum Publications, 1956, pp. 293.
Data on 162 pools in Lea County, New Mexico; chronology of pool discoveries and production records through 1955.

oswell Geological Society, *The Oil and Gas Fields of Southeastern New Mexico,* Roswell, N. Mex., the Society, 1957, pp. 376.
Structural features and geologic history of southeastern New Mexico; petroleum exploration in area, pipe lines, refineries; detailed review of fields.

ean E. Winchester, *The Oil and Gas Resources of New Mexico,* Socorro, N. Mex., New Mexico School of Mines (Bulletin No. 9), 1933, pp. 223.
General geology of New Mexico, structural and stratigraphic features of oil and gas accumulations, and details of oil and gas developments by fields and basins.

4. CENTRAL UNITED STATES

a. Ohio

Robert Leo Alkire, *Oil and Gas Production, History, Regulation, Secondary Recovery, and Bibliography,* Columbus, Ohio Department of Natural Resources, Division of Geological Survey, 1951, pp. iii + 132.
Part I: Drilling activity in Ohio.
Part II: Geology, producing horizons, history of discovery and development, secondary recovery, and bibliography of oil and gas in Ohio.

John Adams Bownocker, *The Occurrence and Exploitation of Petroleum and Natural Gas in Ohio,* Columbus, Geological Survey of Ohio (4th Series, Bulletin No. 1), 1903, pp. 325.
History of oil and gas in Ohio, description of fields.

Contributions to the Oil and Gas Industry in Ohio, Columbus, Division of Geological Survey, State of Ohio, 1959, pp. 35.

Papers on deep possibilities in Ohio, cutting operating costs, repressuring.

A. L. Fleury, *A New Source of National Wealth. Report on the Oil Impregnated Rock of Mecca,* Washington, McGill & Witherow, 1866, pp. 12.
Oil region of Mecca, Trumbull County, Ohio; methods of drilling and production; quality of oil, its use as lubricant.

William D. Humphrey, *A Brief History of Gas and Oil in Findlay,* Findlay, Ohio, the author, 1940, pp. vii + 160.
Discovery and use of gas in Findlay in 1838, said to be first west of Alleghenies; oil and gas development in Ohio half-century later; completion of Hugh McMurray No. 1, world's largest oil well at that time.

John Strong Newberry, *The Rock Oils of Ohio* (from Ohio Agricultural Report for 1859), pp. 14.
Discusses nature, origin, and distribution of petroleum, with particular attention to geology and structure in Ohio; drilling and production at Mecca. Uses of oil, pumping, and refining.

Edward Orton, *Preliminary Report Upon Petroleum and Inflammable Gas,* Columbus, Geological Survey of Ohio, 1886, pp. iii + 76. 2nd Ed. 1887, pp. 200.
Geological scale and structure of Ohio; production of petroleum and natural gas; history and description of each field; possible new areas.

Edward Orton, *First Annual Report of the Geological Survey of Ohio,* Columbus, Westbote Co., 1890, pp. vi + 323.
Geology of Ohio; origin and accumulation of petroleum; gas, sources of oil within Ohio; utilization of natural gas.

George A. Whitney, *History of Oil Development in Ohio,* Oil City, Penna. Derrick Publishing Co., 1924, pp. 20.
Veteran oil scout briefly summarizes oil developments in Ohio.

b. Kentucky

Frank E. Force, *A History of the Oil Fields of the Western Kentucky District,*

Bowling Green, Ky., Clarence McElroy Gaines, 1921, pp. 120.
Contains "Kentucky Oil History," by Frank E. Force; also review of oil activities in Tennessee.

J. B. Hoeing, *The Oil and Gas Sands of Kentucky,* Lexington, Ky., Geological Survey of Kentucky (Preliminary Part, Bulletin No. 1), 1904, pp. 233.
Geology of oil and gas in Kentucky; well records by counties; production, transportation.

Willard Rouse Jillson, *The Oil and Gas Resources of Kentucky,* Frankfort, Department of Geology and Forestry, 1919, pp. xvi + 630. 2nd Ed. (reprint) Kentucky Geological Survey, Frankfort, 1920.
Past development and current status of oil and gas in each of 120 counties in Kentucky; geology of oil and gas pools, with record of drilled wells.

Willard Rouse Jillson, *Oil Field Stratigraphy of Kentucky,* Frankfort, Kentucky Geological Survey, 1922, pp. viii + 738.
Oil sands of Kentucky, by counties, as interpreted by 1200 well logs.

Willard Rouse Jillson, *New Oil Pools of Kentucky,* Frankfort, Kentucky Geological Survey, 1926, pp. viii + 394.
Geological data on more important new oil and gas pools in Kentucky.

Willard Rouse Jillson, *Oil and Gas in Western Kentucky,* Frankfort, Kentucky Geological Survey, 1930, pp. 632.
Summary of drilling, exploration, and production; records of 494 wells in 23 counties in western Kentucky.

Willard Rouse Jillson, *Geology of the Deep Wells in Kentucky,* Frankfort, Kentucky Geological Survey, 1931, pp. 647.
Covers stratigraphy and structure of sedimentary rocks in Kentucky, with records of 377 deep wells in 36 counties.

Edward Orton, *Report on the Occurrence of Petroleum, Natural Gas and Asphalt Rock in Western Kentucky,* Frankfort, Geological Survey of Kentucky, 1891, pp. 233.
Early and modern history, origin and geology of oil and gas; utilization of gas; geological scale and structures i western Kentucky. Based on examina tions made in 1888 and 1889 by autho

c. Tennessee

J. B. Killebrew, *Oil Region of Tennessee With Some Account of Its Other Re sources and Capabilities,* Nashville "The American" Printing Co., 1877, pp 116.
Oil prospects and exploration in Tennes see.

d. Illinois

Alfred Hannam Bell, *Oil Resources an Possibilities in Illinois,* Urbana, Ill. Illinois State Geological Survey, 1955 pp. 11.
Oil development in Illinois; classifica tion map; future prospects.

Willis Stanley Blatchley, *The Petroleum In dustry of Southern Illinois,* Urbana, Ill. Illinois State Geological Survey, 1906 pp. 109.
Oil developments in Illinois to 1904 with description of fields.

Willis Stanley Blatchley, *Oil Resources of Illinois,* Urbana, Ill., Illinois State Geo logical Survey, 1910, pp. 134.
General geology of Illinois relating to oil and gas; detailed geology of central and southern Illinois, with description of oil fields and prospective territory.

Don Llewellyn Carroll, *The New Oil Fields of Southern Illinois,* published by Illinois Chamber of Commerce, in cooperation with Illinois State Geological Survey, no date, but about 1941, pp. 30.
Discovery and development of new oil fields in southern Illinois, with list and map of fields; geology, exploration, drilling, natural gas.

William C. Jones, *Oil Industries of Illinois,* Robinson, Ill., the author, 1908, pp. 32.
Early oil exploration and developments in Illinois; details of companies.

Louis Aubrey Mylius, *Oil and Gas Development and Possibilities in Parts of Eastern Illinois,* Urbana, Ill., Illinois Geological Survey, 1923, pp. 64.

Geologic structure, producing sands, well data, future prospects.

ɔuis Aubrey Mylius, *Oil and Gas Development and Possibilities in East and Central Illinois,* Urbana, Ill., Illinois Geological Survey, 1927, pp. 205.
History, geology, methods and problems of operation, description of pools, recommendations for future prospects. Well data, 101 pages, bound separately.

Marvin Weller, *Geology and Oil Possibilities of Extreme Southern Illinois,* Urbana, Ill., Illinois Geological Survey, 1940, pp. 71.
Structures favorable for oil or gas accumulation and possible producing beds; well records.

e. Indiana

Villiam Newton Logan, *Petroleum and Natural Gas in Indiana,* Indianapolis, Department of Conservation, Division of Geology, 1920, pp. 279.
County reports, logs of wells, review of oil developments.

Villiam Newton Logan, *The Geology of the Deep Wells in Indiana,* Indianapolis, Department of Conservation, Division of Geology, 1926, pp. 540.
Logs of wells, by counties.

f. Michigan

I. E. Downer, *The Oil Region of Michigan,* Michigan, n. pub., 1864, pp. 7.
Description of Baker Tract, near Lakeport, Michigan; source and accumulation of oil and "rock oil in Michigan."

ₐ. B. Newcombe, *Oil and Gas Fields of Michigan,* Lansing, Geological Survey Division, 1933, pp. xvii + 293.
Major geological structure; origin and growth of Michigan Basin; history, economic and technical aspects of development of known oil and gas fields; drilling in undeveloped structures outside known fields.

ₐ. B. Newcombe, *Oil and Gas Development in Michigan,* Lansing, Geological Survey Division (Part III, Mineral Resources of Michigan), 1928, pp. 141–299.
State geological report.

R. A. Smith, *The Occurrence of Oil and Gas in Michigan,* Lansing, Geological Survey Division, 1914, pp. 281.
State geological report.

g. Iowa

Jesse V. Howell, *Petroleum and Natural Gas in Iowa,* Des Moines, Iowa Geological Survey, 1919–20, pp. 48.
Geological conditions and structure in Iowa; occurrence of oil and gas; prospects.

W. G. Osborn, *There Is Petroleum and Natural Gas in Iowa,* Des Moines, Iowa Petroleum Club, 1923, pp. 25.
Written as answer to *Petroleum and Natural Gas in Iowa,* being generally critical of report.

h. North Dakota

Wilson Morrow Laird, *Selected Deep Well Records,* Grand Forks, N.D., North Dakota Geological Survey, 1941, pp. 31.
Logs of 11 deeper wells drilled in North Dakota.

Arthur Gray Leonard, *Possibilities of Oil and Gas in North Dakota,* Bismarck, North Dakota Geological Survey, 1920, pp. 9.
Brief statement on oil and gas possibilities in North Dakota, geological formations, gas discoveries.

i. South Dakota

Roy Arthur Wilson, *The Possibilities of Oil in South Dakota,* Vermillion, S.D., University of South Dakota, 1922, pp. 97.
Geologic report on petroleum possibilities.

j. Nebraska

George Evert Condra, Eckard Frank Schramm, and Alvin Leonard Lugn, *Deep Wells of Nebraska,* Lincoln, Ne-

braska Geological Survey, 1931, pp. 288.
Records of deep wells drilled in Nebraska, logs of wells in other states near Nebraska border; drilling information, statutory requirements.

William C. Finch, Ed., *The Oil and Gas Fields of Nebraska: A Symposium,* Denver, Rocky Mountain Association of Geologists, 1955, pp. 264.
Review of structure and stratigraphy of Nebraska, pipe lines, refineries; oil field data up to Aug. 1, 1955.

Nebraska Writers' Project, *The Search for Oil in Nebraska,* Works Projects Administration, 1942, pp. 107.
Brief history of drilling for oil in Nebraska, 1865 to July 27, 1940, when Bucholz well, near Fall City, became Nebraska's first producing oil well. List and map of oil drillings.

k. Missouri

Malcolm Earl Wilson, *The Occurrence of Oil and Gas in Missouri,* Rolla, Mo., Missouri Bureau of Geology and Mines, 1922, pp. xi + 284.
Oil and gas occurrences in Missouri.

l. Mid-Continent Fields

1. General

Thomas Owen Bosworth, *Geology of the Mid-Continent Oil Fields: Kansas, Oklahoma and North Texas,* New York, Macmillan Co., 1920, pp. xii + 314.
History of oil developments, geological structure of oil field regions.

William Roy King, Ed., *Pre-Permian Handbook of the Hugoton Embayment,* Liberal, Kan., Liberal Geologic Society, 1956, pp. x + 212.
Geographic, geologic, and drilling data on 27 counties located in Hugoton Embayment, embracing parts of southwestern Kansas, southeastern Colorado, Texas Panhandle, Oklahoma Panhandle.

Luther Crocker Snider, *Oil and Gas in the Mid-Continent Fields,* Oklahoma City, Harlow Publishing Co., 1920, pp. 393.

Geologic features of fields in Kansas Oklahoma, and Texas; prospects.

2. Kansas

Hubert G. Hotchkiss, *Oil in Southwester Kansas,* Wichita, Kan., the author, 193 pp. 20.
Geologic cross-section of southwe Kansas; oil review by counties.

John Mark Jewett and George Elmer Abe nathy, *Oil and Gas in Eastern Kansas* Lawrence, Kan., University of Kansas Press, 1945, pp. 244.
Structural features of eastern Kansas oil and gas development by counties.

Kansas University, *Kansas Oil and Ga Pools,* Lawrence, Kan., Kansas Geo logical Society, 1956, pp. 96.
Geological and production data for 2 oil fields in southcentral Kansas.

Matthews & McMahan, Comp., *Kansas Oil Field,* Chanute, Kan., the Firm 1904, pp. 55.
Handbook devoted mainly to differen companies operating in Kansas, wit details on personnel, capitalization, op erations of each company.

Raymond Cecil Moore and Winthrop F Haynes, *Oil and Gas Resources of Kansas,* Lawrence, Kan., State Geologica Survey, 1917, pp. 391.
Historical review of oil and gas industry of Kansas; discussion of properties, ori gin, general geology; production of oi and gas; stratigraphy; physical an chemical properties of Kansas petro leum; oil and gas production in Kansas forms, oil and gas laws; list of refineries

Margaret Elizabeth Nessly, *Illustrate Directory of Kansas Oil Men,* Chicago Municipal Publicity Co., 1918, pp. 95 Brief history of Butler County field; oi companies; individuals.

Walter August Ver Wiebe, *Oil and Gas Re sources of Western Kansas,* Lawrence Kan., University of Kansas, 1938, pp 179.
Development of oil and gas industry in Kansas, producing horizons, geology oil and gas development by counties.

3. Oklahoma

rdmore Geological Society, *Petroleum Geology of Southern Oklahoma,* Tulsa, American Association of Petroleum Geologists, 1956, Vol. I, pp. 402.
Papers dealing with specific fields and geologic formations of southern Oklahoma.

. L. Hutchinson, *Preliminary Report on the Rock Asphalt, Asphaltite, Petroleum and Natural Gas in Oklahoma,* Norman, Okla., Oklahoma Geological Survey, 1911, pp. xiv + 256.

oy M. Johnson, Ed., *Oklahoma History South of the Canadian,* Chicago, S. S. Clarke Publishing Co., 1925, 3 vols.
General local history edited by one of the discoverers of the Healdton field, about which there is considerable firsthand information in Vol. 3. Also numerous other oil references.

lay J. Kessler, *Oklahoma Geophysical Prospects,* Tulsa, Rinehart Oil News Co., 1948, var. pag.
Comment on 189 active geophysical prospects in 41 Oklahoma counties.

ack Lance, *The Oklahoma City Oil Field in Pictures,* Oklahoma City, the author, 1931, pp. 63.
Early drilling in Oklahoma City, events leading to discovery of Mary Sudik well, biographies of individuals and companies.

Mid-Continent Oil and Gas Association, *Oil and Gas in Oklahoma,* Tulsa, the Association, 1943, pp. 67.
Historical review and description of oil industry of Oklahoma; tables on taxes, costs, production.

Margaret Elizabeth Nessly, *Art Edition of Oklahoma Oil Men,* Chicago and Detroit, Municipal Publicity Co., 1919, pp. 126.
Activities of selected geologists, contractors, producers, refiners, marketers associated with oil industry in Tulsa and surrounding territory.

Oklahoma Geological Survey, *Preliminary Report on the Mineral Resources of Oklahoma,* Norman, Okla., the Survey, 1908, pp. 84.

Chapter on oil and gas, pp. 15–23; early wells, oil sales, refining.

Oklahoma Geological Survey, *Oil and Gas —Oklahoma,* Norman, Okla., the Survey (Bulletin No. 40), 1928 and 1930, 3 vols., pp. 1440.
Vol. I: Papers on geology and other phases of oil industry, previously published separately, 1926–28.
Vol. II: Counties of western Oklahoma, structural geology, stratigraphy.
Vol. III: Geology, stratigraphy, oil field development in eastern Oklahoma.

E. R. Perry and L. L. Hutchinson, *History, Geology and Statistics of the Oklahoma Oil and Gas Fields,* n.p., n. pub., 1909, pp. 14.
Early attempts to discover oil in Oklahoma, beginning with Cherokee and Choctaw actions in 1884 legalizing oil prospecting; brief review of Oklahoma geology; statistics.

Riverside Oil & Refining Company, *Done in Oil,* Tulsa, the Company, 1925, pp. 250.
Minutes of special meeting of stockholders of company dealing with litigation involving title to bed of Cimarron River, Oklahoma; includes historical data on Cushing field, which bordered river.

C. W. Shannon and L. E. Trout, *Petroleum and Natural Gas in Oklahoma,* Norman, Okla., Oklahoma Geological Survey (Bulletin No. 19), 1915 and 1917, 2 parts, pp. 669.
Part I: History of development of Mid-Continent oil field, geology, discoveries, refining, prices, natural gas.
Part II: Investigations of untested and undeveloped parts of Oklahoma.

Luther Crocker Snider, *Petroleum and Natural Gas in Oklahoma,* Oklahoma City, Harlow-Ratliff Co., 1913, pp. viii + 196.
Geology of Oklahoma; methods of prospecting for oil and gas; use of geology as a guide.

4. Williston Basin

Emory Neudeck Kemler, *The Williston Basin,* Spring Park, Minn., Summary Reports, 1954, pp. 210.

Past developments and future prospects.

Petroleum Information, *An Introduction to the Williston Basin,* Denver, Petroleum Information, 1952, pp. 173.
Search, discovery, leasing, production and disposition of oil in Williston Basin, with well data.

5. ROCKY MOUNTAIN STATES

Petroleum Information, *29th Annual Resumé, Rocky Mountain Oil and Gas Operations for 1958,* Denver, Petroleum Information, 1959, var. pag.
Reviews drilling, discoveries, and production in 11 states.

a. Colorado

Clark Fred Barb, *The Oil and Gas Industry of Colorado,* Golden, Colo., Colorado School of Mines (*Quarterly,* Vol. 37, No. 2), 1942, pp. 129.
Data on oil and gas fields of Colorado; reserves; costs; refining industry, with description of each plant; consumption; pipe lines; natural gas; oil shale and coal substitutes; oil laws.

Clark Fred Barb, *Selected Well Logs of Colorado,* Golden, Colo., Colorado School of Mines (*Quarterly,* Vol. 41, No. 1), 1946, pp. 435.
Supplement to *The Oil and Gas Industry of Colorado.* Contains 490 well logs, listed by counties; typical logs in each producing field, and wells regarded as wildcats. (Colorado Industrial Development Research Petroleum Report No. 1.)

Fred S. Jensen, Ed., *The Oil and Gas Fields of Colorado: A Symposium,* Denver, Rocky Mountain Association of Geologists, 1954, pp. 302.
Petroleum exploration and development in Colorado, 1862–1954, geologic history, structural and stratigraphic features, pipe lines, refineries, with detailed review of fields.

b. Wyoming

S. Aughey, *Report on the Wyoming Oil Springs,* Omaha, John D. Mortimer, 1882, pp. 61.

Report on Shoshone and Beaver basins in Wyoming Territory, based explorations during 1880 and 1881; geology, oil seepages, dug wells; quality oil as lubricant. Covering property Rocky Mountain Oil, Mining & Transportation Co., incorporated 1879.

Federal Trade Commission, *Report of the Federal Trade Commission on the Petroleum Industry of Wyoming,* Washington, Government Printing Office, 1921, pp. 54.
Development and control of production transportation by pipe lines, and refining of crude oil in Wyoming, 1916–19, with brief discussion of production in other Rocky Mountain States. Lists important companies.

Alfred James Mokler, *History of Natrona County, Wyoming, 1888–1922,* Chicago, R. R. Donnelley & Sons Co., 1923, pp. xiv + 477.
Contains chapter reviewing oil history of Wyoming.

Harold DeWitt Roberts, *Salt Creek, Wyoming. The Story of a Great Oil Field,* Denver, Midwest Oil Corp., 1956, pp. 211.
History of Salt Creek from early developments in Territorial days through formation of Salt Creek Unit and its final approval on Sept. 1, 1939, with epilogue covering subsequent 16 years.

Loyal Wingate Trumbull, *Light Oil Fields of Wyoming,* Cheyenne, S. A. Bristol Co. (State of Wyoming, Geologist's Office, Bulletin No. 12, pp. 121–130), 1916.
Twenty-six Cretaceous oil and gas fields of Wyoming; discusses geology, structure; quality of oil; possibilities.

Loyal Wingate Trumbull, *Petroleum Geology of Wyoming,* Cheyenne, G. G. Bovee, 1917, pp. 81.
Geological history of Wyoming, oil productive horizons, oil and gas fields favorable prospective districts, well logs.

Wyoming Geological Association, Symposium Committee, *Wyoming Oil and Gas Fields. Symposium,* n.p., the Association, 1957, pp. 464.
Data and maps for 257 oil and gas fields discovered in Wyoming up to 1956; geo

logic history and structure of Wyoming. First systematic review of oil and gas fields of Wyoming was Bulletin 418, United States Bureau of Mines, presenting developmental history, statistics and maps for 75 commercially productive fields discovered up to July, 1938.

c. Montana

illings Geological Society, *Montana Oil and Gas Fields,* Billings, Mont., the Society, 1958, pp. 247.
Review of 61 oil and gas fields of Montana; structure maps, electric logs, statistics.

harles Horace Clapp, Arthur C. Bevan, and Gerald S. Lambert, *Geology and Oil and Gas Prospects of Central and Eastern Montana,* Butte, Mont., State School of Mines, 1921, pp. 95.
General geology and stratigraphy of central and eastern Montana; production; possibilities.

ugene Sheridan Perry, *Oil and Gas in Montana,* Butte, Mont., Montana School of Mines, 1953, pp. vii + 54.
General geology and structure of eastern and central Montana, and formations; description of oil and gas fields.

d. Idaho

'irgil Raymond Drexel Kirkham, *Petroleum Possibilities of Certain Anticlines in Southeastern Idaho,* Moscow, Idaho, University of Idaho (Bureau of Mines and Geology Bulletin, No. 4), 1922, pp. 36.
Structural geology and stratigraphy in southeastern Idaho, on or near Wyoming border, regarded as "least unlikely" for production of oil.

e. Utah

;eorge H. Hansen and Mendell M. Bell, *The Oil and Gas Possibilities of Utah,* Salt Lake City, Utah Geological and Mineralogical Survey, 1949, pp. xiii + 341.
Papers on general geology, structure, and stratigraphy of Utah; table of wells drilled in Utah, 1891–1948; oil and gas leasing; history of oil and gas possibilities by areas.

George H. Hansen and H. C. Scoville, *Drilling Records for Oil and Gas in Utah,* Salt Lake City, Utah Geological and Mineralogical Survey, 1955, pp. 116.
Summary of exploration for oil and gas; information on wells drilled in Utah; data and maps by counties.

Intermountain Association of Petroleum Geologists, *Guidebook to the Geology of the Paradox Basin,* Salt Lake City, the Association, 1958, pp. 308.
Papers on geology and stratigraphy of Paradox Basin Region, oil and gas developments and fields in Utah, Colorado, and Arizona.

f. Arizona

Gurdon Montague Butler and Milton Arthur Allen, *Petroleum,* Tucson, Arizona Bureau of Mines, 1921, pp. 45.
Origin, accumulation, properties of petroleum, its discovery and development; search for oil in Arizona.
Petroleum, Tucson, University of Arizona, Arizona Bureau of Mines, pp. 50.
Updated reprint of above.

D. A. Holm, *The Oil Possibilities of Arizona,* Phoenix, Works Projects Administration, 1938, pp. ix + 47.
Geology of Arizona, based on field surveys, with classification of lands into potential and nonpotential oil lands.

g. Four Corners

Paul J. Kuhn, *Oil and Gas in the Four Corners,* Amarillo, Tex., National Petroleum Bibliography, 1958, pp. iii + 298.
Discovery and development of fields in Arizona, Colorado, New Mexico, and Utah.

Ira Rinehart, *Reference Book on Four Corners Area,* Dallas, Rinehart Oil News Co., 1955, pp. 172.
Historical background and possible future oil development in Four Corners Area of southeast Utah, southwest Colorado, northwest New Mexico, and northeast Arizona; records of discoveries, producing zones, drilling.

h. Nevada

Joseph Lintz, Jr., *Nevada Oil and Gas Drilling Data, 1906–1953,* Reno, University of Nevada, 1957, pp. xlii + 80.
Oil possibilities in Nevada; summary of drilling results; data, by counties, of wells drilled in Nevada for oil and gas, 1906–1953.

6. PACIFIC COAST

a. California

Thomas Antisell, *Geological Report,* Washington, United States Senate, 1856, pp. 204, 24 plates. Vol. VII, *Explorations and Surveys to Ascertain the Most Practicable and Economical Route for a Railroad from the Mississippi River to the Pacific Ocean,* Executive Document No. 78, 33rd Congress, 2nd Session.
Geological examinations from Nov. 22, 1854, to Apr. 5, 1855, in California; one chapter lists 13 localities with account of production and use.

James W. Beebe, *Geological Information for Petroleum Investors, with Special Reference to the San Joaquin Valley, California,* Fresno, Cal., the author, 1934, pp. 24, 3rd Ed., 1936, pp. 28.
California oil developments; oil-bearing formations; geophysical exploration; favorable areas.

James W. Beebe, *Kettleman Hills and Dudley Ridge Gas Area, 1900 to 1932,* Fresno, Cal., the author, 1932, pp. 47.

State of California Assembly Committee, *State-Federal Cooperation in the Discovery, Production, Transportation, Refining, and Use of Petroleum Oil and Its Products,* Sacramento, Assembly of the State of California, 1951, pp. 210.
Final report of legislative committee to assemble data on ownership of petroleum deposits beneath tide, submerged, and reclaimed lands.

California Petroleum Company, *Report of the Directors of the California Petroleum Co., to Stockholders at Annual Meeting, Philadelphia, March 14, 1866,* New York, Francis & Loutrel, 1866, pp.

14. Facsimile reprint by Paul Pain Los Angeles, 1946.
Statements by geologists to vindica Professor Silliman in connection wi his favorable report upon the proper of the company.

A. S. Cooper, *The Genesis of Petroleum ar Asphaltum in California,* Sacrament California State Mining Bureau Bullet No. 16, 1899, pp. 89.
Discusses possible source beds, modes accumulation of petroleum in vario areas, with chapter on prospecting f petroleum.

Charles Tenison Deane, *The Oil Industr of California,* San Francisco, Californi Petroleum Miners' Association, 1901 1907, Bulletin Nos. 1 to 6, pp. 110.
Bulletin 2: *The Burning of Crude O for Steam Purposes.*
Bulletin 3: *The Oil Fields of Californi From a Commercial Standpoint.*
Bulletin 6: *Oil Conditions in Californic 1907.*

E. DeGolyer, *Professor Benjamin Sillimar Jr., and Early California Oil,* pape presented before Mississippi Valle Historical Society, April, 1955.
Reviews activities involved with fore going reports.

Federal Trade Commission, *Report of th Federal Trade Commission on th Pacific Coast Petroleum Industry,* Wash ington, Government Printing Office Parts I and II, 1921–22, pp. xi + 538.
Based on S. Res. 138, 66th Cong. 1s Sess. Part I deals with supply of petro leum for Pacific Coast territory, effect of oil lands withdrawal; organization affiliations, investments of large com panies in Pacific Coast industry; detail of investments, costs, and earnings fo production, transportation, and refinin; of petroleum.
Part II presents price statistics for crud petroleum and products, describe marketing agencies, shows importanc of each of 5 large oil companies an conditions of competition.

R. G. Follis, *Crude Oil Production an Imports on the Pacific Coast,* San Fran cisco, Standard Oil Co. of California 1953, pp. 14.
Demand for petroleum products in Fa

West, crude oil supply situation, need for higher-gravity crudes, isolated position of California from crude oil supply areas; charts.

ames P. George, *Dollars and Sense, Geological Information and Useful Allied Knowledge and Data for Petroleum Investors*, San Francisco, the author, 1941, pp. 46.
Historical review of California oil; discussion of oil geology and occurrences in San Joaquin Valley.

.dwin Higgins, *California's Oil Industry: An Outline of Its History, Development, Present Importance and Inherent Hazards*, Los Angeles, Chamber of Mines and Oil, 1928, pp. 39.
History, uses, origin, development, prospecting, production methods, transportation, conservation, refining, shipping, Panama Canal.

.enneth E. Hill and John G. Winger, *Future Growth of the West Coast Petroleum Industry*, New York, Chase Manhattan Bank, 1957, pp. 44.
Energy sources and consumption in 5 Western states; natural gas and its effect on oil demand; onshore and offshore oil supply; ultimate output; estimates for 1966.

)laf P. Jenkins, Ed., *Geologic Formations and Economic Development of the Oil and Gas Fields of California*, Sacramento, State Printing Office (Bulletin No. 118, Division of Mines, Department of Natural Resources, State of California), 1943, pp. xvi + 773.
Definitive treatise on California oil fields with detailed history, maps, and statistics of each field. Bibliography.

:harles W. Jennings and Earl W. Hart, *Exploratory Wells Drilled Outside of Oil and Gas Fields in California to Dec. 31, 1953*, San Francisco, California Division of Mines (Special Report 45), 1956, pp. 104.

Frank Forrest Latta, *Black Gold in the Joaquin*, Caldwell, Idaho, Caxton Printers, 1949, pp. 344, no index.
Oil history of San Joaquin Valley, 1830 through development of Kettleman Hills a century later.

Roy Parmelee McLaughlin and C. A. Waring, *Petroleum Industry of California*, San Francisco, California State Mining Bureau, (Bulletin No. 69), 1914, pp, 519.
Extent and location of California oil deposits, history of development of fields, cost of extracting oil, and marketing and financial conditions governing industry.

Gordon B. Oakeshott, Lewis T. Braun, Charles W. Jennings, and Ruth Wells, *Exploratory Wells Drilled Outside of Oil and Gas Fields in California to Dec. 31, 1950*, San Francisco, California Division of Mines (Special Report 23), 1952, pp. 77.
Lists 4000 wells drilled outside of principal oil and gas fields; geologic and other data.

Oil Producers Agency of California, *The Agency Date Book. 100 Years of Events in the California Oil Industry, Etc., Mexican Period to 1947*, Los Angeles, the Agency, 1944, pp. 201, with appendices, 1st Ed.
Dates of important events in California oil industry, name of person or company concerned; chronological and alphabetical lists of oil and gas discoveries.

Edmond O'Neill, *The Development of the Petroleum Industry*, Berkeley, Cal., Reprint from University of California *Chronicle*, Vol. IV, No. 3, June 1901, pp. 176–202, pp. 29.
California oil developments, production, refining, transportation, utilization.

Palmer Union Oil Company, *California's Greatest Industry. A Review of Its Resources and Prospects*, San Francisco, the Company, 1912, pp. 95.
California oil history and developments. Devotes main attention to Santa Maria (now Orcutt) field; folded map of field.

Paul W. Prutzman, *Production and Use of Petroleum in California*, San Francisco, California State Mining Bureau (Bulletin No. 32), 1904, pp. 230.
History, geology, drilling, production, field operations in California oil industry; uses of crude oil for fuel and other purposes, refining, and chemistry of California petroleum.

Paul W. Prutzman, *Petroleum in Southern California,* San Francisco, California State Mining Bureau (Bulletin No. 63), 1913, pp. vii + 430.
Oil development in California south of the Tehachapi; details of wells and companies; analyses of oils.

Benjamin Silliman, Jr., *A Description of the Recently Discovered Petroleum Region in California, With a Report on the Same,* New York, Francis & Loutrel, 1865, pp. 24.
Report of Professor Silliman upon outcrops of mineral oil, or petroleum, which appear on the Ranch of Ojai, near Buenaventura, Santa Barbara County, in area of present Ventura Field. Property owned by California Petroleum Co., organized by Thomas Scott of the Pennsylvania Railroad. Historical review of petroleum in California, with discussion of transportation and markets. Report dated San Francisco, Sept. 1, 1864.

Professor Silliman's Report Upon the Oil Property of the Philadelphia and California Petroleum Co. of Philadelphia, situated in Santa Barbara and Los Angeles Counties, Calif., Philadelphia, 1865, pp. 36, also New York, 1865, pp. 24.
Extracts added from field notes made on survey and exploration for railroad, in 1850 and 1857, by Colonel J. Williamson, Chief Engineer for the Survey.

Professor Silliman's Report Upon Oil Properties of the Pacific Coast Petroleum Co. of New York, New York, 1865.

Lawrence Vander Leck, *Petroleum Resources of California,* Sacramento, California State Printing Office (Bulletin No. 69, California State Mining Bureau), 1921, pp. 186.
Geology governing origin and accumulation of petroleum in California; possibilities of oil discovery in various areas of state.

W. L. Watts, *Oil and Gas Yielding Formations of Los Angeles, Ventura, and Santa Barbara Counties,* Sacramento, California State Mining Bureau (Bulletin No. 11), 1897, pp. ix + 94.
Geology, drilling, production of oil and gas in southern California; refining drilling machinery; use of oil as fu in Los Angeles; resumé of research analyses; refinery methods.

W. L. Watts, *Oil and Gas Yielding Form tions of California,* Sacramento, Ca fornia State Mining Bureau (Bullet No. 19), 1900, pp. 236.
Oil developments in California; descri tion of oil-yielding formations; c history in California.

b. Oregon

Roscoe Emerson Stewart, *Oil and Gas E ploration in Oregon,* Portland, Depar ment of Geology and Mineral Indu tries, 1954, pp. 53.
Reviews indications of oil and gas Oregon, with well records by countie

c. Washington

Sheldon Latta Glover, *Preliminary Repo on Petroleum and Natural Gas in Was ington,* Olympia, Department of Co servation and Development, Divisio of Geology, 1936, pp. 24.
Discusses by counties areas in Washin ton favorable or unfavorable for pr duction of oil and gas.

Sheldon Latta Glover, *Oil and Gas Explor tion in Washington,* Olympia, Divisio of Mines and Geology, 1947, pp. 49.
Exploration in Washington; data; tab lations.

Vaughn E. Livingston, Jr., *Oil and G Exploration in Washington, 1900–195.* Olympia, Division of Mines and Geo ogy, 1958, pp. 61.
Reviews of past exploration; give tabulation, by counties, of 323 oil an gas test wells.

Charles Edwin Weaver, *Geology and I Relation to the Occurrence of Oil i Washington,* Seattle, University Washington, 1938, pp. 16.
Discusses possibilities of oil and ga production in Washington.

d. Alaska

Anchorage Chamber of Commerce, *Alaska 1957 Oil Discovery and Its Strateg*

Importance, Anchorage, the Chamber, 1957, pp. v + 10.
Discusses Alaska's commercially pro-

ductive oil well, discovered July 23, 1957, northern end of Kenai Peninsula.

D. MEXICO

Clarence Walker Barron, *The Mexican Problem,* Boston, Houghton Mifflin Co., 1917, pp. xv + 136.
Development of oil production in Mexico; social, political, and economic problems connected therewith; Edward L. Doheny's role in Mexican oil development.

Carl Hugh Beal, *Reconnaissance of the Geology and Oil Possibilities of Baja California,* New York, Geological Society of America (Memoir 31), 1948, pp. x + 138.
Physiography, stratigraphy, geologic structure, history, and notes on oil possibilities of Baja California, based on field observations.

José Colomo and Gustavo Ortega, *The Mexican Petroleum Law. Its Basis and Its Aims. Early History and Development of the Oil Industry in Mexico,* Mexico, D. F., Government of Mexico, 1927, pp. 41.
Review of background, interpretation of Mexican petroleum law and regulations; origin and development of Mexican oil industry.

Leonard Derbyshire, *Mexico, The Solution of our Fuel Oil Problem,* Philadelphia, Sutton & Derbyshire, 1920, pp. 21.
Pamphlet reviewing Mexican oil developments, including political situation; list of principal oil companies operating in Mexico, wells, production, and holdings.

Elmer Dean Fuller, *The Oil Situation in Mexico In Relation to American Investments,* New York, the author, 1917, pp. 10.
Plea on behalf of small independent oil operators in Mexico, to be heard and

represented in matters related to Mexican oil situation.

John Malcolm Muir, *Geology of the Tampico Region, Mexico,* Tulsa, American Association of Petroleum Geologists, 1936, pp. xix + 280.
Covers stratigraphy of Tampico area, oil structures of northern and southern oil fields, developments, with bibliography.

Pan American Petroleum & Transport Company, *Mexican Petroleum,* New York, the Company, 1922, pp. xiv + 300.
Oil developments in Mexico, information concerning refining, transportation, distribution activities of company, and review of geographical distribution of petroleum. Pan American was Doheny's company.

Petroleos Mexicanos, *Poza Rica, Mexico,* D. F., Petroleos Mexicanos, 1950, pp. 47.
Describes Mexico's largest oil field, discovered 1930, its development, plant, facilities, and output data, 1937–1950.

Israel Charles White, *Report and Appraisal Prospectus of the Mexican Petroleum Co., Ltd.,* n.p., n.pub., 1911, pp. 18.
2nd Report on the Properties of the Mexican Petroleum Co., Ltd., 1913, pp. 14, with folded chart.
3rd Report on the Properties of the Mexican Co., Ltd., Dr. White was State Geologist of West Virginia. Reports comment on oil geology and oil-bearing strata of Mexico, well logs, drilling operations of company; provide competent record of early oil activities in Mexico.

E. SOUTH AMERICA

1. GENERAL

Frederick Gardner Clapp, *South America. Big Field for Petroleum Development,*

New York, New York Commercial, n.d., pp. 20.
Review, by countries, of explorations and development in South America.

Joseph E. Pogue, *Oil and the Americas,* New York, Chase National Bank, 1944, pp. 28.
Divergent oil policies of Latin America, requirements for adequate oil development, social and economic benefits from development of oil resources. Reprint of address.

2. VENEZUELA

Harry Lee Franklin and W. Doyle Miller, *Operating Requirements, Techniques, and Procedures for Prospective Oil and Gas Operators in Venezuela,* Dallas, the authors, 1957, pp. vi + 224.
Problems and costs of operations in Venezuela, oil industry personnel, exploration data, drilling practices and costs, production practices, pipe lines, and refineries.

International Labour Office, *Freedom of Association and Conditions of Work in Venezuela,* Geneva, International Labour Office (Studies and Reports, New Series No. 20), 1950, pp. 185.
Report of I.L.O. mission to Venezuela; development of petroleum industry, political events and changes, trade union movement, living and working conditions.

International Labour Office, *Observations of the Government of Venezuela on the Report of the I.L.O. Mission,* Geneva, International Labour Office (Studies and Reports, New Series No. 21 A), 1951, pp. iv + 97.
Observations of Venezuelan Government on visit of I.L.O. mission, presenting contrary viewpoints to much of the report.

Myrick and Barbara Land, *Jungle Oil. The Search for Venezuela's Hidden Treasure,* New York, Coward-McCann, 1957, pp. 96.
Oil development in Venezuela, from first oil well (1880) and first refinery up to present; brief account of social and physical benefits; iron ore developments.

Jonathan Norton Leonard, *Men of Maracaibo,* New York, G. P. Putnam's Sons, 1933, pp. 287.
Accounts of oil country and oilmen in early oil-boom days in Lake Maracaibo

area of Venezuela, when activity ha slackened.

Ralph Alexander Liddle, *The Geology Venezuela and Trinidad,* Fort Wort Texas, J. P. MacGowan, 1928, pp. xxx + 550. 2nd Ed. Ithaca, N.Y., Paleo tological Research Institute, 1946, p xlvii + 890.
First part deals with various areas Venezuela; second part with Trinida Geological map showing principal mi eral deposits, major structural feature and chart showing correlation of sed ments; physiography; general, stru tural, and economic geology; aspha and petroleum; production data; d scription of fields.

Edwin Lieuwen, *Petroleum in Venezuel A History,* Berkeley, Cal., University California Press, 1954, pp. 160.
General history of petroleum in Ven zuela, showing oil development again a political background.

Rodolfo Luzardo, *Venezuela: Busine and Finances,* Englewood Cliffs, N. J Prentice-Hall, 1957, pp. xii + 167.
Economic conditions in Venezuela an association of petroleum industry ther with; principal attention to monetar policy of Venezuela.

C. C. McDermond, *Who's Who in Ven zuela, as of Aug. 1, 1929,* Maracaibc Venezuela, the author, 1929, pp. 99. 2n Ed. 1932, pp. viii + 278.
Reviews oil production generally; d tails of Venezuelan oil industry, o companies, personnel, and general con mercial data on Venezuela and leadin business concerns.

Ministry of Mines and Hydrocarbons, *N tional Petroleum Convention,* Caraca Venezuela, the Ministry, 1951, pp. 41
Papers by government and oil industr personnel on geology, exploration, o field development, production, transpo tation, refining, taxes, utilization o natural gas.

Ministry of Mines and Hydrocarbon *Venezuelan Crude Oils,* Caracas, Ven zuela, the Ministry, 1951, pp. 172.
Sixty-five active oil fields in Venezuela tables of properties of important crud oils, amounts and properties of prod

ucts. Map of fields, refineries, pipe lines. Appendix describes method of evaluating Venezuelan crude oil analyses.

inistry of Mines and Hydrocarbons, *Venezuela and Other World Crude Oils,* Caracas, Venezuela, the Ministry, 1952, pp. 100.
Significant properties of crude oils and petroleum products; analyses of typical crude oils of Venezuela, Middle East, and United States, by gravities, and examples of evaluation.

lichael James O'Shaughnessy, *Venezuelan Oil Handbook,* New York, the author, 1924, pp. 32.
Oil history of Venezuela, fields discovered, companies operating, with folded map of Maracaibo Basin showing holdings of various companies, producing and shipping fields, pipe lines, etc.

lichael James O'Shaughnessy, *Venezuelan Oil Fields: Developments to September 1, 1924,* New York, the author, 1924, pp. 26.

oseph E. Pogue, *Oil in Venezuela,* New York, Chase National Bank, 1949, pp. 49.
Economic study of role of Venezuelan oil in world trade and national economy; standards for oil policy in Venezuela.

3. OTHER SOUTH AMERICA

Margaret Charlotte Alexander Marsh. *The Bankers of Bolivia. A Study in American Foreign Investment,* New York, Vanguard Press, 1928, pp. xvi + 233.
Contains discussion of Bolivian oil, early laws, concessions, and exploration.

Feliz Mendoza and Benjamin Alvarado, *The Petroleum Industry in Colombia,* Bogotá, Ministry of National Economy, Petroleum Department, 1939, pp. 217.
Brief historical account; production, exploration, refining in Colombia; oil geology; resumé of petroleum legislation. In Spanish and English.

Federico Moreno, *Petroleum in Peru, From an Industrial Point of View,* Lima, F. Masias & Co., 1891, pp. 161.

Petroleum development in Peru and elsewhere; drilling, transportation, chemistry, refining, and consumption of oil for fuel; map of coastal area and oil deposits. Two reports on oil in Peru, one made to Board of Directors, Peruvian Petroleum Co., dated New York, Feb., 1866, by E. R. Larkin.

Eduardo Ospina-Racines, *Economics of Oil Investments in Colombia,* Bogotá, the author, 1941, var. pag.
Factors governing commercial development of South American oil, with particular attention to Colombia; production, concessions, oil prices, taxation, costs, royalties, pipelines and refineries; commercial relations between oil countries of South America and United States.

Joseph E. Pogue, *Oil in Brazil,* New York, Chase National Bank, 1951, pp. 32.
Brazilian oil legislation, resources, refining, transportation, distribution; suggested design for oil development in Brazil.

F. Ignacio Rickard, *The Mineral and Other Resources of the Argentine Republic (La Plata) in 1869,* London, Longmans, Green & Co., 1870, pp. 323.
Based on extended inspection of mineral districts of Argentina; petroleum seepages in Province of Mendoza; drilling recommended to be undertaken by Argentine government.

Chester Wesley Washburne, *Petroleum Geology of the State of São Paulo, Brazil,* São Paulo Geographic and Geologic Commission, 1930, pp. xiii + 282.
Geology, well logs, etc.; possibility of developing oil fields in state of São Paulo.

4. OTHER WESTERN HEMISPHERE

Thomas Cochrane, 10th Earl of Dundonald, *Brief Extracts from Memoranda of The Earl of Dundonald on the Use, Properties, and Products of the Bitumen and Petroleum of Trinidad,* London, J. Ridgway, 1857, pp. 14.
Describes and illustrates with engravings Pitch Lake of Trinidad and advocates use of bitumen for various purposes. Dundonald, a retired British

admiral, held numerous patents on asphalt for insulation, waterproofing, and paving; he owned access to Pitch Lake and was attempting commercial development.

Edward Hubert Cunningham-Craig, *Report on the Oilfields of Barbados,* T. E. King & Co., Printers to Government of Barbados, 1913, pp. 14.
General description of geological structure, prospective drilling sites, equipment, possible results.

James Dodds Henry, *Oil Fields of the Empire,* London, Bradbury, Agnew & Co., 1910, pp. xxix + 278.
Development of British oil supplies, oil developments in Trinidad and petroleum in Newfoundland, with notes by Sir Boverton Redwood.

Thomas Henry Holland, *Oil Industry of Trinidad,* Port-of-Spain, Trinidad, Government Printing Office (Council Pape No. 86 of 1928), 1928, pp. 32.
Trinidad oil development and prospect leasehold conditions, taxation, organiz: tion of Mines Department, recommen dations.

Clifford Richardson, *Trinidad Pitch,* An nual Report of the Commissioners the District of Columbia for Year Ende June 30, 1892 (Executive Document part 7, 52nd Congress, 2nd Session pp. 464–498.
Describes pitch (asphalt) deposits an pitch lake of Trinidad, theories as t origin and formation, composition an characteristics, collection and shipmen brief review of history of pitch industr and use of Trinidad pitch for street pave ment (first laid in Washington i 1880's). Author was chemist and In spector of Asphalt and Cements, Engi neer Department, District of Columbia

V.

Eastern Hemisphere

A. EUROPE

nglo-Iranian Oil Company, *Petroleum in England. An Account of the Search for Indigenous Petroleum, of the Discovery and Development of the Eakring Oilfield by the D'Arcy Exploration Co., Ltd.*, London, the Company, 1947, pp. 20. Reprinted 1953.
History of search for oil in England, with specific accounts of each area. Production by fields, 1938–52, shown in tables.

ouncil of British Manufacturers of Petroleum Equipment, *British Petroleum Equipment, 1959/1960 Edition*, London, the Council, 1959, pp. 894.
Published alternate years, series initiated with 1947 edition, pp. xlvii + 402. Reviews work of Council, formed 1943, to deal with technical aspects of equipment for petroleum industry. Lists members, committees, and catalogue announcements of members.

conomic Commission for Europe, *Relationship Between Coal and Black Oils in the West European Fuel Market*, Geneva, United Nations, 1954, pp. 77.
Prepared by Industry Division of Commission. Trends in relationships between coal and oil in western Europe, forecast of energy market in 1963, discussion of technical aspects of use of coal and heating oils, and supply conditions for black oil.

E. St. John Fairman, *A Treatise on the Petroleum Zones of Italy*, London, E. & F. N. Spon, 1868, pp. vii + 75.
Petroleum prospects of Italy, with special attention to provinces of Modena and Reggio.

Institute of Petroleum, *The Post-War Expansion of the U. K. Petroleum Industry*, London, the Institute, 1954, pp. 220.
Supply, refining, distribution, and economics; Middle East as source of oil supply.

Stanislaw Janicki, *The History and Present Conditions of the Oil Industry in Galicia*, London, Polish Press Bureau, 1921, pp. 40.
History, geology, production of oil and gas in Poland; refineries, consumption; companies.

Constantin N. Jordan, *The Romanian Oil Industry*, New York, New York University Press, 1955, pp. 357.
Rumanian oil industry in 1947: communization of oil industry, oil field equipment and supplies, labor force, exploration, drilling, production, refining, transport, marketing, consumption; statistics, 1928–1947.

Constantin N. Jordan, *The Romanian Methane Gas Industry*, New York, Mid-European Studies Center, Free Europe Committee, 1955, pp. v + 136.
Account of methane (natural gas) resources and use in Rumania; maps of oil and gas regions and pipe lines.

National Committee for a Free Europe, *The Hungarian Oil Industry*, New York, Mid-European Studies Center, 1954, pp. vi + 110.
Exploration and discoveries before 1920, 1920–1948 period, and recent developments, refining industry, and Plans of 1947 and 1950.

55

Organisation for European Economic Co-Operation, *Europe's Need For Oil,* Paris, the Organisation, 1958, pp. 106.
Present and future effects of Suez crisis on supply of oil to Europe.

Organisation for European Economic Co-Operation, *Oil: The Outlook for Europe,* Paris, the Organisation, 1956, pp. 115.
Oil in economy of Europe, oil consumption in relation to general economic activity, oil-refining industry, future oil demands, energy requirements, etc.

Organisation for European Economic Co-Operation, *Oil Equipment in Europe: Fabrication Possibilities, Production Capacity,* Paris, the Organisation, 1955, pp. 136.
Report of Technical Assistance Mission No. 121. Discusses engineer consultant firms, main classifications of equipment.

Organisation for European Economic Co-Operation, *The Search For and Exploitation of Crude Oil and Natural Gas in the OEEC Area,* Paris, the Organisation, 1957, 2 vols., pp. 79.
Hydrocarbon law; oil geology; oil and gas discoveries; oil prospects, and statistics for OEEC member countries, plus Spain and Yugoslavia. Vol. 2 is cylinder of maps and charts.

Mihail Pizanty, *Petroleum in Roumania, A General Review of the Economic, Statistical and Juridical Situation,* Bucharest, Roumanian Economic Institute, 1930, pp. 100. 1933 Ed., pp. 384.
Detailed review of Rumanian oil industry; numerous tables, illustrations, charts, and maps.

Ira Rinehart, *Report on the Oil Fields of Northwest Germany,* Tulsa, the author 1930, pp. xviii + 87.
Based on author's trip through North German oil district; geology, producing fields, salt domes; operating practices leasing taxes, customs.

The Centenary of Rumania's Oil Industry, Bucharest, Foreign Languages Publishing House, 1959, pp. 36 + 86 unnumbered pages.
Events, including building and operation of oil refinery, marking 1857 a birth year of Rumanian oil industry early oil history to end of First World War, subsequent events up to and after 1948.

Stanislaw Unger and Stanislaw Zarzecki *The Polish Oil Industry,* Warsaw Union of Mineral Oil Producers and Refiners in Poland, 1925, pp. 20 + un numbered section of statistics and map Polish oil fields, drilling methods, producing capacity, trade, capital employed oil policy of Polish government. Pamphlet prepared for members of British Parliament visiting Polish oil fields June, 1925.

Jan H. Wszelaki, *Fuel and Power in Captive Middle Europe,* New York, Mid-European Studies Center, National Committee for a Free Europe, 1952, pp. 63 Fuel and power production in eastern Germany, Czechoslovakia, Poland Hungary, Rumania, Bulgaria, and Albania; chapters on oil, natural gas, and synthetic fuels.

B. RUSSIA (U.S.S.R.)

Amtorg Trading Corporation, *Petroleum Industry of the U.S.S.R.,* New York, the Corporation, 1929, pp. 31.
Operating functions and other aspects of Soviet oil industry, prepared for International Petroleum Exposition, Tulsa.

Council of Petroleum Industry, *New Oil Districts of U.S.S.R. and Their Future Development,* Moscow, n.pub., 1926.
Six booklets, each describing geography

and geology of assigned area, occurrence of oil, history of prospecting and exploitation, with bibliographies.

East European Fund, Inc., *Prospects for Oil Output in the U.S.S.R. by 1960,* n.p. the Fund, 1952, pp. 25.
Survey of Soviet oil production, power, mechanization, capital accumulation, geographical location; present and potential production, with plan objective outlined in appendix.

Alexander Gerschenkron and Nancy Nimitz, *A Dollar Index of Soviet Petroleum Output, 1927–28 to 1937*, Santa Monica, Cal., Rand Corp., 1952, pp. ii + 210.
Measures Soviet output of petroleum products by application of dollar valuations; data on Soviet output of petroleum and refined products.

T. Gonta, *The Heroes of Grozny*, Moscow, Co-operative Publishing Society of Foreign Workers in the U.S.S.R., 1932, pp. 56.
Drilling, oil production, and operations under 5-year plan; counter-plan proposed by Grozny oil workers.

N. Goold-Verschoyle (Translator), *The Victory of the Oil Workers: The Five-Year Plan in Two and a Half Years*, Moscow, n.pub., 1931.
Collection of articles translated from Russian publications on production, drilling, and refining operations in Russian oil fields and centers.

Heinrich Hassmann, *Oil in the Soviet Union: History, Geography, Problems*, Princeton, N.J., Princeton University Press, 1953, pp. 173.
Translated from German by Alfred M. Leeston. Structure of Russian oil industry, its development, oil-producing districts, Russian oil problems, demand, supply. Translator added footnotes, maps, bibliography, some new information.

James Dodds Henry, *Baku, An Eventful History*, London, Archibald Constable & Co., 1906, pp. xviii + 256.
History of Baku and oil and gas developments, refining, leading companies and personalities; about half the book is devoted to a detailed account of the 1905 massacre of Armenians by Tartars; chapter on Batum, Black Sea refining town for Baku oil.

Aleksandr Abramovich Isbakh, *Nefte-Chala, Short Stories of the Fight for Oil*, Moscow, Co-operative Publishing Society of Foreign Workers in the U.S.S.R., 1932, pp. 80.
Oil developments in Nefte-Chala district, near Caspian Sea, with accounts of early activities, advent of turbine drilling and review of early Russian oil history.

Alexander H. Japp, *Days With Industrials; Adventures and Experiences Among Curious Industries*, London, Trubner & Co., 1889, pp. viii + 304.
Chapter on petroleum deals largely with oil developments at Baku and reviews some earlier developments.

J. A. Krems, Ed., *The Petroleum Excursion. 17th International Geological Congress, Moscow, 1937*, Moscow and Leningrad, Chief Editorial Office of the Mining-Fuel and Geological-Prospecting Literature, 1937, pp. 345 in 5 fascicles.
Route of excursion; geographic, geologic, and economic description of regions visited; oil development; description of fields. Fasc. 1: Perm District, Bashkirian Autonomous Soviet Socialist Republic, and Samara Bend. Fasc. 2: Azerbaijanian Soviet Socialist Republic. Fasc. 3: Daghestanian Autonomous Soviet Socialist Republic and Grozny Region. Fasc. 4: Georgian Soviet Socialist Republic. Fasc. 5: Kuban-Black Sea Region. Each fascicle with maps, plates, diagrams, bibliography.

Charles Thomas Marvin, *The Region of the Eternal Fire: An Account of a Journey to the Petroleum Region of the Caspian, in 1883*, London, W. H. Allen & Co., 1884, pp. xviii + 413. Popular Ed. 1891, pp. 406.
Author was first writer to attempt to stimulate British interest in petroleum and its development within British Empire. Book gives full account of Russian oil industry, then centered about Baku, including material on activities and accomplishments of Robert and Ludwig Nobel. Marvin also wrote the following "shilling pamphlets" on oil, all published in London:
The Petroleum of the Future: Baku, The Petrolia of Europe, 1883.
The Petroleum Industry of Southern Russia, 1884.
The Moloch of Paraffin, 1886.
England as a Petroleum Power, or The Petroleum Fields of the British Empire, 1887.
The Coming Deluge of Russian Petroleum, and Its Bearing on British Trade, 1887.

The Coming Oil Age: Petroleum—Past, Present and Future: The Great Canadian Oil Fields, 1889.
Our Unappreciated Petroleum Empire, 1889.

John Mitzakis, *The Russian Oil Fields and Petroleum Industry*, London, *Pall Mall* Press, 1911, pp. 106.
Handbook on management of oil properties, history of Russian petroleum industry, survey of oil-bearing lands, legalization of English companies in Russian Empire, Russian mining laws. Designed for investors in, and managers of, Anglo-Russian oil companies.

The Petroleum Industry of Baku and

Nobel Brothers Petroleum Productio Company, St. Petersburg, Trenke Fusnot, 1893, pp. 20.
Role of Robert and Ludwig Nobel i developing Russian oil industry; charts maps.

A. Beeby Thompson, *Oil Fields of Russi and the Russian Petroleum Industry* London, C. Lockwood & Son, 1904, pp xviii + 504. 2nd Ed. 1908, pp. xix - 415.
Practical handbook on exploration, ex ploitation, and management of Russia oil properties; notes on origin and de scription of its use for fuel. 2nd E adds accounts of labor disturbances an use of electrical power.

C. MIDDLE EAST

Advisory Committee on International Technologic Assistance, *The Utilization of Waste Gases in Saudi Arabia*, Washington, National Academy of Sciences, National Research Council, 1954, pp. 165.
Technological and economic considerations of flared gas; local utilization; use in manufacturing and power production; projects for transportation to Europe by pipe line or in liquefied form.

Anglo-Persian Oil Co., Ltd., *The Persian Oil Industry: An Account of Its Origin and Development*, London, the Company, 1927, pp. 27.
Discovery and development of oil in Persia, transportation, refining, gas recovery; medical and staff services.

Arabian American Oil Co., *Summary of Middle East Oil Developments*, New York, 1947, pp. ii + 27, maps. 2nd Ed. 1948, pp. ii + 30. 3rd Ed. 1952, pp. 20.
Exploration, development, and production of oil in Middle East; relationships with governments; refineries; pipe lines; properties of Middle East crude oil; summaries of operations in Iran, Iraq, Kuwait, Saudi Arabia, Bahrein, Qatar.

Michael Sheldon Cheney, *Big Oil Man From Arabia*, New York, Ballantine Books, 1958, pp. 282.
Author's experiences working 7 years in oil fields of Saudi Arabia, laying Trans-Arabian pipe line, living in oil

camps and desert; social, economic, an political changes from oil developmen

Khodadad Farmanfarmaian, *An Analys of the Role of the Oil Industry in th Economy of Iran*, n.p., the autho 1955, pp. xiii + 234.
Doctoral thesis reviewing history o Iranian oil industry from origina D'Arcy concession through 1951 natior alization; distribution of economic bene fits of oil industry; oil industry i Iranian economy under 1954 agreemen and in future.

Richard Finnie, *Bechtel in Arab Lands: 15th-Year Review of Engineering an Construction Projects*, San Franciscc Bechtel Corp., 1958, pp. 149.
Oil developments in Arab countries an participation since 1943 in constructio of facilities for gathering, transporting and refining oil in Middle East; plu variety of public works in these coun tries.

Lorania K. Francis, *Dispatches From th Middle East*, n.p., n. pub., 1951, pp. 24
Articles describing author's visit to oi producing countries of Middle East.

International Labour Office, *Labour Con ditions in the Oil Industry in Iran* Geneva, International Labour Office 1950, pp. 87.
Mission of International Labour Offic

visit to Abadan refinery, oil fields, and other locations in Iran and Iraq. Describes oil areas, labor force, recruitment and training, working conditions, social services, trade union situation, labor-management relations.

Government of Iran, *Some Documents on the Conditions of the Iranian Workers under the Ex-Anglo Iranian Oil Co.,* Teheran, Iranian Government, 1952, pp. 47.
Contradicts portions of International Labour Office Report (above); presents notes, memoranda, and documents evidently acquired during period of nationalization.

Iraq Petroleum Company, *Guide to Kirkuk,* London, the Company, 1955, pp. 33 unnumbered.
Guidebook to Kirkuk oil field, Iraq, covering oil production and equipment employed; medical, educational, production data; illustration of underground section, maps.

Roy Lebkicher, George Rentz, and Max Steineke, *The Arabia of Ibn Saud,* New York, Russell F. Moore Co., 1952, pp. xiii + 179.
Subsequent 3 parts of American Employees Handbook series.

Stephen Hemsley Longrigg, *Oil in the Middle East,* London, Oxford University Press, 1954, pp. xiii + 305.
Covers Middle East countries from Egypt to Turkey, tracing history of oil development in Arab countries and Persia from early times to 1953; devoted mainly to exploratory and productive efforts of past 50 years, with many details of operations in area. Author was oil company executive in this area.

Hakon Mielche, *Lands of Aladdin,* trans. from Danish by M. A. Michael, London, William Hodge & Co., 1955, pp. 241.
History of oil industry and developments in Middle East; author's travels in Middle East, with comments on recent oil activities in area.

Wayne Mineau, *The Go Devils,* London, Cassell & Co., 1958, pp. xi + 243.
Development of Middle East oil, beginning with D'Arcy in Persia and continuing with development in other areas; based on tour of oil fields and interviews with oilmen and others.

Jamal Muzaffar, *Middle East Oil Transportation,* n.p., n.pub., 1957, pp. 28.
Geography of Middle East, oil producing and transit countries, pipe lines, Suez Canal, new routes, and markets for Middle East oil.

E. H. Pascoe, *Geological Notes on Mesopotamia, with Special Reference to Occurrences of Petroleum,* Calcutta, Government of India (Memoirs of The Geological Survey of India), 1922, pp. vii + 90 with 10 plates.
Based on geological reconnaissance of Mesopotamia 1918–19; 14 reports on areas visited, with summary review. Author concluded "country will probably take a not unimportant place among the world's sources of petroleum."

Petroleum Times, *Review of Middle East Oil,* London, *Petroleum Times,* 1948, pp. xlix + 115.
Comprehensive illustrated review of all aspects (including history) of oil developments in Middle East, based on tour by Dr. C. T. Barber, with articles by others. Geology, concessions, development, operations in Iran, Iraq, Bahrein, Saudi Arabia, Kuwait; refineries.

G. E. Pilgrim, *The Geology of the Persian Gulf and Adjoining Portions of Persia and Arabia,* Calcutta, Superintendent of Government Printing (Memoirs of The Geological Survey of India, Vol. XXXIV, part 4), 1908, pp. xx + 177, with 16 plates.
Based on 1904–05 field trip; discusses possible petroleum development, specific discussion of Bahrein. Comments indicating little promise of oil finding influenced British views on oil prospects and interest in area.

Samir Shamma, *The Oil of Kuwait,* Beirut, Lebanon, Middle East Research and Publishing Center, 1959, pp. viii + 90.
Examines background and present state of oil industry in Kuwait, various concession agreements with foreign oil companies, and recommendations regarding future oil policy of Kuwait.

Angus Sinclair, *Bahrein and The Bahrein Petroleum Company,* Washington, the author, 1953, pp. 68. Rev. Ed. 1954.
History of sheikhdom of Bahrein, sovereignty controversy, granting of oil concession; establishment and development of Bahrein Petroleum Co., wartime and postwar operations.

Standard Oil Company (New Jersey), *Standard Oil Company (New Jersey) and Middle Eastern Oil Production,* New York, the Company, 1947, pp. 15. Rev. Ed. 1954, pp. 35.
Historical background of oil develop-

ment in Middle East; early German at tempts through World War II, with discussion of expanding oil markets. Revised edition contains chronology of events affecting Middle East oil development, 1901–52.

John W. Williamson, *In a Persian Oil Field* London, Ernest Benn, 1927, pp. 189. 2nd Ed. 1930, pp. 192.
Application of scientific knowledge and methods in Persian oil industry. 2nd Ed includes larger international aspects of petroleum industry.

D. BURMA

Burma Research Society, *The Burma Petroleum Industry,* London, Longmans, Green & Co., 1946, pp. 64.
Historical review of Burma oil industry, companies involved; recent developments including destruction of wells, equipment, and refineries in 1942 in advance of Japanese invasion; geology, oil field development, production, labor; contribution of petroleum industry to Burma.

Government of Burma, *The Burma Oil-Fields Manual,* Rangoon, Burma, Superintendent of Government Printing, 1920, pp. 64. Reissued 1938 and to July 1, 1946, pp. 89. Published 1947.
Rules and regulations under the Burma Oil-Fields Act, 1918; designation and boundaries of oil fields.

Union of Burma, *Report of the Ad Hoc Oilfields Enquiry Committee,* Rangoon, Burma, Superintendent of Government Printing and Stationery, 1950, pp. 76.
History of Burma oil industry, Burmah Oil Company, prewar conditions, the war period, postwar developments, insurrection, subsequent developments; present conditions; recommendations.

Hiram Cox, *Journal of a Residence in the Burmhan Empire, and More Particularly at the Court of Amarapoorah,* London, John Warren and G. & W. B. Whittaker, 1821, pp. viii + 431.
Includes account of visit to oil wells at Yenangyaung in 1797, with description of operations. States there were 520

hand-dug wells registered by Government with estimated annual production of 412,360 hogsheads, or about 2000 United States barrels daily.

John Crawfurd, *Journal of an Embassy from the Governor General of India to the Court of Ava,* London, Henry Colburn, 1834, 2 vols., pp. 1023, maps and drawings, 2nd Ed. (First apparently issued in 1829.)
Journal of British envoy to Burma in 1826; history, language, customs, military affairs, manufactures, flora, fauna, natural phenomena of the Burmese Empire. Entry of Sept. 22, 1826 (Vol. I) describes extent and operating methods of Burmese oil-producing industry Author estimated some 200 hand-dug wells then in operation, averaging about 200 ft. deep. Oil raised to surface in earthen pots, transported in crocks by ox teams and river boat, sold at 5d. to 7d. per cwt. for use unrefined as burning fluid and for saturating timber against termites.

Friedrich Wilhelm Noetling, *The Occurrence of Petroleum in Burma and Its Technical Exploitation,* Calcutta, Government of India Central Printing Office (Memoirs of the Geological Survey of India, Vol. XXVII, part 2), 1898, pp. iv + 226, with 17 plates and map.
Historical summary from legendary times up to 1886; review of petroleum occurrence in various areas, its economic importance, costs, prices, and

trade value; extended review of Yenang-yaung oil field, including early history and hand-dug wells.

ξ. H. Pascoe, *The Oil-Fields of Burma,* Calcutta, Superintendent of Government Printing (Memoirs of the Geological Survey of India, Vol. XL, Part 1), 1912, pp. xlix + 269, with 54 plates.
Geology, oil development and production, including history of early native industry.

Michael Symes, *An Account of an Embassy to the Kingdom of Ava Sent by the Governor General of India in the Year 1795,* London, Printed by W. Bulmer & Co., 1800, pp. xxiii + 503.
Includes account of visits of Yenang-

yaung oil field, which has history of exploitation covering longer period of time than any other field in world.

Henry Yule, *A Narrative of the Mission Sent by the Governor-General of India to the Court of Ava in 1855, with Notices of the Country, Government, and People,* London, Smith, Elder & Co., 1858, pp. vi + 391.
Account of visit to oil wells in 1855. Capt. Yule was accompanied by Thomas Oldham, Supt. of Geological Survey of India, who prepared "Notes on the Geological Features of the Banks of the Irawadi, and of the Country North of Amarapoora," published as appendix. During visit at Yenangyaung, Oldham first observed association of anticlinal structure with petroleum.

E. OTHER EASTERN HEMISPHERE

Anglo-Persian Oil Company On Behalf of the Government of the Commonwealth of Australia, *The Oil Exploration Work in Papua and New Guinea, 1920–1929,* London, Harrison & Sons, 1930, 6 vols., 2 atlases.
Covers first geological expedition, 1920–23, and second expedition, 1927–29, with report on drilling operations.

Thomas Sutton Bowman, *Report on Boring for Oil in Egypt,* Cairo, Government Press (Mines and Quarries Department, Ministry of Finance, Egypt), 1925 to 1931, Sections I, II, and III, pp. xxviii + 511.
Sect. I: *Government Petroleum Research Operations:* record of test borings for petroleum undertaken by Egyptian Government. Sect. II: *Sinai:* operations of several oil companies in Sinai area, discussion of drilling and consideration of results. Sect. III: *Eastern Desert and Adjoining Islands:* area embracing African Coast of Gulf of Suez, in which 128 wells had been drilled; early prospecting and drilling, results; geological summary; engineering notes; description of Hurghada oil field.

Eric J. Bradshaw and Henry Crookshank, *The Search for Oil in Pakistan,* Karachi, Geological Survey of Pakistan (Vol. 2, Part 1), 1950, pp. 14.

Review of oil prospecting and discovery in Punjab, Baluchistan, and elsewhere in Pakistan.

Grant W. Corby, *Geology and Oil Possibilities of the Philippines,* Manila, Bureau of Printing (Department of Agriculture and Natural Resources, Technical Bulletin No. 21), 1951, pp. 363.
Descriptive geology of island and areas of Philippines; discussion of petroleum possibilities.

John Gunn and Arthur Justin Hancock, *Royal Commission on Mineral Oils and Petrol and Other Products of Mineral Oils,* Canberra, Australia, Commonwealth Government Printer, 1935, pp. 198. (Includes Report by Sydney Ernest Lamb, Chairman, pp. 124.)
Presents results of inquiry initiated April 7, 1933, into landed cost, wholesale and retail selling price, capital employed, profits, losses, customs and excise duties, taxation, etc., resulting in comprehensive report on Australia's oil trade.

J. Henderson, *Petroleum in New Zealand,* Wellington, N.Z., E. V. Paul, 1937, Extract, pp. 401–426, from *New Zealand Journal of Science and Technology,* Vol. XIX, No. 7 (Bulletin No. 60, Department of Scientific and Industrial Research.)

General geology of New Zealand, structure and oil possibilities of various districts.

James Dodds Henry, *Oil Fields of New Zealand,* London, Bradbury, Agnew & Co., 1911, pp. xxvi + 337.
Endeavors to develop oil production in New Zealand, beginning near close of 1865; review of shale oil industry of New Zealand.

Chi-ch'ing Huang (and others), *Report on Geological Investigation of Some Oil-Fields in Sinkiang,* Nanking, National Geological Survey of China (Series A, No. 21), 1947, pp. vii + 118.
Report, Sept., 1943, of first geological expedition sent by Central Government of China into Province of Sinkiang. Covers stratigraphy, structure, development of oil fields, production and refining, composition of oil, with discussion of oil geology and prospects throughout area.

Government of India, *Report of the Tariff Board Regarding the Grant of Protection to the Oil Industry,* Calcutta, Central Publication Branch, 1928, pp. x + 101.
Reports from inquiry initiated March 26, 1928, when oil-producing companies of India asked protection in price war caused by kerosene imported from Russia. Describes oil industry of India and companies, kerosene pool, origin of price war, world parity price, United States Gulf Coast prices, freight; petroleum products demand in India, 1920–27; need for protection; recommendations.

Benjamin Smith Lyman, *A Report of Progress for the 1st Year of the Oil Surveys,* Tokyo, Public Works Department, 1877, pp. v + 63.
Includes complete description of well digging, including lighting.

Benjamin Smith Lyman, *Report on the 2nd Year's Progress of the Survey of the Oil Lands of Japan,* Tokyo, Public Works Department, 1878, pp. iv + 67.

Benjamin Smith Lyman, *Reports of Progress for 1878 and 1879,* Tokyo, Public Works Department, 1879, pp. x + 266.
Includes data on 2513 oil wells in Japan, covers costs, oil refining, and products.

E. H. Pascoe, *The Petroleum Occurrences of Assam and Bengal,* Calcutta, Superintendent of Government Printing (Memoirs of the Geological Survey of India, Vol. XI, Part 2), 1914, pp. 270–329, plates 55–69.
Geological report and appraisal.

E. H. Pascoe, *Petroleum in the Punjab and North-West Frontier Province,* Calcutta, Superintendent of Government Printing (Memoirs of the Geological Survey of India, Vol. XL, part 3) 1920, pp. 330–493, plates 70–88.
Geological report.

Symposium on the Development of Petroleum Resources of Asia and the Far East, *Proceedings,* Bangkok, United Nations Economic Commission for Asia and the Far East (Mineral Resources Development Series No. 10), 1959, pp. xiv + 251.
Geology, potentialities, exploration, development, associated petroleum matters relating to Asia and Far East.

Boris Pavlovich Torgasheff, *Digest of Coal, Iron and Oil in the Far East,* Honolulu, Institute of Pacific Relations, 1929, pp. 63.
Section on oil gives summary data on petroleum in Japan, Russia, Far East, China, Formosa, Philippines, and Kamchatka.

W. G. Woolnough, *Report on Tour of Inspection of the Oil-Fields of the United States and Argentina and On Oil Prospects in Australia,* Canberra, Australia, Government Printers, 1931, pp. 118.
Prospects for obtaining oil in various parts of Australia, against background of visit to United States and Argentina.

VI.

Natural Gas and Natural Gasoline

A. NATURAL GAS

Alaska Development Board, *Possibility of Commercial Development of Gubik Gas Field and Use of Natural Gas as a Source of Heat and Power in the Railbelt Area of Alaska,* Juneau, the Board, 1954, pp. iv + 75.
Oil explorations in Naval Petroleum Reserve No. 4, area of 37,000 square miles in Northern Alaska, describes discoveries of oil and gas, discusses potential gas markets, development of gas reserves, construction of pipe line and distribution facilities.

V. J. Altieri, *Gas Analysis and Testing of Gaseous Materials,* New York, American Gas Association, 1945, pp. xi + 567.
Standards for sampling, analyzing, and testing gases and gaseous materials, composition of gases, measurement of quantity and flow, apparatus and methods.

V. J. Altieri, *Gas Chemists' Book of Standards for Light Oils and Light Oil Products,* New York, American Gas Association, 1942, pp. xiii + 352.
Details of current specifications, definitions, tests, and facilities in matters relating to light oils, benzene, toluene, and other light oil products. Prepared to meet wartime needs as part of revision of *Gas Chemists' Handbook.*

American Gas Association, *Fuel Flue Gases. A Digest of Their Properties, Behavior, and Utilization,* New York, the Association, 1940, pp. x + 198. Reprinted, with corrections, 1941.
Nature of gas, applicable laws, methods of analysis, composition of typical gases, physical tests, composition of fuel gases, other aspects related to combustion.

American Gas Association, *Gas Facts. A Statistical Record of the Gas Utility Industry in 1958,* New York, the Association, 1959, pp. xiv + 250.
Annual series initiated with edition covering 1945–46, published 1947. Reviews year on: energy reserves, production, transmission, distribution, sales, utilization, finance, employment, prices. Data on Canadian industry added 1950; on underground storage, 1952. Glossary.

American Gas Association, *Historical Statistics of the Gas Industry, 1956,* New York, the Association, 1956, pp. x + 313.
Organized on basis comparable with *Gas Facts;* provides historical data through 1954. Planned for revision and reissue every 5 years, with intervening supplementary information issued as inserts.

American Gas Association, *Survey of Residential Gas Service by County,* New York, the Association, 1953, pp. i + 280.
Gas and gas appliance utilization and marketing. Data for each state show county totals of population, dwellings, customers using gas for cooking and heating fuel, name of utility company serving each community, types of service, etc. Association previously published similar volume with comparable data as of Oct. 1, 1949.

American Gas Association, *Proceedings, 39th Annual Convention,* New York, the Association, 1958, pp. cviii + 306.
Held Oct. 7–9, 1957, at St. Louis, Mo. Reports of accounting, industrial, commercial, and residential gas sections, rate committee, operating section; list

of papers and reports presented at 12th Annual Research and Utilization Conference, May 7–9, 1957, Cleveland, Ohio.

American Gas Institute, Technical Committee, Sub-committee on Chemical Tests, *Gas Chemist's Handbook,* New York, the Institute, 1917, pp. 354. 2nd Ed. 1922, pp. 608. 3rd Ed. 1929, pp, 795.

American Petroleum Institute, *Field Handling of Natural Gas,* Austin, Petroleum Extension Service, University of Texas, Texas Education Agency, and Central Committee on Training, New York, the Institute, 1954, pp. 139.
Growth of natural gas industry, conservation, standards and practices adopted to meet problems of producing and transporting.

American Petroleum Institute, *Gas Measurement for Field Production Workers,* Preliminary issue prepared, 1945, by Division of Extension, University of Texas, New York, the Institute.
This issue was distributed to oil and gas industry. On the basis of comments the manual was divided into four parts: Part I: Introduction to the Study of Natural Gas; Part II: Field Handling of Natural Gas; Part III: Gas measurement With Portable Equipment; Part IV: Gas Measurement with Orifice Meters. Parts I, III, IV then published. Part II published in 1954.

American Society for Testing Materials, *ASTM Standards on Gaseous Fuels,* prepared by ASTM Committee D-3 on Gaseous Fuels, Philadelphia, the Society, 1954, pp. vi + 176. 2nd Ed. 1949. 3rd Ed. 1951, pp. vi + 136.
ASTM methods of testing gaseous fuels; includes sampling and measurement, methods of testing and analysis; sampling and testing of liquefied petroleum gases.

Charles A. Ashburner, *The Geology of Natural Gas in Pennsylvania and New York,* reprint of paper read before American Institute of Mining Engineers, Halifax meeting, Sept., 1885, pp. 11.
History of natural gas development in Pennsylvania; geology associated with discoveries in Pennsylvania and New York; "belt" theory and anticlinal theory in relation to gas findings.

L. Bannister, *Something About Natural Gas. Its Origin, Extent and Development. The Piping Systems, Safety Appliances and Devices for Its Safe and Economic Utilization. Gas the Fuel of the Future,* New York, Baldwin & Gleason, 1886, pp. 39.
Regarded as first book or pamphlet devoted to production and use of natural gas.

C. T. Barber, *The Natural Gas Resources of Burma,* Calcutta, Government of India, 1935, pp. xxviii + 172, 14 plates.
Tertiary geology of Burma; natural gas in Yenangyaung structure and other areas; origin and accumulation of gas; its conservation and utilization.

Bechtel International Corporation, *Natural Gas Supply for Europe,* San Francisco, the Company, 1951, pp. 16.
Preliminary study of proposed natural gas pipe line from Kirkuk to Paris; estimates of costs of system, delivered cost of gas, markets; appendices; alternate routes.

Frederick Frank Blachly and Miriam Eulalie Oatman, *Natural Gas and the Public Interest,* Washington, Granite Press, 1947, pp. viii + 159.
Control of natural gas industry; discusses basic factors, private integration, state regulation, federal control, views of opponents and advocates of regulation and need for national policy.

John W. Boatwright, *Reasonable Market Prices,* New York, American Petroleum Institute, 1957, pp. 15.
Background Information Bulletin. "Cost of service" yardstick as basis for regulating natural gas prices.

British Productivity Council, *Gas,* London, the Council, 1953, pp. xv + 194.
Report of Productivity Team representing British Gas Industry which visited United States in 1952 and made survey of American gas industry; includes general structure and administration of industry; use of refinery and liquid petroleum gases; purification, distribution, storage; application of gas for

domestic, commercial, and industrial purposes.

R. E. Buffington, *Natural Gas,* Washington, Association of American Railroads, 1944, pp. ix + 60.
First report of Group 7, Sub-committee for Economic Study, Railroad Committee for Study of Transportation. Factors affecting substitution of natural gas for solid and liquid fuels transported by rail; review of industry; legislative and regulatory influences; future markets.

John C. Diehl, *Natural Gas Handbook,* Erie, Penna., American Meter Co., Metric Metal Works, 1927, pp. 578.
Continuation of *Hand Book of Natural Gas* by H. P. Westcott. History, properties, pressures, measurement; meters, leases, contracts, field work, wells, pipe lines, distribution, consumption, heating value, analysis.

Report of Engineering Committee, *Texas Panhandle Field, etc.,* Dallas, printed by Harben-Spott Co., 1934, pp. 26, tables.
Report of Committee of Engineers affiliated with operating companies on wastage of gas in Panhandle Field; proposal for returning excess gas to formation.

Edward Falck and Francis X. Welch, *Federal Regulation of Natural Gas in the United States,* Washington, E. Falck & Co., 1958, pp. 100.
Enactment of Natural Gas Act; federal regulation; certificates of public convenience and necessity; rates, export and import licenses, etc. Cites leading cases.

William Frederick Heisler, *Natural Gas. Vocational Training Courses,* Stillwater, Okla., College Book Store, Oklahoma Agricultural and Mechanical College (Course No. S4), 1937, pp. 302.
Textbook for natural gas industry, for study in production and distribution of natural gas as fuel. History, geology, etc. Fourth of special instructional group of vocational education courses, petroleum industry series, set up by Joint Educational Committee of American Petroleum Institute and Departments of Industrial Education, University of Texas and Oklahoma Agricultural and Mechanical College.

Richard C. Henshaw, Jr., *Natural-Gas Statistics,* Austin, University of Texas, 1955, pp. 127. (Supplement to Research Monograph No. 15, Economics of Natural Gas in Texas.)

R. V. Higgins, G. B. Shea, and William H. Kerns, *A Study of the Economic Practicability of a Natural Gas Pipeline from the Gubic Field to Fairbanks and Anchorage, Alaska,* n.p., n. pub., 1958, pp. 67.
Discovery and reserves of Gubic field; proposed route of line; estimated requirements, costs of line, gas delivery.

Independent Natural Gas Association of America, *Compilation of Papers Given at Annual Meeting,* Washington, the Association, 1958, pp. 81.
Eighth Annual Meeting, held at New Orleans, Sept. 15–16, 1958. Published annually beginning with meeting held Sept. 24, 1951, at Oklahoma City, pp. 101.

William Iulo, *Natural Gas in the Pacific Northwest. Some Economic Aspects,* Pullman, Wash., State College of Washington (Bulletin No. 25), 1953, pp. xvi + 110.
History and development of industry; utilization; energy use pattern of Pacific Northwest; markets in area; notes on competing pipe lines.

Willard Rouse Jillson, *The Conservation of Natural Gas in Kentucky,* Louisville, Ky., John P. Morton & Co., 1922, pp. 152.
History of gas development in Kentucky; description of fields; manufacture of carbon black; critical comment on production; problems of conservation.

Willard Rouse Jillson, *Natural Gas in Eastern Kentucky,* Lawrence, Ky., Standard Printing Co., 1937, pp. xii + 237.
Occurrence; production; geology of each field.

Willard Rouse Jillson, *Natural Gas in Western Kentucky,* Frankfort, Kentucky Geological Survey (Series 6, Vol. 38), 1931, pp. 190.
Occurrence; production; geology of each field.

Donald LaVerne Katz, et al., *Handbook of Natural Gas Engineering,* New York, McGraw-Hill Book Co., 1959, pp. vii + 802.
Presents procedures for conduct of engineering calculations for design of equipment required to produce and deliver natural gas, including engineering principles governing operations.

T. H. Kerr, *Natural Gas in Ohio. A History,* Columbus, Ohio State University (Circular No. 52, Engineering Experiment Station), 1950, pp. 116.
Natural gas in Appalachian area; history of companies; gas-measuring devices; storage, pipe lines.

Joseph Alton Kornfeld, *Natural Gas Economics,* Dallas, Transportation Press, 1949, pp. xiv + 261.
Role of natural gas in energy sources; place in national economy; modern conservation; synthetic fuels; reserves; production, demand; pipe line construction; underground storage; regulation, pricing.

Henry A. Ley, Ed. *Geology of Natural Gas,* Tulsa, American Association of Petroleum Geologists, 1935, pp. xii + 1227.
Thirty-eight papers by 47 authors; comprehensive geologic treatise on occurrence of natural gas on North American continent; discusses methods of estimating natural gas reserves; summary of industry.

Lester Clyde Lichty, *Natural Gas. Measurement, Compression and Transmission,* New York, John Wiley & Sons, 1924, pp. v + 523.
Fundamental laws applicable to natural gas; decline of gas wells; methods and apparatus for measurement; compression; separation of natural gasoline from natural gas; transmission in pipe lines.

James W. McKie, *The Regulation of Natural Gas,* Washington, American Enterprise Association, 1957, pp. 49.
Structure of industry, relation to other fuels; history of pipe line contracts; Supreme Court decision subjecting field price to Federal Power Commission control; legislative attempts to exempt natural gas from certain aspects of regulation.

Jerome J. Morgan, *Gasification of Hydrocarbons,* New York, Moore Publishing Co., 1953, pp. 180.
Manufacture of gas to supplement natural gas for peak loads; oil gas and water gas; catalytic cracking, etc.

Paul W. Mullen, *Modern Gas Analysis,* New York, Interscience Publishers, 1955, pp. ix + 354.
Theory; equipment; absorptiometric and instrumental analysis; advantages and disadvantages of each.

Natural Gas Association of America, *Proceedings, Natural Gas Association of America,* Kansas City, Mo., the Association, 1909, pp. 566.
First volume covers organization meeting, Feb. 20, 27, and March 20, 1906, Kansas City; papers and discussions on geology; field operations; commercial problems presented at first 4 meetings. Subsequent volumes covered annual meeting through 22nd meeting, May 9–12, 1927. Papers and discussions extended to include conservation, transportation, accounting, valuation, natural gasoline extraction, etc. Natural Gas Association of America merged with American Gas Association in 1927. Proceedings of annual meetings of Natural Gas Department of American Gas Association were published beginning with volume for 1928, and continued yearly until terminated with volume for 1952, pp. 112.

Robert Peeples Nevin, *Les Trois Rois,* Pittsburgh, Jos. Eichbaum & Co., 1888, pp. iv + 185.
Transportation, iron, fuel, in relation to Pittsburgh; reviews development and distribution of natural gas in area.

Oscar E. Norman, *The Romance of the Gas Industry,* Chicago, A. C. McClurg & Co., 1922, pp. 203.
Production, distribution, uses; development as household and industrial fuel; chronology of early industry.

Organisation for European Economic Co-operation, *Gas in Europe. Production, Availabilities, Consumption.* A Study by Gas Committee, Organization for European Economic Co-operation, Paris, the Organisation, 1958, pp. 146.
First report of a committee established

1956 to study problems of production, transportation, distribution, utilization of manufactured and natural gas. Economic considerations; present position and possible lines of development; separate chapters on gas in 16 member countries. Covers 1954–56, with forecasts to 1960.

Organisation for European Economic Co-operation, *Long-Distance Gas Transport in the United States,* Paris, the Organisation, 1946, pp. 183.
Report of fact-finding mission (Project No. 118) representing 8 member nations, to United States to study facilities and operations for transportation of natural gas; treatment before transmission; compressor stations; underground storage; operation and control; conclusions and recommendations.

Henry Ozanne, *The Gas Record, 1955,* Washington, Petroleum Industry Projects, 1955, 2 vols., pp. 645. Also published in 1953 and 1954.
Operating and financial data on about 273 companies in production, transportation, distribution of natural gas. After 1955, production and pipe line data presented in *Oil Record.*

Pacific Coast Gas Association, *Gas Engineers' Handbook,* New York, McGraw-Hill Book Co., 1934, pp. x + 1017.
Mathematical, chemical, and physical data for solving problems in gas manufacture, transmission, distribution, and utilization.

Joseph Dominic Parent, *The Storage of Natural Gas as Hydrate,* Chicago, Institute of Gas Technology (Bulletin No. 1), 1948, pp. iv + 40.
Based on research project sponsored by Natural Gas Department of American Gas Association; presents survey of technical and patent literature pertaining to reaction of paraffin hydrocarbon gases with water to form solid hydrates and to storage and degasification.

Eugene S. Perry, *Natural Gas in Montana,* Butte, Mont., Montana School of Mines (Memoir No. 3), 1937, pp. viii + 96.
Geology; occurrence and production; description of producing districts; prospective and unproductive areas.

Francis C. Phillips, *Report on the Composition and Fuel-Value of Natural Gas,* Harrisburg, Board of Commissioners for Geological Survey (Part II, Annual Report of Geological Survey of Pennsylvania), 1887, reprint, pp. 41.
Selection and collection of samples, calculation of fuel value, results of analysis of natural gas from 8 pools in Pennsylvania, and one of Fredonia gas in New York. First systematic investigation of composition of natural gas in Pennsylvania was made by Pennsylvania Geological Survey in 1875; results published in Report on the Use of Natural Gas in Iron Manufacture, 1876.

Charles O. Sawyer, *Our Gas Fields. Story of Development and Potential Possibilities,* Horseheads, N.Y., *Chemung Valley Reporter,* 1932, pp. 80.
Geology, developments, possibilities of Pennsylvania and New York natural gas fields.

Gilbert E. Seil, *Dry Box Purification of Gas,* New York, American Gas Association, 1943, pp. x + 289.
Technical book on gas measurement and purification.

Louis Shnidman, *Gaseous Fuels. A Digest of Their Properties, Behavior, and Utilization,* New York, American Gas Association, 1948, pp. xii + 368. 2nd Ed. 1954, pp. xvii + 453.
History of fuel gases, basic gas laws, physical measurements, gas analyses, burners, furnaces, operation.

Paul Stanley Stacey, *Natural Gas and Its Ethical Implications,* Washington, Catholic University of America, 1952, pp. 15.
Lecture under auspices of American Catholic Philosophical Association; derivatives and uses of natural gas.

Maynard Moody Stephens, *Natural Gas Engineering,* University Park, Penna., Pennsylvania State University, 1939, pp. xi + 553. Reprinted 1941. 2nd Ed. 1948, pp. viii + 565. 3rd Ed. 1954, pp. viii + 578. Reprinted 1957.
Natural gas economics; developments; measuring, properties; gas well completion and operation; processing, well capacities and property valuation; gathering, compression, and transmis-

sion; regulation. One of a textbook series.

John R. Stockton, Richard C. Henshaw, and Richard W. Graves, *Economics of Natural Gas in Texas,* Austin, University of Texas, 1952, pp. xvi + 316.
Review of industry, utilization, production, reserves, transportation, taxation, public control, conservation, employment in petrochemical industries; competition with other fuels, their relation to Texas.

Louis Stotz, *History of the Gas Industry,* New York, the author, 1938, pp. 534.
One hundred and twenty years of natural gas history; uses of gas; management problems; pipe line systems; regulation of public utilities. Written when Natural Gas Act of 1938 was under consideration in Congress.

George E. Taylor, *The Conservation of Natural Gas in West Virginia,* Morgantown, W. Va., West Virginia University (College of Engineering Bulletin Series 4, No. 1), 1918, pp. 32.

Lyon F. Terry and John G. Winger, *Future Growth of the Natural Gas Industry,* New York, Chase Manhattan Bank, 1957, pp. 28.
Energy supply and consumption in United States, by sources; reserves, finding rate and costs; future supply; estimates of ultimate reserves of oil and gas.

The Texas Company, *Regulation of Producers' Natural Gas Prices: Is Anyone Benefiting?,* New York, American Petroleum Institute, 1957, pp. 4. Background Information Bulletin. Reprint from *Texaco Star.*

Benjamin Howarth Thwaite, *Gaseous Fuel, Including Water Gas. Its Production and Application,* London, Whittaker & Co., 1889, pp. 32.
Smoke pollution of atmosphere; origin, production, chemistry of natural gas; distribution and utilization. Lecture delivered March 29, 1889, under auspices of Manchester and Salford Noxious Vapours Abatement Association. Also *Liquid Fuel,* London, 1887.

University of Oklahoma, School of Natural Gas Engineering, College of Engineering, and Business and Industrial Services, Extension Division, *Gas Conditioning Conference: Proceedings,* Norman, Okla., the University.
1956, pp. 82. 6 papers on gas treating and conditioning. *1957,* pp. 136. 7 papers. *1958,* pp. 114. 8 papers.

Westcoast Transmission Company, Ltd., *Natural Gas in the Economy of Alberta and British Columbia,* Calgary, the Company, 1951, pp. xv + 153.
Resources of Alberta, including principal energy sources; industrial advancement; development of natural gas; exportation, economic benefits, pipe line to British Columbia; exportation and national defense.

Henry P. Westcott, *Hand Book of Natural Gas,* Erie, Penna., Metric Metal Works, 1913, pp. xiv + 529. 2nd Ed. 1915, pp. xv + 616. 3rd Ed. 1920, pp. xvi + 725.
Data on natural gas production etc., as provided by F. H. Oliphant, United States Geological Survey, were presented in commercial catalogs, but with expanded industry, company in 1913 decided to publish book devoted entirely to production, transportation, distribution of natural gas. Series continued by John C. Diehl.

Henry P. Westcott, *Measurement of Gases Where Density Changes,* Erie, Penna., Metric Metal Works, 1915, pp. 59. 2nd Ed. 1923, pp. 60.
Text and tables with formula to determine quantity of natural gas when measured above normal pressure.

Henry P. Westcott, *Measurement of Gas by Orifice Meter,* Erie, Penna., Metric Metal Works, 1918, pp. 408. 2nd Ed.: *Measurement of Gas and Liquids by Orifice Meter,* 1922, pp. 434.
History and types of orifice meters; their use in measuring gas and liquids.

West Virginia University, *Proceedings of the 17th Annual Appalachian Gas Measurement Short Course, 1957,* Morgantown, W. Va., the University (Engineering Experiment Station Technical Bulletin No. 50), 1958, pp. 614.
Course established by gas engineering department of Public Service Commission of West Virginia; sponsored by

School of Mines, West Virginia University, et. al., to provide training in installation, use, maintenance of equipment to measure gas quantities; presentation of new developments. Papers.

Samuel S. Wyer, *Natural Gas, Its Production, Service and Conservation,* Washington, United States National Museum (The Mineral Industries of the United States, Bulletin No. 102, part 7), 1918, pp. 67.
Natural gas geology; production, transmission, distribution; waste and conservation. Based on study by Bureau of Standards, First World War.

Samuel S. Wyer, *Study of Ohio's Natural Gas Situation,* Columbus, East Ohio Gas Co., 1930, pp. 38.
Review of public interest in natural gas, production, distribution, use.

Samuel S. Wyer, *Study of Natural Gas Situation,* Columbus, Fuel-Power-Transportation Educational Foundation, 1931, pp. 46.
Enlargement of preceding publication; discusses carbon black; conservation difficulties.

Vincente Trevino Ximenes, *Natural Gas in New Mexico,* Albuquerque, University of New Mexico (New Mexico Studies

in Business and Economics, No. 3), 1954, pp. 73.
History of developments; location of major producing areas; estimate and ownership of reserves; production, storage, waste, costs and revenue, public interest.

Clinton Mason Young, *Natural Gas,* Lawrence, Kan., University of Kansas, 1934, 2 vols., pp. 532. Rev. Ed. Edited by Eugene A. Stephenson, 1956.
Home study course prepared at request of American Gas Association. Geology, prospecting, production, transportation, utilization. Rev. Ed. presents 37 papers by various authors.

J. Carlisle Youngberg, *Natural Gas. America's Fastest Growing Industry,* San Francisco, Schwabacher-Frey Co., 1930, pp. 185, index and appendix.
History of industry; summary of resource and statistical data; devoted mainly to description of companies and groups in industry.

John A. Zublin, *Gas Conservation, etc.,* Los Angeles, Universal Engineering Co., 1936, pp. ix + 76.
Necessity for gas conservation, purpose, legal aspects, methods; analysis of flow of oil and gas in porous formations and through tubing; description of gas extractor.

B. NATURAL GASOLINE

George Granger Brown, Donald L. Katz, George G. Oberfell, and Richard C. Alden, *Natural Gasoline and the Volatile Hydrocarbons,* Tulsa, Natural Gasoline Association of America, 1948, pp. 92.
Properties of volatile hydrocarbons; application to natural gasoline extraction processes and cycling operations. Marked as Section 1, but no subsequent sections published.

George Arthur Burrell, *The Recovery of Gasoline from Natural Gas, etc.,* New York, Chemical Catalog Co., 1925, pp. 600.
Natural gasoline industry from its reported inception in Pennsylvania in 1903; theories underlying practices of

industry; compression; oil absorption; charcoal processes of extracting gasoline from natural gas; removal of sulphur; operations; discusses motor fuels in general.

George Arthur Burrell, *Gasoline Industry. Technology of Natural Gas As Applied to Making Gasoline and Absorption Processes,* Oil City, Penna., Derrick Publishing Co., 1916, pp. 20.
Properties and characteristics of paraffin hydrocarbons; testing natural gas for gasoline content; methods and practices in extracting natural gasoline, etc.

Richard Lee Huntington, *Natural Gas and Natural Gasoline,* New York, McGraw-Hill Book Co., 1950, pp. vii + 598.

For use in engineering courses dealing with production of natural gas and manufacture of liquefied products from gas; estimation of reserves; plant location and design; gathering raw gas and return of residue gas; dehydration; natural gasoline processing; storage; transportation.

Natural Gasoline Association of America, *Proceedings, Natural Gasoline Association of America,* 37th Annual Meeting, Tulsa, the Association, 1958, pp. 124.
Annual publication of proceedings, 1st meeting held April 27–28, 1922, Tulsa, pp. 27. 24th meeting, 1945, cancelled on account of war.

Natural Gasoline Association of America, in cooperation with Natural Gasoline Supply Men's Association, *Engineering Data Book,* Tulsa, the Association, 1935. 2nd Ed. 1936, pp. 104. 3rd Ed. 1937. 4th Ed. 1941. 5th Ed. 1946. 6th Ed. 1951. 7th Ed. 1957, pp. 174. Reprinted 1958.
Technical data on gas measurement, compressor, storage, fluid flow, water treating, cooling tower, gas processing, etc. "K" charts are revision of 1955 edition, pp. 132, of *Equilibrium Ratio Data Book,* published by Natural Gasoline Association of America.

Natural Gasoline Association of America, *Technical Standards of the Natural Gasoline Association of America,* Tulsa, the Association, n.d., loose-leaf.
Official testing methods and specifications of Association; testing methods developed in cooperation with other organizations; provides complete compilation of testing procedures for natural gasoline and cycling industries.

George G. Oberfell and R. C. Alden, *Natural Gasoline. Testing, Manufacturing and Properties,* Chicago, W. B. Conkey Co., 1924, pp. xviii + 533.
Methods of testing gas, gasoline, and absorbent oils; methods of manufacture; oil absorption and charcoal process plants; properties of natural gasoline.

Henry P. Westcott, *Hand Book of Casing-head Gas,* Erie, Penna., Metric Metal Works, 1916, pp. ix + 274. 2nd Ed. 1918, pp. xviii + 577. 3rd Ed. 1922, pp. xvii + 642.
Physical properties, wells, pipe lines, measuring, compression and absorption methods of extraction; transportation of gasoline.

C. LIQUEFIED PETROLEUM GASES

Carl Abell, *Butane-Propane Power Manual, Principles of LP-Gas Carburetion,* Los Angeles, Jenkins Publications, 1952, pp. 384. 2nd Ed. 1953, pp. 360.
Basic facts on LP-Gas; relation to other fuels; use in internal combustion motors; carburetion, installation of equipment, ignition, etc.

Earle A. Clifford, *A Practical Guide to LP-Gas Utilization,* New York, Moore Publishing Co., 1952, pp. 405. 2nd Ed. 1957, pp. 362.
Service and installation handbook; distribution, installation; uses of liquefied petroleum gases.

Cramer-Krasselt Company, *Cities Service Liquefied Petroleum Gas Survey,* Milwaukee, Wis., Cramer-Krasselt Co., 1930, pp. 170.
Survey of all phases of market possibilities of liquefied petroleum gases.

George H. Finley, *The Handbook of Butane-Propane Gases,* Los Angeles, Western Business Papers, 1932, pp. 279. 2nd Ed. 1935, pp. 375. Revised 1938, pp. 415. 3rd Ed. 1942, pp. 482.
History; early types of gases, chronology of development; properties of gases; manufacture; transportation; distribution; utilization of liquefied petroleum gases. 3rd Ed. reprinted 1945, 1947, and 1951. In 1956 Chilton Company, Philadelphia, acquired Handbook, other LPG textbooks, and *Butane-Propane News* and *Gas* from Jenkins Publications, successor to Western Business Papers, Inc.

Liquefied Petroleum Gas Association, *Market Facts. LP-Gas Industry, 1957,* Chicago, the Association, 1958, pp. 24. 1st issued 1956, pp. 42 with cumulative data through 1955. 2nd Ed. 1957, pp. 20. Statistics and charts on liquefied petroleum gas production, storage, transportation, sales, equipment, carburetion, appliances.

Charles Courtland Turner, *The LP-Gas Man's Encyclopedia of Methods and Equipment,* New York, Moore Publishing Co., 1955, pp. 276.
Extensive listing of definitions and descriptions of words and phrases used in liquefied petroleum gas industry; numerous illustrations; discussion of uses.

Charles Courtland Turner, *The Bottled Gas Manual,* Los Angeles, Jenkins Publications, 1944, pp. v + 348.
Textbook and field guide for distributors, dealers, servicemen, salesmen, users of liquefied petroleum gases, equipment, and appliances.

Charles Courtland Turner, *Basic Facts for Bulk Plant Employees,* New York, Moore Publishing Co., 1957, pp. 71.
Specialized training course in operational practices and procedures at LP-Gas bulk plants.

VII.

Oil Shales and Shale Oil

Victor Clifton Alderson, *The Oil Shale Industry,* New York, Frederick A. Stokes Co., 1920, pp. xi + 175.
Nature, origin, and distribution of oil shale; history; mining, retorting and reduction; experimental and research work; economic factors, appraisal of future.

Harold Sill Bell, *Oil Shales and Shale Oils,* New York, D. Van Nostrand Co., 1948, pp. vii + 157.
History and exploitation of oil shale sources of world; characteristics of shale and shale oils; open-cut and underground mining; retorting and refining of oil from shale; relative costs.

Harry Brenan Cronshaw, *Oil Shales,* London, John Murray, 1921, pp. ix + 80.
Occurrence, characteristics, and uses of oil shales of British Empire and foreign countries.

Charles Reinhard Fettke, *Oil Resources in Coal and Carbonaceous Shales of Pennsylvania,* Harrisburg, Pennsylvania Geological Survey, 4th series, Bulletin M-2, 1923, pp. vi + 119.
Coal and carbonaceous shale deposits of Pennsylvania; testing; results of carbonization tests; composition of oils and tars.

J. Arthur Greene, *A Treatise on British Mineral Oil,* London, Charles Griffin & Co., 1919, pp. xi + 233.
Papers on geology, retorting, refining, chemistry, and other aspects of destructive distillation of coals, shales and similar materials for production of oil.

George W. Halse, *Oil and Retortable Materials,* London, Charles Griffin & Co., 1927, pp. vi + 146.
Processes for obtaining liquid fuels from coals, torbanites, cannel coals, and oil shales.

Institute of Petroleum, *Oil Shale and Cannel Coal,* London, the Institute, 1938 and 1951, 2 vols. pp. xxxix + 1308.
Papers covering mining and technical achievements in distillation and treatment.

Peter Otto Krumin, *Review of the Estonian Oil Shale Industry,* Columbus, Ohio State University, 1949, pp. 126.
History of Estonian oil shale industry; mining and retorting; properties and recovery of crude shale oil; discussion of German and Russian interests. Account of oil shale resources in United States, production, retorting, and refining.

Ernest Elmer Lyder, *The Thermal Decomposition of Oil Shales,* New York, the author, 1921, pp. 36.
Thesis submitted to Columbia University.

Paul De Vries Manning, *The Genesis of Oil Shale and Its Relation to Petroleum and Other Fuels,* New York, the author, 1927, pp. 73.
Thesis submitted to Columbia University.

Ralph H. McKee, Ed., *Shale Oil,* New York, Chemical Catalog Co., 1925, pp. 326.
Twelve articles giving general view of shale oil industry; origin, geology, distribution of oil shales; oil-yielding materials, analysis and evaluation; refining of shale oil; nitrogen constituents; economic considerations; abstracts of articles and patents.

Organisation for European Economic Co-Operation, *Swedish Shale Oil,* Paris, the Organisation, 1952, pp. 65.
Report of technical mission to Sweden, covering mining of oil shale, retorting, treatment, products.

Harold Henry Parker, *Some Fundamental*

Problems of An American Shale Indus-try, New York, the author, 1927, pp. 55.
Critical temperatures and oil cracking; water supply in shale retorting. Thesis submitted to Columbia University.

Iltyd I. Redwood, *A Practical Treatise on Mineral Oils and Their By-Products,* London, E. & F. N. Spon, 1897, pp. 336. Reprinted 1914, pp. xiv + 336.
Development of the Scottish shale oil industry, with detailed descriptions of manufacturing processes.

Alexander McIntosh Reid, *The Oil Shale Resources of Tasmania,* Hobart, Tasmania, Tasmania Department of Mines, 1924, pp. vi + 119.
Geographic and geologic background of oil shale industry; shale fields; the search for petroleum.

Waldemar Scheithauer, *Shale Oil and Tars and Their Products,* trans. from German by Charles Salter, London, Scott, Greenwood & Son, 1913, pp. 183. 2nd Ed. 1923, pp. 283.
Production and utilization of distillation tars; apparatus of German lignite industry, and Scottish shale oil industry; operating methods; products; manufacture of paraffin and candles.

Scottish Oils, Ltd., *A Brief Description of the Operations of The Scottish Shale Oil Industry,* Glasgow, the Company, 1948, pp. 32.
History and account of operations in Scottish shale oil industry; mining, transportation, retorting, and refining.

John Cassius Stauffer, *The Nitrogen Compounds of Colorado Shale Oil,* New York, the author, 1926, pp. 61.
Thesis submitted to Columbia University.

Kunio Uwatoko, *The Oil Shale Deposit of Fushun, Manchuria,* Sapporo, Japan, the author, 1931, pp. 92.
Geological occurrence, origin and sedimentation, petrographical and chemical characteristics, classification, etc., of Fushun oil shale field, northeast of Mukden.

VIII.

Conservation of Petroleum

American Bar Association, Section of Mineral Law, Committee on Conservation of Mineral Resources, *Report of the Committee on Conservation of Mineral Resources of the Section of Mineral Law,* Baltimore, The Lord Baltimore Press, 1929, pp. 30.
Proposals for voluntary or compulsory unit development of oil fields to prevent wasteful competitive drilling of oil and gas pools; drafts of suggested legislation.

American Bar Association, Section of Mineral Law, *Legal History of Conservation of Oil and Gas,* Chicago, the Association, 1938, pp. 302.
Eleven papers on legal history of regulation of oil and gas production in interest of conservation.

American Petroleum Institute, Special Study Committee and Legal Advisory Committee on Well Spacing and Allocation of Production of Central Committee on Drilling and Production Practice, Division of Production, *Progress Report on Standards of Allocation of Oil Production Within Pools and Among Pools,* New York, the Committee, 1942, pp. 98.
Principles for allocating production within pools and among pools; factors that should be considered in proper application. Third progress report, first to be published separately. First report appeared in *Drilling and Production Practice, 1934* and second in Section 1, *Proceedings* of the 8th Mid-Year Meeting of the American Petroleum Institute. DeGolyer, in preface, hails report as hardly less important than Miller's notable *Function of Natural Gas in Production of Oil.*

Barnabas Bryan, Jr., *Petroleum Control in the United States,* New York, American Council of the Institute of Pacific Relations, 1933, pp. 36.

Control of oil production in United States by proration and unitization.

Stuart E. Buckley, Ed., *Petroleum Conservation,* New York, American Institute of Mining and Metallurgical Engineers, 1951, pp. xix + 304.
Ten papers on conservation and mechanics of efficient oil and gas recovery, principles underlying conservation, petroleum reservoirs, characteristics of reservoir fluids, efficient operation of oil and gas reservoirs, state regulation, cooperative development, unit operation.

E. DeGolyer, *Report of the Engineering Committee of the Interstate Oil Compact Commission,* April 14, 1941, n.p., n.pub., pp. 11.
Findings, objectives, or recommendations concerning production of oil and gas and operation of oil and gas fields.

Hiram M. Dow, *New Mexico's Conservation Achievement,* Albuquerque, N. Mex., New Mexico Oil Conservation Commission, 1939, pp. 17.
Drilling and production of oil under New Mexico conservation legislation.

Northcutt Ely, *Oil Conservation Through Interstate Agreement,* Washington, Government Printing Office, 1933, pp. x + 398.
Prepared for Federal Oil Conservation Board. Broad discussion of State as agency to coordinate oil supply with demand and authority to effect conservation, need for interstate cooperation, and proposal for interstate agreement.

Northcutt Ely, *The Oil and Gas Conservation Statutes, (Annotated),* Washington, Government Printing Office, 1933, pp. vii + 432.
Emphasizes increased recognition of states' responsibility in preservation of reservoir energy, allocation of produc-

74

tion among pools for maximum oil recovery; voluntary allocation of production among states.

Federal Oil Conservation Board, *A Comparative Analysis of the Present Oil and Gas Conservation Laws of the Principal Oil States,* Washington, Government Printing Office, 1931, pp. 40.

Federal Oil Conservation Board, *Report of the Federal Oil Conservation Board to the President of the United States,* Part 1, 1926, Washington, 1926, pp. 127. (Report No. I)
Has been characterized as "one of the most incisive comments yet written upon the oil industry and its relation to the public interest"; Board took first authoritative notice of Henry L. Doherty's theory of the role of gas conservation in the conservation of oil.

Report II, 1928, pp. vi + 40.
Deals with possible substitute motor fuels such as shale oil.

Report III, 1929, pp. v + 218.
The importance of conservation of reservoir energy; examination of legal problems of unit operation. Appendices include Report of the Committee on Conservation of Mineral Resources of the American Bar Association, and report on petroleum resources of foreign countries and outlying possessions of the United States.

Report IV, 1930, pp. v + 24.
Petroleum situation during 1929. Particular attention to Federal forecasts of oil supply and demand, in hope that industry would use the information to avoid tremendous overproduction of crude oil and refined products then current.

Report V, 1932, pp. iii + 61.
Petroleum situation first half of 1932, with important appendix outlining specific program for interstate oil conservation pact. A landmark report, largely ignored at the time, pointing the way to the eventual solution of conservation legal dilemma.

Federal Oil Conservation Board, *Complete Record of Public Hearings, Feb. 10–11,* *1926,* Washington, Government Printing Office, 1926, pp. ix + 171.
Initial public hearings of Federal Oil Conservation Board, constituted by President Coolidge, Dec. 19, 1924, and consisting of Secretaries of War, Navy, Interior, and Commerce. Hearings heard oil industry leaders.

Federal Oil Conservation Board, *Public Hearing, May 27, 1926,* Washington, Government Printing Office, 1926, pp. v + 74.
Meeting addressed by Charles Evans Hughes, counsel for American Petroleum Institute, to which remarks and supplemental response were made by Henry L. Doherty.

Stanley Gill, *A Report on the Petroleum Industry of the United States,* Houston, n.pub., 1934, pp. 382.
Prepared on behalf of independent oil producers' group; views of those opposed to oil regulatory legislation then under consideration by House of Representatives. Excerpts and comments on conservation, curtailment, and proration.

Robert E. Hardwicke, *Antitrust Laws, et al. versus Unit Operation of Oil and Gas Pools,* New York, American Institute of Mining and Metallurgical Engineers, 1948, pp. ix + 300.
Reviews effort to promote conservation of oil, plan of H. L. Doherty for unit operation, appointment and work of Federal Oil Conservation Board, questions of law. Appendices: Mr. Doherty's letter to President; influence of East Texas field; Cotton Valley suit; table of cases.

James John Hayden, *Federal Regulation of the Production of Oil,* Washington, Catholic University of America, 1929, pp. x + 132.
Discusses constitutional aspects of conservation; extent of power of Federal Government to regulate production.

LeRoy H. Hines, *Unitization of Federal Lands,* Denver, F. H. Gower, 1953, pp. 70.
Definitions; discusses reasons for unitization, legislative background, statutory authority, procedure, cooperative and communization agreements. Author of

pamphlet, *Some Aspects of Unit Operation of Oil and Gas Pools and Fields,* published by United States Geological Survey, 1934.

Leo J. Hoffman, *Voluntary Pooling and Unitization—Oil and Gas,* Albany, Matthew Bender & Co., 1954, pp. xiii + 336.
Legal principles, problems in pooling and unitization of separately owned oil and gas properties.

Interstate Oil Compact Commission, *Oil For Today—And For Tomorrow,* Oklahoma City, the Commission, 1953, pp. 83.
Summary of genesis and early history of oil, occurrence and production; development, application, and operation of oil and gas conservation programs.

Interstate Oil Compact Commission, *A Summary of the Background, Organization, Purposes, and Functions of the Interstate Compact to Conserve Oil and Gas,* Oklahoma City, the Commission, 1954, pp. 17.
Pre-organization background, drafting, growth, purpose of Compact, with review of activities.

Interstate Oil Compact Commission, Engineering Committee, *Oil and Gas Production, An Introductory Guide to Production Techniques and Conservation Methods,* Norman, Okla., University of Oklahoma Press, 1951, pp. xv + 128.
Rudiments of oil geology and production necessary to an understanding of the technology of good conservation practice.

James Edward Jones, *And So—They Indicted Me! A Story of New Deal Persecution,* New York, J. Edward Jones Publishing Corp., 1938, pp. 253.
Experiences in connection with oil activities under New Deal and N.R.A. Relates circumstances which resulted in termination of Federal Oil Conservation Board.

Park J. Jones, *Oil and Gas Conservation, Development and Production,* Houston, Gulf Publishing Co., 1950, pp. viii + 138.
Characteristics of reservoirs, properties

of reservoir gas and liquids; economics, pressure maintenance with water and gas; economics of flooding; natural gas and condensate production; oil and gas conservation.

J. B. Aug. Kessler, *Cooperative Plan for World Petroleum Industry,* New York, World Petroleum, 1931, pp. 35.
Plan for reducing oil production in principal producing countries to some point below consumption, so excessive stocks might be lowered.

Richard H. Leach and Redding S. Sugg, Jr., *The Administration of Interstate Compacts,* Baton Rouge, La., Louisiana State University Press, 1959, pp. vi + 256.
Study of development of interstate agencies under Compact Clause of United States Constitution, including relations with state and federal agencies, powers, personnel, staffing, and operations, including references to Interstate Compact to Conserve Oil and Gas.

Leonard Marion Logan, Jr., *Stabilization of the Petroleum Industry,* Norman, Okla., University of Oklahoma Press, 1930, pp. 248.
Economic aspects of oil industry, stabilization efforts, proration, unit operation, relationship of industry with government. Reflects petroleum industry viewpoint immediately prior to discovery of East Texas oil field.

E. W. Marland, *Shall There Be Communism in Oil?* Ponca City, Okla., the author, 1924, pp. 18.
Address before National Editorial Association opposing regulation of oil industry. Decade later, Mr. Marland, then Governor of Oklahoma, took lead in establishing Interstate Compact to Conserve Oil and Gas.

Mid-Continent Oil and Gas Association, *Handbook on Utilization of Oil Pools,* Tulsa, issued by Association, 1930, pp. 141.
Unitization of oil pools, with examples and benefits illustrated. Competitive vs. unitized operation, principles and rules of practice in support of unitization.

Lee Silas Miller, *Oil and Gas Conservation*

in Michigan, Lansing, Department of Conservation, 1954, pp. 29.
History of first 15 years of administration of Michigan oil and gas conservation law.

Blakely M. Murphy, Ed., *Conservation of Oil & Gas. A Legal History, 1948,* Chicago, Section of Mineral Law, American Bar Association, 1949, pp. xvii + 754.
Comprehensive coverage of United States conservation, history and developments leading up to it, summary of state and federal law, chapters on producing and conservation history of each state. Prepared by qualified authorities, many of whom were chief participants in the events whereof they write. Best single volume on conservation for interest, authority, and completeness.

Raymond M. Myers, *The Law of Pooling and Unitization; Voluntary, Compulsory,* New York, Banks & Co., 1957, pp. xix + 833.
Conservation, history of unitization, pressure maintenance, secondary recovery operations, creation of units, voluntary unit agreements, compulsory pooling and unitization procedures, taxation, titles, legal problems.

National Conservation Commission, *Report,* Washington, Government Printing Office (Senate Document No. 676, 60th Congress, 2nd Session), 1909, pp. 793.
Vol. 3 contains chapters on petroleum and natural gas resources of United States. Descriptions of known fields, probable supply, duration of production, nature and extent of waste in extraction of petroleum, methods of preventing or lessening waste. Natural gas chapter includes discussion of production, waste of gas, waste prevention.

National Resources Board, *Energy Resources and National Policy,* Washington, Government Printing Office (House Document No. 160, 76th Congress, 1st Session), 1939, pp. vii + 435.
Message from the President of the United States transmitting a comprehensive study of the nation's energy resources prepared by National Resources Committee in cooperation with other federal agencies. Discussion of petroleum and natural gas reserves, phases of technology in petroleum industry, Connally Act and experience of states in petroleum production control and conservation measures.

Oklahoma Corporation Commission, *Oklahoma Oil and Gas Conservation Laws,* Guthrie, Okla., Co-operative Publishing Co., 1950, 2 vols., pp. xvi + 798.
Vol. I: Text of laws, rules, and regulations, with reprint of *Legal History of Conservation of Oil and Gas.*
Vol. II: Orders issued by Oklahoma Corporation Commission, June, 1947, to Jan., 1949.

Earl Oliver, *The So-Called A.P.I. Report. An Analysis,* Ponca City, Okla., the author, 1925, pp. 11.
Submitted "in protest" against the so-called A.P.I. report being accepted as representing the sentiment of the oil industry.

Petroleum Administrative Board, *Operation of the New Pool Plans of Orderly Development Under Code of Fair Competition for the Petroleum Industry,* Washington, Government Printing Office, 1936, pp. iv + 87.
Purposes and procedure for control of new oil pool development under Petroleum Code; review by States of approved plans; economic advantages of controlled development and production.

Samuel Barrett Pettengill, *Hot Oil. The Problem of Petroleum,* New York, Economic Forum Co., 1936, pp. xviii + 308.
Review of problems studied by Sub-Committee on Petroleum Investigation, Committee on Interstate and Foreign Commerce, House of Representatives, 73rd Congress, of which author was member. A witty, wise, and highly readable account of industry's current ills, proposed legislation, statements and views of industry witnesses; background of Connally Act and Interstate Oil Compact.

F. C. Proctor, *The Oil Problem,* Houston, the author, 1927, pp. 32.
Author opposes establishment of state commissions to restrict oil production, adoption of gas-oil ratios, and unit plans of operation.

Stephen Raushenbush, *Our Conservation Job,* Washington, Public Affairs Institute, 1949, pp. 64.
Basic conservation to be done in field of petroleum and other petroleum problems; use and rates of natural gas.

Research Associates, *The Unit Operation of Oil and Gas Fields,* Oklahoma City, Research Associates, 1957, 16 parts, var. pag.
Discusses compulsory and voluntary unit operation; rules and regulations by States; appendices contain table of cases, administrative material, forms, directory of administrative and leasing agencies.

Resources for the Future, Inc., *Perspectives on Conservation: Essays on America's Natural Resources,* Baltimore, Md., Johns Hopkins Press, 1958, pp. xii + 260.
Twenty-three essays exploring development and specific aspects of natural-resource conservation.

Benjamin F. Rice and Thomas D. Lyons, *Waste of Oil and Gas,* Tulsa, the authors, 1918, pp. 32.
Oklahoma laws for oil and gas conservation, particular attention to definitions of waste and provisions for control of production. Authors were Tulsa oil and gas lawyers.

George Ward Stocking, *The Oil Industry and the Competitive System, A Study in Waste,* Boston, Houghton Mifflin Co., 1925, pp. 323.
Competent, well-documented exposé of waste in oil fields arising from law of capture; author favored governmental control of oil production rates to eliminate this condition. A milestone in literature of conservation.

United Nations, *Proceedings of the United Nations Scientific Conference on the Conservation and Utilization of Resources: Vol. III, Fuel and Energy Resources,* New York, United Nations, 1951, pp. 333.
Papers on techniques of oil and gas discovery and production; techniques for increasing production, oil chemistry; petroleum conservation, secondary recovery of oil, oil shale, petroleum refining in United Kingdom, petroleum chemicals industry, synthetic fuel production.

United States Attorney General, *Report of the Attorney General Pursuant to Section 2 of Joint Resolution July 28, 1955, Consenting to an Interstate Compact to Conserve Oil and Gas,* Washington, Government Printing Office, 1956, pp. iv + 94. *2nd Report,* 1957, pp. iv + 159. *3rd Report,* 1958, pp. iii + 92. *4th Report,* 1959, pp. i + 101.
Attorney General's annual reports on operation of Interstate Oil Compact as required by Act of Congress in 1955.

Charles Richard Van Hise, *The Conservation of Natural Resources in the United States,* New York, Macmillan Co., 1910, pp. xiv + 413. (Reprinted annually through 1918.)
Substance of lectures given at University of Wisconsin, revised and amplified to provide handbook in reference to conservation, including discussion of petroleum and natural gas.

Volunteer Committee on Petroleum Economics, *Survey of National Petroleum Requirements for Seasonal Periods of 1932–1931–1930,* Washington, Government Printing Office, 1932, pp. iii + 43.
Reports covering period April 1, 1930, through December 31, 1932.

Myron W. Watkins, *Oil: Stabilization or Conservation? A Case Study in the Organization of Industrial Control,* New York, Harper & Bros., 1937, pp. 269.
Review of conservation and production limitation plans under N.R.A. code by author, who questioned background and basis for oil regulation.

James Horatio Westcott, *Oil, Its Conservation and Waste,* New York, Beacon Publishing Co., 1928, pp. iv + 213. 4th Ed. 1930, pp. xiii + 273.
Conservation in oil industry and reduction of waste in its operations; conservation of crude oil through use of cracking processes.

Ray Lyman Wilbur and William Atherton Du Puy, *Conservation in the Department of the Interior,* Washington, Government Printing Office, 1932, pp. xii + 253.
Conservation activities and responsibil-

ities of Department of the Interior; discussion of oil and gas conservation; attempts to develop Kettleman Hills Field (California) on a unit basis; actions of states to promote oil conservation through the Oil States Advisory Committee.

René de Visme Williamson, *The Politics of Planning in the Oil Industry Under the Code,* New York, Harper & Bros., 1936, pp. 90.
Planning under the Petroleum Code, including characteristic features of such planning, and related objectives of planning for national security and stabilization of the economy.

Erich Walter Zimmerman, *Conservation in the Production of Petroleum, A Study in Industrial Control,* New Haven, Yale University Press, 1957, pp. xxii + 417. Authoritative monograph on conservation of oil and gas, discussion of economic and sociological aspects and evaluation of achievements, responses to earlier critics, appraisal of weaknesses and unsolved problems associated with conservation procedure. Covers state laws, federal participation, interstate coordination.

IX.

World Oil Fields,
International Oil Relations

A. GENERAL

Robert Page Arnot, *The Politics of Oil,* London, Labour Publishing Co., 1924, pp. 94.
Alleges oil to be imperialist monopoly.

Benjamin T. Brooks, *Peace, Plenty and Petroleum,* Lancaster, Penna., Jaques Cattell Press, 1944, pp. 197.
Changes in uses of oil, petroleum in war, world power politics, hazards involved in foreign operations, postwar prospects, increasing dependence on imported oil.

E. H. Davenport and Sidney Russell Cooke, *The Oil Trusts and Anglo-American Relations,* London, Macmillan & Co., 1923, pp. xii + 272.
Great Britain as oil power, oil policy of United States, oil in international conferences, political principles, and oil resources of world. Refers to article by Sir Edward Mackay Edgar, London, Sept., 1919, which disturbed American oilmen.

Francis Delaisi, *Oil. Its Influence on Politics,* trans. from French by C. Leonard Leese, London, Labour Publishing Co. and George Allen & Unwin, 1922, pp. vi + 94. First published in France, 1920.
Sensationalist account of period following World War I when United States, announcing its "open-door policy" in mandated areas, was stirred by indications of scarcity at home and British supremacy abroad, with France involved through San Remo Agreement.

Ludwell Denny, *We Fight For Oil,* New York, Alfred A. Knopf, 1928, pp. 297.

Disputes in various countries over oi property rights; United States Goverr ment backing of American oil com panies; Anglo-American competition fo foreign oil concessions.

European Gas & Electric Company, *Stand ard Oil Company (New Jersey) an Oil Production in Hungary by Maor 1931–1948,* New York, the Compan 1949, pp. 65.
Account of seizure of Hungariar American Oil Co. (Maort) by Hunga ian Government in 1948, includin responses to allegations contained i *Grey Book,* a report issued Sept. 2 1948, by Hungarian Ministry of Hom Affairs.

Leonard M. Fanning, *Foreign Oil and th Free World,* New York, McGraw-Hi Book Co., 1954, pp. xiii + 400.
Authoritative survey of growth of inte national oil business, case histories o individual ventures in various oil-pro ducing countries throughout the worl world refining; Russian oil; cartels, com petition. Financial and production sta tistics; tables of investment and payou of selected companies.

Leonard M. Fanning, *The Shift of Worl Petroleum Power Away from the Unite States,* Pittsburgh, Gulf Oil Corp., 195 pp. 23, plus 30 unnumbered pages c tables.
Review in text and tables of change during past two decades in position c United States among world oil pro ducers; movement abroad of America

producers; increased interest in foreign oil; review of costs and production characteristics.

Ierbert Feis, *Petroleum and American Foreign Policy, Food Research Institute,* Stanford University, Cal., 1944, pp. vi + 62.
Earlier oil disputes, petroleum situation in United States and Middle East, Petroleum Reserves Corp. and pipe line project, suggestions of Middle East Oil Agreement, major elements of petroleum policy for United States, recommendations by American companies.

Ierbert Feis, *Seen From E. A.: Three International Episodes,* New York, Alfred A. Knopf, 1947, pp. xi + 313.
Author was Economic Adviser (E.A.) in Department of State. Book deals with three episodes in American search for national security, two of which relate to oil: (1) attempt by Petroleum Administration for War to purchase Middle East oil and develop Anglo-American Petroleum Agreement; (2) oil for Italy.

ouis Fischer, *Oil Imperialism, The International Struggle for Petroleum,* London, George Allen & Unwin, 1926, pp. 256.
Left-wing view of international oil affairs subsequent to World War I. Author wrote extensively and sympathetically of Soviet Russia, and had access to oil documents in Russian Government files.

Ienry S. Fraser, *Diplomatic Protection of American Petroleum Interests in Mesopotamia, Netherlands East Indies, and Mexico,* Washington, Government Printing Office (79th Congress, 1st Session, Document No. 43), 1945, pp. 73.
Study prepared for Special Committee Investigating Petroleum Resources. Diplomatic protection afforded American oil in Mesopotamia (1920–32), Netherlands East Indies (1920–28), Mexico (1915–28). Intended to illustrate, without appraisal, methods, scope, nature, and results of diplomatic support extended.

Valentine Richard Garfias, *Petroleum Resources of the World,* New York, John Wiley & Sons, 1923, pp. xi + 243.
Producing and prospective oil fields;

petroleum legislation in principal oil countries of the world.

L. Vernon Gibbs, *Oil and Peace,* Los Angeles, Parker, Stone & Baird Co., 1929, pp. 204.
International competition for oil between nations following World War I and threat to peace.

Narain Gupta, *Oil in the Modern World,* Allahabad, India, Kitab Mahal, 1949, pp. 184.
Particular attention to India and Burma, as background for "new order" in oil involving exploitation of oil by state or its nationals and exclusion of foreign interests, with technical assistance, financing, and operation through United Nations or other agencies.

Frank Cleary Hanighen, *The Secret War,* New York, John Day Co., 1934, pp. 316.
International oil conflicts and rivalries in various parts of world.

Frank Cleary Hanighen and Anton Zischka, *The Secret War. The War for Oil,* London, George Routledge & Sons, 1935, pp. xii + 250.
Much the same as previous title.

Frederick Haussmann, *World Oil Control, Past and Future, An Alternative to "International Cartelization,"* New York, New School for Social Research, 1942, pp. 21.
Proposes International Oil Institute under United Nations to develop world oil policy, mediate disputes between governments and companies, undertake continuing study of technical and economic problems in oil.

Louis Heyman, *The New Aspect of the Oil Problem,* London, The Petroleum Times, 1933, pp. 112. Translated from French edition, published 1931, at Brussels.
Earlier fears of oil scarcity, accomplishments in oil finding with resulting overproduction, followed by attempts to restrict output.

Paul van Hissenhoven, *The Petroleum Industry in Depression and Recovery,* Brussels, Belgium, L'Imprimerie Puvrez, 1938, pp. 25.
Continental viewpoint of oil industry

during depression and succeeding recovery years; governmental policies on oil.

International Labour Organization, Petroleum Committee, *Preliminary Report for the First Meeting of the Petroleum Committee,* Montreal, International Labour Office, 1946, pp. 106.
Covers organization of Petroleum Committee, international character of petroleum industry, employment problems, labor conditions, social services, industrial relations.

International Labour Organization, Petroleum Committee, *Notes of Discussion, First Session,* Geneva, 1947, pp. xxiii. *Record of the First Session,* Geneva, 1948, pp. 192.

International Labour Organization, Petroleum Committee, *General Report, Recruitment and Training, Safety in the Petroleum Industry, Industrial Relations,* Geneva, 1948, pp. 197. *Record of the Second Session,* Geneva, 1950, pp. 146.

International Labour Organization, Petroleum Committee, *Notes on Proceedings of Third Session, General Report, Social Conditions in Petroleum Industry,* Geneva, 1950, pp. 211. *Summary Record of the Third Session,* Geneva, 1952, pp. 44.

International Labour Organization, Petroleum Committee, *Notes on Proceedings of Fourth Session, General Reports, Principles and Methods Used in Determining Wages in Petroleum Industry, and Social Services in Petroleum Industry,* Geneva, 1952, pp. 417. *Summary Record of the Fourth Session,* Geneva, 1955, pp. 43.

International Labour Organization, Petroleum Committee, *General Reports, Contract Labour in Petroleum Industry, Human Relations in Petroleum Industry, Use of Visual Aids for Training and Instructional Purposes,* Geneva, 1955, pp. 314. *Note on the Proceedings of the Fifth Session,* Geneva, 1956, pp. 46.
Events and developments in world oil industry, as reported by missions sent to oil-producing countries pursuant to

International Labour Organization resolutions. Other reports review employment in petroleum industry, recruitment qualifications, education and training trade union recognition, collective bargaining, settlement of disputes, and other aspects of industrial and social relations in petroleum industry.

Interstate Oil Compact Commission, *Reply to the Staff Report to the Federal Trade Commission on the International Petroleum Cartel,* Oklahoma City, the Commission, 1952, pp. 8.

Alfred M. Leeston, *A World Tour in Oil,* Dallas, the author, 1948, pp. 35.
Brief review of oil producing countries of world and oil developments. Reprinted from *Drilling* Magazine, Jan. Apr. 1948.

Alfred M. Leeston, *Magic Oil, Servant of the World,* Dallas, Juan Pablos Books, 1951, pp. 237.
Quick survey of oil production, transportation, refining, in United States, Middle and Far East, Russia, Europe and South America.

Pierre Paul Ernest L'Espagnol de la Tramerye, *The World Struggle for Oil,* trans. from French by C. Leonard Leese, New York, Alfred A. Knopf, 1922, pp. 259.
World's oil resources, competition between companies, and conflicts between governments.

Amicia Moore Melland, *World Oilmen,* London, Sylvan Press, 1955, pages unnumbered.
Men at work in various areas of world oil industry. Bibliography.

Anton Mohr, *The Oil War,* trans. from Norwegian, New York, Harcourt Brace & Co., 1926, pp. vii + 267.
Political intrigue as dominant force in oil industry.

Scott Nearing, *Oil and The Germs of War,* Ridgewood, N.J., Nellis Seeds Nearing, 1923, pp. 32.
Oil provides incentive for world conflict.

Harvey O'Connor, *The Empire of Oil,* New York, Monthly Review Press, 1955, pp. 372.

Sensational, left-wing view of international oil industry and its "control" of State Department and foreign ministries abroad; need for international control of oil through cooperative alliance; holds up nationalized Mexican industry as "beacon of hope."

Michael O'Shaughnessy, *Oil Tariff and World Zoning,* New York, South American Oil Reports, 1931, pp. 40.
Proposes stabilization of world's oil industry through restriction of crude oil production by economically demarked zones, based on gasoline consumption and refinery output in each.

Sylvia Pankhurst, *The Truth About the Oil War,* London, Dreadnaught Publishers, n.d. (early 1920's), pp. 29.
British, French, and American rivalry for oil resources following World War I, with attention to San Remo Agreement.

Floyd William Parsons, *Petroleum and Prosperity,* New York, Publishers Printing Co., 1924, pp. 25.
Discussion in support of United States backing of private American oil enterprises to secure their equal treatment in foreign lands.

William H. Peterson, *The Question of Governmental Oil Import Restrictions,* Washington, American Enterprise Association, 1959, pp. 71.
Background of government oil import policy, economics of oil imports, import controls and international trade, national security.

Petroleum Industry Research Foundation, Inc., *World Oil: Fact and Policy. The Case for a Sound American Petroleum Policy,* New York, the Foundation, 1944, pp. 79.
Oil supply, oil use in war and peace, Petroleum Reserves Corporation, Arabian pipeline, principles and plan of foreign oil policy, Anglo-American Petroleum Agreement.

Wallace E. Pratt and Dorothy Good, Eds., *World Geography of Petroleum,* New York, American Geographical Society, 1950, pp. 464.
How petroleum is formed, reasons why it is found only in certain regions;

organization of industry; chief productive regions; problems in oil hunting and development; geography of world use.

Ronald S. Ritchie, *Oil in World Affairs,* Toronto, Canadian Institute of International Affairs, 1951, pp. 15.
Importance of oil in world affairs, international factors involved in oil development, British problems, strategic considerations.

Standard Oil Company (New Jersey), *Oil for the World,* New York, the Company, 1944, pp. 16.
Advocates world oil policy "based on freedom of enterprise to promote the discovery of oil, and a policy based on international cooperation to prevent squandering of a resource essential to the world's prosperity."

Department of State, *Petroleum and Kerosene Oil in Foreign Countries,* Consular Reports No. 37, Washington, Government Printing Office, 1884, pp. vii + 399–547.
Part I: *Petroleum in the Orient.* Extracts from reports by consuls on quality and packaging of illuminating oils.
Part II: *Petroleum and Petroleum Development in Foreign Countries.* Reports received by Department of State during preceding 4 years. Includes report on oil development in Venezuela (1880) and in Argentina.

A. Beeby Thompson, *Oil Field Atlas,* Surrey, England, The Technical Press, 1952.
Main oil field areas of world, size and productivity of oil fields and wells, future oil reserves.

A. Beeby Thompson, *The Petroleum Problem As Affecting British Industry,* London, London Chamber of Commerce, 1921, pp. 12.
World oil situation at close of World War I, with particular attention to British achievements in oil developments. British "have scoured the world for new sources of supply whilst America has rested content with her home resources."

Twentieth International Geological Congress, *Symposium on Deposits of Petro-*

leum and Gas (Title in Spanish), Mexico, D. F., Editorial Stylo, 1956, 5 vols.
Papers presented at 20th International Geological Congress (1956) in English, French, German, Spanish; papers for italicized countries in English.
Vol. I: *Africa*, pp. 218. *Union of South Africa*, Algeria, Cameroun Belgian Congo, *Gold Coast*, *Ethiopia*, Gabon, *Kenya*, Madagascar, French Morocco, *Uganda*.
Vol. II: *Asia and Oceania*, pp. 235. *Saudi Arabia*, *Iran*, *Iraq*, *Japan*, *Kuwait*, *Malaya*, *Qatar*, *Australia*, New Caledonia, *Papua*, *New Guinea*.
Vol. III: *North America*, pp. 562. *Canada*, *United States*, *Mexico*.
Vol. IV: *South America and Antilles*, pp. 322. Bolivia, *Brazil*, *Ecuador*, Peru, Dominican Republic, Venezuela.
Vol. V: *Europe*, pp. 372. Germany, *Denmark*, *Spain*, France, *Hungary*, *United Kingdom*, *Ireland*, *Turkey*.

United Nations Secretariat, *Pollution of the Sea by Oil*, New York, United Nations, 1956, pp. iii + 235.

Report of inquiry by United Nation Secretariat, pursuant to resolution International Conference on Pollutio of the Sea by Oil, London, 1954.

United States Senate, Staff Report Federal Trade Commission Submitte to Subcommittee on Monopoly of Se lect Committee on Small Business, *Th International Petroleum Cartel*, Wash ington, Government Printing Offic 1952, pp. xii + 378.
Resources and alleged concentration world petroleum industry; partnershi ventures in international petroleum i dustry; production and marketin agreements.

David White, *The Petroleum Resources the World*, Philadelphia, America Academy of Political and Social Scienc 1920, pp. 24.
Author, prinicipal geologist of Unite States Geological Survey, attracted wic attention with his predictions of in minent exhaustion of United States p troleum resources.

B. UNITED STATES

Bernard Brodie, *American Security and Foreign Oil* (pp. 298–311, Foreign Policy Reports, Vol. XXIII, No. 24), New York, Foreign Policy Association, 1948. (Revision of *Foreign Oil and American Security*, New Haven, Conn., Yale Institute of International Studies, 1947, pp. 29.)
Actual and potential oil resources in United States, other Western Hemisphere areas; substitute fuels; Middle East oil; discussion of suggested United States oil policies.

J. H. Carmical, *The Anglo-American Petroleum Pact, A Case-History in the Negotiation of Postwar Agreements*, New York, American Enterprise Association, 1945, pp. 46.
Reviews international oil proposals, background and analysis of original Anglo-American Oil Agreement, revised document and oil industry suggestions, with discussion of foreign oil policy.

John Davis, *Natural Gas and Canad United States Relations*, n.p., Nation Planning Association (USA) and Pr vate Planning Association of Canad 1959, pp. xii + 32.
Review of natural gas development Canada, reserves and potential r sources, prospective markets, gover ment regulation, and common needs United States and Canada.

John Davis, *Oil and Canada-United Stat Relations*, n.p., Canadian-America Committee, sponsored by Nation Planning Association (USA) and Pr vate Planning Association of Canad 1959, pp. xii + 36.
Problems of expanding oil productic in Canada; trade restrictions; possib export outlets; Montreal market.

Federal Trade Commission, *Foreign Owne ship in the Petroleum Industry*, Was ington, Government Printing Offic 1923, pp. xxii + 152.

Submitted in response to Senate Resolution 311, 67th Congress, 2nd Session, describes organization, development, and status of Royal Dutch-Shell Group, special reference to holdings in United States; discrimination of foreign governments against United States nationals in acquisition and development of petroleum production in foreign lands.

oreign Operations Committee (Petroleum Administrator for War), *A Foreign Oil Policy for the United States,* Washington, the Committee, 1943, pp. 12.
American interest in international oil developments, immediate problems, oil policy essentials, design for International Oil Compact.

hn Ise, *The United States Oil Policy,* New Haven, Yale University Press, 1926, pp. x + 547.
History of oil development in various states, overproduction, waste, monopoly, conservation, public lands, substitutes and foreign oil. States: "Great problem is that of conserving our oil resources."

ational Petroleum Council, *A National Oil Policy for the United States,* Washington, the Council, 1949, pp. 23.
A report by Council which outlines aims, fundamental principles, and elements of national oil policy,

ational Resources Board, *A Report on National Planning and Public Works in Relation to Natural Resources and Including Land Use and Water Resources, with Findings and Recommendations,* Washington, Government Printing Office, 1934, pp. vii + 455.
Described as "first attempt in our national history to make an inventory of our national assets and of the problems related thereto."

enry Ozanne, *United States Foreign Oil Policy,* New York, Petroleum Industry Research Foundation, 1945, pp. 79.
Oil diplomacy background, State Department policy, and treaty stage; international cartels, foreign policy principles, foreign policy in oil.

etroleum Industry Research Foundation, *United States Oil Imports. A Case Study in International Trade,* New York, the Foundation, 1958, pp. ix + 113.
History of American oil imports, government policy, importing companies, economic reasons for imports and relation of imports to foreign trade, national security, and domestic production.

Petroleum Industry War Council, *United States Foreign Oil Policy and Petroleum Reserves Corp., An Analysis of the Effect of Proposed Saudi Arabian Pipe Line,* Washington, the Council, 1944, pp. 29. Report of National Oil Policy Committee of Petroleum Industry War Council summarizing history of foreign oil policy of United States and actions involving Petroleum Reserves Corporation, including various official papers and statements and resolutions adopted by Council on problems of foreign oil development and policy.

President's Materials Policy Commission (Paley Commission), *Resources for Freedom. A Report to the President,* Washington, Government Printing Office, 1952, 5 vols., pp. xxiii + 819.
Commission appointed by President Truman, under chairmanship of William S. Paley, to "study the broader and longer range aspects of the Nation's materials program." Vol. I: Foundations for Growth and Security; II: The Outlook for Key Commodities; III: The Outlook for Energy Sources; IV: The Promise of Technology; V: Selected Reports to the Commission.

Public Advisory Board for Mutual Security, *A Trade and Tariff Policy in the National Interest,* Washington, Government Printing Office, 1953, pp. v + 78.
Contains discussion of petroleum import policy and recommendation on imports.

Sebastian Raciti, *The Oil Import Problem,* New York, Fordham University Press, 1958, pp. 100.
History and background of oil imports, case for independents and majors, need for compromise solution.

Emmette Shelburn Redford, *Public Administration and Policy Formation,* Austin, University of Texas Press (Studies in Oil, Gas, Banking, River Development, and Corporate Investigations), 1956, pp. xiv + 319.

Standard Oil Company (New Jersey), *Facts*

About Oil Imports, New York, the Company, 1953, pp. 42.
Views of Standard Oil Company (N.J.) with data, concerning limitation of imports and establishment of quotas.

C. MEXICO

Association of Oil Producers in Mexico, *Documents Relating to the Attempt of the Government of Mexico to Confiscate Foreign-Owned Oil Properties,* New York, the Association, 1919, pp. 82.
Chronological compilation of documents and translations on measures of Mexican Government "to divest present owners and lessees of oil-bearing lands."

Association of Oil Producers in Mexico, *The Mexican Oil Question,* New York, the Association, 1919, pp. 95, documents and translations.
Title and taxation aspects of Mexican oil question, excerpts from Mexican Constitution, laws, decrees, various notes and press statements.

Association of Oil Producers in Mexico, *The Mexican Oil Controversy. As Told in Diplomatic Correspondence Between United States and Mexico,* New York, the Association, 1920, pp. 31.
Review and discussion of notes on oil question exchanged between United States and Mexico, with texts of numerous notes and documents.

Association of Oil Producers in Mexico, *The Petroleum Bill of Mexico, as Passed by the Mexican Senate, December 8, 1919,* New York, the Association, 1920, pp. 37.
Presents draft of law, as enacted, putting into effect Article 27 of Mexican Constitution, with comments and statements.

Association of Oil Producers in Mexico, *Reprint of Correspondence Between the Government of the United States and Mexico, As Released for Publication by the Department of State, November 24, 1926,* New York, the Association, 1926, pp. 70.
Contains notes exchanged July 31, 1926, to Nov. 17, 1926, between United States

secretary of state and Mexican minister for foreign affairs.

Amos L. Beaty, *Rules of American Law Invoked by the Mexican Government in the Amparo Proceedings Brought by the Oil Companies,* New York, no publisher, 1918, pp. 26.
Review of American and other laws and decisions pertaining to ownership of subsurface minerals, responding to action of Mexican Government under Article 27 of 1917 Constitution, against which oil companies sought injunctive action. Includes Spanish version.

Paul Boracrès, *The Mexican Problem* *"Stolen Property?",* Mexico, D. F., Union of Petroleum Workers of Mexico, 1939, pp. 63.
Viewpoint of Mexican oil workers on expropriation.

Lázaro Cárdenas del Rio, *Messages to the Mexican Nation on the Oil Question,* Mexico, D. F., Government of Mexico, 1938, no pag.
Contains message of March 18, 1938 announcing decree of expropriation, address at parade of March 23, 1938, and manifesto of March 26, 1938.

Alejandro Carrillo, *The Mexican People and the Oil Companies,* Mexico, D. F., the author, 1938, pp. 30.
Reviews Mexican oil conflict from viewpoint of Mexican oil workers. Address delivered at Institute of Public Affairs July 8, 1938, at Charlottesville, Va. where author represented Confederation of Mexican Workers.

Howard Francis Cline, *The United States and Mexico,* Cambridge, Mass., Harvard University Press, 1953, pp. xvi + 452.
Covers events leading up to oil expropriation, settlement of dispute, subsequent operations and operations of Pemex, the government oil monopoly

Roscoe B. Gaither, *Expropriation in Mexico, The Facts and The Law,* New York, William Morrow & Co., 1940, pp. xi + 204.
Analysis of Mexican law as to legality of seizure of oil properties by Mexican Government on March 18, 1938, by author who has written extensively on legal matters pertaining to Mexico.

Antonio Gomez Robledo, *The Bucareli Agreements and International Law,* trans. from Spanish, Mexico, D. F., National University of Mexico Press, 1940, pp. xii + 228.
Written in 1937, with epilogue on expropriation of British and American oil properties in Mexico added in 1938, presents Mexico's contentions in international differences caused by Mexican land laws and oil question.

Wendell Chaffee Gordon, *The Expropriation of Foreign-Owned Property in Mexico,* Washington, American Council on Public Affairs, 1941, pp. viii + 201.
History of oil development in Mexico, oil dispute and resulting expropriation, solution as test of "good neighbor" policy. Author was with Department of Economics, University of Texas.

William H. Gray, *Defense of a Tariff on Mexican Oil,* n.p., the author, 1921, pp. 23.
Two addresses delivered in Texas on history of tariff on oil, oil developments in Mexico, and need for tariff to protect small wells in United States.

Huasteca Petroleum Company, Mexico, *Expropriation of Foreign-Owned Oil Properties, 1938,* n.p., the Company, 1938, pp. v + 144.
Communications sent by Huasteca Petroleum Company to Department of State between March 31 and Oct. 6, 1938; public statements by Secretary Hull and President Cárdenas; notes between Great Britain and Mexico leading to severance of diplomatic relations.

Patrick J. Hurley, *The Struggle for the Mexican Oil,* Mexico, D.F., Editorial Cultura, 1940, pp. 25.
Statement before Railroad Commission of Texas concerning negotiations concluded with Mexican Government with reference to Sinclair oil properties in Mexico.

Frederic Rogers Kellogg, *The Mexican Situation,* New York, Association of Producers of Petroleum in Mexico, 1927, pp. 16.
Argument supporting position of Department of State in Mexican oil controversy.

William E. McMahon, *Two Strikes and Out,* Garden City, New York, Country Life Press Corp., 1939, pp. 156.
Economic, social, and political events and oil company-government relations to show "significant facts connected with the Mexican Government's program of confiscation of foreign-owned oil properties." Chronology of controversy.

Salvador Mendoza, *Why Mexico Expropriates,* Mexico, D.F., Editorial "Mexico," 1939, pp. 14.
Statement on background of oil expropriation by former professor of law at National University of Mexico City.

Government of Mexico, *The True Facts About the Expropriation of the Oil Companies' Properties in Mexico.* Mexico, D.F., published by Government of Mexico, 1940, pp. 271.
Response of Government of Mexico to *Present Status of the Mexican Oil Expropriation,* published by Standard Oil Company (N.J.), following same order, "so as to present in a proper manner the various aspects of the controversy." Also published in Spanish.

Government of Mexico, *Mexico's Oil,* Mexico, D.F., 1940, pp. iii + 881. English edition in black cloth cover; Spanish edition in red.
Compilation of official documents in oil conflict, introduction summarizing its cause and consequence; early historical material on oil and Spanish law.

The Mexican Expropriations in International Law, New York, 1940, pp. 165.
Background of oil expropriation, question of constitutionality, notes exchanged, capacity to pay, questions of international law and distinction between oil and agricultural land expropriations.

Oscar Morineau, *The Good Neighbor,* Mexico City, the author, 1938, pp. 19.
Mexican point of view on expropriation of oil industry in Mexico.

National Association for the Protection of American Rights in Mexico, *Plow with Petroleum,* New York, the Association, 1920, pp. 12.
Advocates protection by United States Government of those who "risk their lives and money in other countries in an effort to develop a foreign petroleum supply." Title related to agricultural uses of petroleum products.

Harlow Stafford Person, *Mexican Oil, Symbol of Recent Trends in International Relations,* New York, Harper & Bros., 1942, pp. 83.
Historical background of Mexico, oil problems from inception through expropriation and indemnification for expropriation, with agreements between Mexico and United States as to amount and terms of indemnification. Author was staff chief of American experts serving with United States representative in negotiations.

Jack Richard Powell, *The Mexican Petroleum Industry, 1938–1950,* Berkeley, Cal., University of California Press, 1956, pp. xiv + 269.
Records history of Petroleos Mexicanos (Pemex) in period following expropriation, to determine extent to which Mexico achieved objectives of oil expropriation.

Donald R. Richberg, *The Mexican Oil Seizure,* New York, Arrow Press, 1939, pp. 56.
Review by counsel for companies involved in Mexican expropriation of foreign-owned oil properties of its development, conflicts of interests, efforts for their adjustment, and proposed agreement for oil company operation of expropriated properties under long-term contracts and negotiations for settlement.

Merrill Rippy, *The National Oil Industry of Mexico, 1938–1955,* Beaumont, Tex., Lamar State College of Technology (Research Series Paper No. 3), 1957, pp. 18.

Comparisons indicating major change in Mexican oil industry since expropriation.

John Serocold, *Oil in Mexico,* London Chapman & Hall, 1938, pp. 71.
Events preceding Expropriation Decree of March 18, 1938, but devotes more attention to events which followed submission of British and United State notes, responses thereto, and difference in position reflected in notes.

Standard Oil Company (New Jersey), *Confiscation or Expropriation? Mexico' Seizure of the Foreign-Owned Oil Industry,* New York, the Company, 1940 pp. 105.
Contains numerous articles published separately.

Standard Oil Company (New Jersey) *Mexico Labor Controversy, 1936–1938 Memoranda on the Controversy Arising Out of Mexico's Impositions on Foreign Oil Companies in Mexico Leading Up to the Expropriation Decree of March 18, 1938,* New York, the Company, 1940, pp. vii + 226.
Contains 8 principal memoranda, dated from Sept. 21, 1936, to May 9, 1938 submitted to Department of State by oil companies in connection with controversy between companies and Mexico.

Standard Oil Company (New Jersey), *Denials of Justice,* New York, the Company, 1940, pp. 167.
Brief analysis of decree of Mexican Supreme Court, Dec. 2, 1939, concerning properties of United States, British, and Dutch oil companies, with full text of decision.

Standard Oil Company (New Jersey), *The Reply to Mexico,* New York, the Company, 1940, pp. v + 126.
Company's response to *The True Facts About the Expropriation of the Oil Companies,* which was issued, 1940, by Government of Mexico. Contains several appendices reviewing historical and other aspects of case.

Standard Oil Company (New Jersey), *Present Status of the Mexican Oil "Expropriations,"* 1940, n.p., the Company 1940, pp. 170. (Edition without appendices, pp. 79.)

Presents Company's viewpoint concerning expropriation, describing it as matter of confiscation. Appendices contain various memoranda outlining Company's position in detail.

Guy Stevens, *Current Controversies With Mexico,* New York, Association of Oil Producers in Mexico, 1929, pp. 376.
Background on Mexican oil controversy as it existed a decade before expropriation. Concludes with discussion of position of American oil companies in Mexico on March 27, 1928, when Department of State pointed out that practical conclusion had been reached. Other addresses by Guy Stevens on Mexican oil question published by Association, as follows:
The Mexican Question, Address before Foreign Policy Association, Feb. 19, 1927, Providence, R.I., pp. 11.
The Mexican Situation, Address before Foreign Policy Association, April 19, 1927, Hartford, Conn., pp. 22.
Brief Statement of Facts Relating to The Mexican Oil Controversy, Address at Institute of Politics, Aug. 6, 1927, Williamstown, Mass., pp. 37.
Understanding the Mexican Situation, Address at Conference on Latin American Relations, July 25, 1927, Durham, N.H., pp. 37.
Next Steps in the Policy of the United States Toward Mexico and Nicaragua, May 11, 1927, New York.

George Ward Stocking, *The Mexican Oil Problem,* Dallas, Southern Methodist University, 1938, pp. 22.
Deals with Articles 27 and 123 of Mexican Constitution, Morrow settlement, oil controversy and prospects for settlement.

Napoleon Bonaparte Tanner, Jr., *Diplomacy of the Expropriation of the American Oil Industry in Mexico,* Kingsville, Tex., the author, 1940, pp. 74.
Thesis submitted to Texas College of Arts and Industries. Background of oil expropriation, decade of controversy, expropriation, and diplomatic exchanges since expropriation.

Arthur Thomson, *Mexico and the Oil Interests,* Los Angeles, Citizen Print Shop, 1921, pp. 16.

Discussion of oil company position in support of Mexican viewpoint.

Charles Alexander Thomson, *The Mexican Oil Dispute,* New York, Foreign Policy Association (pp. 122–132, Foreign Policy Reports, Vol. XIV, No. 11), 1938.
Events leading to and following expropriation of foreign oil properties.

William Cameron Townsend, *The Truth about Mexico's Oil,* Los Angeles, Summer Institute of Linguistics, 1940, pp. iv + 86. Events witnessed by author during period of Mexican oil expropriation, described from Mexican viewpoint.

Twelve Oil Companies, *The Mexican Oil Strike of 1937,* New York, the Companies, 1938, 3 vols.
Vol. I: Early phases of Mexican oil controversy, union demands, assembly to reach conciliatory agreement, strike movement when assembly failed to reach agreement.
Vol. II: Events after union voluntarily lifted strike and took case to Federal Labor Board as "economic issue," presenting viewpoint of oil industry in Mexico regarding examination of its economic and financial position.
Vol. III: Decision rendered by Federal Labor Board, considerations of Board in dictating award, clauses which Board ruled should be included in general contract and injunction proceedings of companies against award.

Evelyn Arthur St. John Waugh, *Robbery Under Law: The Mexican Object-Lesson,* London, Chapman & Hall, 1939, pp. viii + 286.
Based on travel in Mexico and written as "political book" from viewpoint of British who "remained indifferent when a rich and essential British industry was openly stolen in time of peace," discusses events leading to oil confiscation and resulting situation.

Worker's University of Mexico, *The Oil Conflict in Mexico, 1937–1938,* Mexico, D. F., Universidad Obrera de México, 1938, pp. 110.
Documents bearing on labor problems

in Mexico and expropriation of Mexican oil industry, beginning with demands of

workers, in July, 1936, concluding with Expropriation Decree of March, 1938

D. BOLIVIA

Defraudation. History of an Oil Enterprise in Bolivia, (Reprint from *Bolivia,* Vol. VII, No. 6, 1939), New York, L. & S. Printing Co., 1939, pp. 24.
Bolivian refutation of statements in *Confiscation,* by Standard Oil Company.

Standard Oil Company of Bolivia, *Confiscation, A History of the Oil Industry in Bolivia,* New York, the Company, 1939, pp. iii + 39.

Story of seizure of oil properties by Bolivian Government, under decree of March 13, 1937, with English translations of various documents.

Standard Oil Company (New Jersey), *Bolivia Takes What It Wants,* New York the Company, 1941, pp. 17.
Review of events and oil company position regarding seizure of oil properties by Bolivian Government.

E. MIDDLE EAST

Anglo-Iranian Oil Company Case (*United Kingdom v. Iran*), *Pleadings, Oral Documents, Judgment of July 22, 1952,* The Hague, Netherlands, International Court of Justice, 1953, pp. 809.
Contains application instituting proceedings, with annexes, Agreement of April 29, 1933, correspondence concerning nationalization of Iranian oil industry and arbitration, memorial submitted by United Kingdom on nationalization, with statement of relevant facts up to May 1, 1951, Iranian document (in French), observations and submissions by United Kingdom, and oral proceedings, pleadings and arguments, rejoinders, and correspondence.

Anglo-Iranian Oil Company Case (*United Kingdom v. Iran*), *Reports of Judgments, Advisory Opinions and Orders, Preliminary Objections, and Judgment of July 22, 1952,* The Hague, Netherlands, International Court of Justice, 1952. (French and English editions.)
Numerous pamphlets and documents relating to nationalization of Iranian oil industry have been published. These include Anglo-Iranian Oil Co. compilation of Chairman's statements to stockholders in annual reports for 1948, 1949, 1950, 1951, and 1952 regarding Company's interest in Iran, chronology of main events, 1948, to May 1953; compilation of Some Documents on the

Nationalization of the Oil Industry of Iran, published by Iranian Embassy, Washington, D.C.

Ray Brock, *Blood, Oil and Sand,* Cleveland and New York, World Publishing Co., 1952, pp. 256.
Middle East; degrees of political reliability and military preparedness among potential western allies and probable enemies.

Michael Brooks, *Oil and Foreign Policy,* London, Lawrence & Wishart, 1949, pp. 143.
Oil matters in Middle East and Indonesia, in tune with statement that "oil is more than a shadow behind international affairs."

W. Byford-Jones, *Oil on Troubled Waters,* London, Robert Hale, 1957, pp. 255.
Israeli and Anglo-French military actions involving Suez Canal; pipe line transportation; destruction of lines.

Ian Campbell, *The Future of Oil,* London, Union of Democratic Control Publications, 1957, pp. 16.
Middle East oil; recommendations on British policy for cooperation with oil-producing countries and nationalization of British oil market.

Olaf Caroe, *Wells of Power. The Oilfields*

of South-Western Asia, London, Macmillan & Co., 1951, pp. xx + 240.
Developments in Middle East and adjacent countries, companies involved, entry of American companies, human aspects, political developments; oil resources and world peace.

aurence Paul Elwell-Sutton, *Persian Oil. A Study in Power Politics,* London, Lawrence & Wishart, 1955, pp. 343.
Anglo-Iranian Oil Co. and Persian Government; events associated with oil development in Persia (Iran) to 1955 when petroleum consortium was established.

Nasrollah Saifpour Fatemi, *Oil Diplomacy. Powderkeg in Iran,* New York, Whittier Books, 1954, pp. 405.
Oil industry in Iran; competition among world powers; problems; position of Iranians; review and analysis of mistakes made on both sides.

David H. Finnie, *Desert Enterprise. The Middle East Oil Industry in Its Local Environment,* Cambridge, Mass., Harvard University Press (No. 1, Harvard Middle Eastern Studies), 1958, pp. x + 224.
Problems; employee, governmental, and social relations of companies operating in Middle East. Concessions, operations, and relations with people and leaders. Author was research fellow of Center for Middle Eastern Studies, Harvard University.

Alan W. Ford, *The Anglo-Iranian Oil Dispute of 1951–1952. A Study of the Law in the Relation of States,* Berkeley, Cal., University of California Press, 1954, pp. xii + 348.
Anglo-Iranian oil dispute through July, 1952, when International Court of Justice dismissed application for judicial determination; role of law.

Foreign Petroleum Supply Committee Under the Voluntary Agreement and the Activities of the Middle East Emergency Committee and Its Subcommittees Under the Plan of Action, *Report to the Secretary of the Interior from the Director of the Voluntary Agreement Relating to Foreign Petroleum Supply,* Amended May 8, 1956, Report of Committees dated June 30, 1957, 6 vols.,

pp. 1367, including appendices.
Vol. I: Chronological account of activities.
Vol. II: Minutes of meetings, Foreign Petroleum Supply Committee, Voluntary Agreement, Plan of Action, etc.
Vol. III: Minutes of meetings, Middle East Emergency Committee.
Vol. IV: Minutes of meetings: Supply and Distribution, Production, and Pipeline Transportation Subcommittees.
Vol. V: Minutes of Meetings: Statistical, Tanker, Refining, and Information Subcommittees.
Vol. VI: Reports: Supply and Distribution, Tanker Transportation, and Refining Subcommittees.

Herbert Hoover, Jr., *Oil, National Security and the Lessons of Suez,* New York, American Petroleum Institute, 1957, pp. 7.
Background Information Bulletin. Status of our oil reserves, with suggestions of the author.

Stanton Hope (W. E. Stanton-Hope), *The Battle for Oil,* London, Robert Hale, 1958, pp. 198.
Story of "unending struggle against Nature to locate oil and produce oil, coupled with lively international competition to acquire concessions in certain zones within oil-bearing lands." Oil developments in Middle East and elsewhere; author visited Qatar and Borneo.

Halford L. Hoskins, *Middle East Oil in United States Foreign Policy,* Washington, Legislative Reference Service, Library of Congress (Public Affairs Bulletin No. 89), 1950, pp. 118, plus exhibits.
Oil in international politics; petroleum in United States; oil problem in Europe; Middle East oil production; place of oil in strategic planning.

Iranian Embassy, *Some Documents on The Nationalization of The Oil Industry in Iran,* Washington, the Embassy, 1951, pp. 46.
Text of oil nationalization law and regulations; history of oil in Iran; measures adopted by Iranian Government; text of Prime Minister's report to Majles, Aug. 5, 1951; correspondence pertaining to American attempt to bring dispute to an end.

Norman Kemp, *Abadan. A First-Hand Account of the Persian Oil Crisis,* London, Allan Wingate, 1953, pp. 270.
Account of the controversy between Iranian Government and Anglo-Iranian Oil Co. to departure of British nationals employed by Company.

Morden Lazarus, *Oil and Turmoil,* Toronto, Across Canada Press, 1956, pp. 54.
Oil in Middle East; companies involved; problems in Canada and Latin America. Proposals of International Cooperative Alliance; United Nations investigation recommended.

William S. McCrea, *A Comparative Study of the Mexican Oil Expropriation (1938) and the Iranian Oil Nationalization (1951),* Washington, copyright by author, 1955, pp. 419.
Thesis submitted to Georgetown University. Mexico and Iran: social and political backgrounds; problems engendered by oil industry; effects of expropriation and nationalization; negotiations in each case; analyses of causes of disputes; comparison of results.

Daniel van der Meulen, *The Wells of Ibn Saud,* New York, Frederick A. Praeger, 1957, pp. ix + 270.
Written against background of 3 decades of contact, through Dutch consular service, with Saudi Arabia and adjacent areas, rulers and people; events and historical relationships of period encompassing entry of Americans in Arabian oil developments; resulting social and economic changes; current situation.

A. G. Mezerik, *Oil in the Middle East,* New York, International Publications (International Review Service, Vol. 4, No. 46, Sept., 1958), 1958, pp. 29.
Brief review of development of oil in Middle East, its importance to other nations and effect on Middle East countries both socially and economically.

Middle East Emergency Committee, *Emergency Oil for Europe,* New York, American Petroleum Institute, 1957, pp. 7.
Background Information Bulletin. Report on emergency "oil lift" to western Europe during Suez Canal closure.

Raymond Frech Mikesell and Hollis B Chenery, *Arabian Oil. America's Stak in the Middle East,* Chapel Hill, N.C University of North Carolina, 1949, pp xi + 201.
Events establishing American positio in Middle East, development of Arabia oil by American firms, foreign economi policy of United States on strategi materials, diplomatic actions; Middl East oil policies; suggestions for foreig petroleum policy.

A. B. Rajput, *Iran Today,* Lahore, Pakistan Lion Press, 1945, 2nd Ed. 1946. 3rd Ed 1953, pp. x + 351.
Iranian oil industry from an Irania viewpoint, from 1901 concession t nationalization, rupture of diplomati relations with Great Britain, and de parture of British staff.

Kermit Roosevelt, *Arabs, Oil and History The Story of the Middle East,* Harper & Bros., New York, and Victor Gollancz London, 1949, pp. 271.
Middle East countries; limited referenc to oil and its development.

Benjamin Shwadran, *The Middle East, Oil and the Great Powers,* New York Frederick A. Praeger, 1955, pp. xii + 501.
Development of oil industry in Middl East, effects on people and on inter national community.

Standard Oil Company (New Jersey), *The Iranian Oil Agreement,* New York, the Company, 1954, pp. 7.
Oil development in Iran; nationalization negotiations leading to consortium brief summary of agreement.

Correspondence between His Majesty's Government in the United Kingdom and Related Documents concerning the Oil Industry in Persia, Feb., 1951, to Sept., 1951, London, His Majesty's Stationery Office (Cmd. 8425), 1951, pp 66. Thirty-nine documents; text of Convention of April 29, 1933.

Guy Wint and Peter Calvocoressi, *Middle East Crisis,* Harmondsworth, England, Penguin Books, 1957, pp. 141.
British viewpoint of Middle East oil

and British requirements; British Middle East policy to assure access to oil

supply; review of events preceding Suez Canal crisis; documents.

F. RUSSIA (U.S.S.R.)

Amtorg Trading Corporation, *Soviet Oil Industry; A Compilation of Statements Regarding Purchases of Soviet Oil by Standard Oil Company of New York and Vacuum Oil Company. Statistics of Oil Industry of U.S.S.R.,* New York, the Corporation, 1928, pp. 31.

Essad Bey (Leo Noussimbaum), *Blood and Oil in the Orient,* trans. from German by Elsa Tolmey, New York, Simon & Schuster, 1932, pp. 315.
Life in Baku oil region before World War I.

Petroleum Industry Research Foundation, Special Report, *The Role of Oil in the Soviet Economy,* New York, the Foundation, 1956, pp. 31.
Meaning of Soviet oil developments to West; Russian oil production from before World War I; Russian oil re-serves, geographical distribution of Soviet oil deposits, drilling methods, transportation, refining, consumption, imports and exports.

L. Sedin, *The Oil Industry in the Soviet Union in the Course of the War,* New York, Russian Economic Institute, 1944, pp. 9.
Oil industry in U.S.S.R. since beginning of World War II, based on survey by author; in Sept., 1943, issue (No. 17), *Bolshevik,* Moscow.

Luigi Villari, *Fire and Sword in the Caucasus,* London, T. Fisher Unwin, 1906, pp. 347.
Baku: history and description; outbreak between Armenians and Tartars; strikes, 1903–1905; damage to oil fields of Apsheron Peninsula.

X.

Properties and Processing
of Petroleum

A. CHEMICAL, PHYSICAL, AND OTHER PROPERTIES
OF PETROLEUM

American Petroleum Institute, *Synthesis of Hydrocarbons in the Gasoline Range, 1938–1953,* New York, the Institute, 1953, pp. vi + 261.
Reprints of papers published under A.P.I. Research Project 45: "Synthesis, Purification and Properties of Hydrocarbons of Low Molecular Weight." Appendices list other papers published in relation to project.

American Petroleum Institute, Department of Information Staff, *Research and Development Expenditures and Personnel in the Oil Industry,* New York, American Petroleum Institute, 1956, pp. 7.
Background Information Bulletin. Oil industry investment in research and development.

American Society for Testing Materials, *Physical Constants of Hydrocarbons Boiling Below 350° F.,* Philadelphia, the Society, 1950, pp. 16.
Tables of physical constants of low-boiling hydrocarbons, covering 6 classes of hydrocarbons.

American Society for Testing Materials, *Knocking Characteristics of Pure Hydrocarbons,* Philadelphia, the Society, 1958, pp. 100.
Data developed under American Petroleum Institute Research Project 45: examination of wide variety of pure hydrocarbons, relating their structures and physical properties to knock limitation,

in variety of engine types and operation procedure.

M. P. Doss, *Physical Constants of the Principal Hydrocarbons,* New York, The Texas Co., 1929. 2nd Ed. 1939. 3rd Ed. 1942, pp. ix + 215.
Tabulation of most of the hydrocarbons physical constants not readily found in laboratory handbooks.

Gustav Egloff, *The Reactions of Pure Hydrocarbons,* New York, Reinhold Publishing Corp., 1937, pp. xvii + 897.
Deals with reactions of pure hydrocarbons which occur as result of thermal, catalytic, photochemical, or electrical treatment in 7 hydrocarbon groups.

Gustav Egloff, *Physical Constants of Hydrocarbons,* New York, Reinhold Publishing Corp., 1939 to 1953, 5 vols., pp. xxxiii + 2733.
Melting and boiling points, specific gravity, and refractive index of all classes of pure hydrocarbons (first 3 volumes); their interrelationships (Vol. 4); Vol. 5 is revision of Vol. 1 in light of later data.

Joseph Escott Faraday, *Encyclopedia of Hydrocarbon Compounds,* New York, Chemical Publishing Co., 1946, with additions and revisions, 14 vols.
Standard record of all known hydrocarbons, with references to original sources concerning each.

S. W. Ferris, *Handbook of Hydrocarbons,* New York, Academic Press, 1955, pp. ix + 324.
Introductory discussion of hydrocarbons, with tables giving most important physical properties of all hydrocarbons whose boiling points have been recorded.

Institute of Petroleum, *Significance of Properties of Petroleum Products,* London, the Institute, 1954, pp. 74.
Papers discussing physical properties of petroleum products as expressed in specifications and their relevance to purposes for which product is used.

George W. Le Maire, *Study of Physical Properties in the Refining of Petroleum,* Golden, Colo., Colorado School of Mines (*Quarterly,* Vol. 49, No. 4), 1954, pp. 87.
Results of investigation to determine and evaluate properties of pure hydrocarbons with those of petroleum fractions.

J. B. Maxwell, *Data Book on Hydrocarbons,* New York, D. Van Nostrand Co., 1950, pp. viii + 259.
Basic data on hydrocarbons and petroleum fractions, application to process design and chemical engineering in oil industry.

K. van Nes and Hendrik Adriaan van Westen, *Aspects of the Constitution of Mineral Oils,* Amsterdam, Elsevier Publishing Co., 1951, pp. xxiv + 484.
Comprehensive survey of knowledge concerning constitution of mineral oils. Revises "ring analysis" of "Waterman analysis," published in original form 1932 and revised 1935.

Brinley Pugh and Jack Milson Alfred Court, *Fuels and Lubricating Oils for Internal Combustion Engines,* London, Sir Isaac Pitman & Sons, 1949, pp. ix + 168.
Hydrocarbon chemistry, manufacture of fuels and lubricants from petroleum, combustion, anti-knock rating of fuels, chemical and physical properties of fuels and their significance.

Frederick Dominic Rossini, Beveridge James Mair, and Anton Joseph Streiff, *Hydrocarbons from Petroleum,* New York, Reinhold Publishing Corp., 1953, pp. vi + 556.
A.P.I. Research Project begun Jan., 1927, on composition of petroleum, fractionation and analysis of hydrocarbons, development of fractionating processes, purification and purity of hydrocarbons, and measurement of physical properties.

Frederick Dominic Rossini (and others), *Selected Values of Physical and Thermodynamic Properties of Hydrocarbons and Related Compounds,* Pittsburgh, Carnegie Press for American Petroleum Institute, 1953, pp. ix + 1050.
Data obtained through 1952 under A.P.I. Research Project 44, Data on Hydrocarbons and Related Compounds, established 1942 for consolidated assembly of all physical and thermodynamic properties of known hydrocarbons. Supplemental sheets issued periodically.

Alexander Nicholas Sachanen, *The Chemical Constituents of Petroleum,* New York, Reinhold Publishing Corp., 1945, pp. 451.
Physical and chemical methods of determining hydrocarbons in distillates, hydrocarbons of straight-run and synthetic distillates, classification of crude oils.

Bruce Hornbrook Sage and William Noble Lacey, *Thermodynamic Properties of the Lighter Paraffin Hydrocarbons and Nitrogen,* New York, American Petroleum Institute, 1950, pp. 221.
Fundamental behavior of lighter hydrocarbons; bibliography.

Bruce Hornbrook Sage and William Noble Lacey, *Some Properties of the Lighter Hydrocarbons,* New York, American Petroleum Institute, 1955, pp. 246.
Monograph on A.P.I. Research Project 37, established 1927 to study effect of gas in oil in reservoir and, since 1930, concentrated on determining fundamental properties of lighter hydrocarbons. Covers experimental work, 1947–53; earlier work described in previous monograph by same authors, above.

B. ANALYSIS, TESTING, STANDARDS, AND MEASUREMENT

Samuel S. Amdursky, Luther G. Marsh, and Edward Norton Hurlburt, *Handbook of the Petroleum Industry,* Rochester, N.Y., Taylor Instrument Co., 1928, pp. vii + 192.
Laboratory practices and tests applied to crude oil and its refined components; instruments used in laboratory practice; tables for testing and inspecting.

American Society for Testing Materials, *ASTM Standards on Petroleum Products and Lubricants,* Philadelphia, the Society, published annually.
Originally published with title, *Report of Committee D-2 on Petroleum Products and Lubricants and Methods of Test Relating to Petroleum Products,* 1923, pp. 96; 1924, pp. 80; 1926, pp. 81; 1927, pp. 245; 1928, pp. 268; 1929, pp. 260; 1930, pp. 284; 1931, pp. 267; 1932, pp. 286; 1933, pp. 292; 1934, pp. 340; 1935, pp. 358; 1936, pp. 372; 1937, pp. 292; 1938, pp. vi + 311; 1939, pp. ix + 336; 1940, pp. ix + 354; 1941, pp. viii + 398; 1942, pp. x + 442; 1943, pp. x + 442; 1944, pp. x + 514; 1945, pp. x + 546; 1946, pp. xii + 615; 1947, pp. xvi + 690; 1948, pp. xviii + 745; 1949, pp. xvi + 535; 1950, pp. xviii + 764; 1951, pp. xviii + 784; 1952, pp. xxi + 810; 1953, pp. xxv + 890; 1954, pp. xxvi + 956; 1955, pp. xxvii + 954; 1956, pp. xxix + 1066; 1957, pp. xxix + 1108.
Prepared by Committee D-2 on Petroleum Products and Lubricants, American Society for Testing Materials, and includes proposed, tentative, and standard methods of tests, specifications, definitions of terms and classifications of petroleum products and lubricants, with related information.

American Society for Testing Materials, *The Significance of Tests of Petroleum Products,* Philadelphia, the Society, 1934, pp. 76.
Responds to "growing demand on the part of the general public for information regarding the significance of tests used in evaluating petroleum products."

American Society for Testing Materials, *Significance of ASTM Tests for Petroleum Products,* Philadelphia, the Society, 1956, pp. xviii + 115.
Methods of tests and their relationship to performance characteristics of specific products.

American Society for Testing Materials, *Evaluation of Petroleum Products, A Resumé of Present Information,* Philadelphia, the Society, 1940, pp. 52.
Papers on production, use of petroleum products and lubricants; gasoline, diesel fuels, other fuel oils; lubricating oils and greases; status of research on fuels and lubricants for aircraft engines.

American Society for Testing Materials, *Symposium on Oil Procurement Practices,* Philadelphia, the Society, 1946, pp. 53.
Methods of oil procurement by various industrial plants, airlines, United States Navy, etc.

American Society for Testing Materials, *ASTM Manual of Engine Test Methods for Rating Fuels,* Philadelphia, the Society, 1948, pp. xvi + 320. 2nd Ed. 1952, pp. xvi + 342.
Presents 5 standardized methods (Motor, D357, Research, D908, Aviation, D614, Supercharge, D909, and Cetane, D613) for rating fuels, which are in world-wide use by automotive and petroleum industries; 6 supplements containing information on best practices currently in use for laboratory facilities, installation of engine test units; provisions for reference materials and electrical, water, and air services; operation and maintenance of units. 2nd Ed. includes changes in 5 test methods and amplifies information in 6 supplements.

American Society for Testing Materials, *ASTM Manual for Rating Motor Fuels by Motor and Research Methods,* Philadelphia, the Society, 1956, pp. xii + 180.
Two methods published separately, having been recommended for consideration as international standards.
1957 Supplement, pp. iv + 82. Includes changes in 1956 *Manual for Rating Motor Fuels by Motor and Research*

Methods and 1952 *Manual of Engine Test Methods for Rating Fuels,* which have been approved, up to July 1, 1957, by Committee D-2 and American Society for Testing Materials.

American Society for Testing Materials, *Manual on Measurement and Sampling of Petroleum and Petroleum Products,* Philadelphia, the Society, 1950, pp. xii + 120. 2nd Ed. 1953, pp. xii + 133. 3rd Ed. 1958, pp. 172.
Gauging, temperature measurement, volume calculations and corrections, water and sediment, gravity, and sampling.

American Society for Testing Materials, *Evaluation of Insulating Oils, European Development,* Philadelphia, the Society, 1954, pp. 72.
European developments in testing of transformer oils; papers covering research in France, Sweden, and England. Sixth of series of symposia on insulating oils, held Nov., 1954, Cleveland, Ohio. Symposia deal with development of test methods and evaluation of test results for use in establishing serviceability of new and used insulating oils.
First. 1946; see ASTM Bulletin No. 146, 1947, pp. 90–100.
Second. 1947; see ASTM Bulletin No. 149, 1947, pp. 58–74.
Third. 1949; see STP No. 95.
Fourth. 1951; see STP No. 135.
Fifth. 1952; see STP No. 152.

American Society for Testing Materials, *ASTM-IP Petroleum Measurement Tables.* American Edition: United States Units of Measurement, Philadelphia, the Society, 1953, pp. xv + 525. British Edition: Tables applicable to units (Imperial) commonly employed in British Commonwealth, London, Institute of Petroleum, 1952, pp. 416.
Uniformly conceived and executed tables required for calculation of quantities of petroleum and petroleum products.

Donald C. Broome and R. O. Child, *The Testing of Bituminous Mixtures,* London, Edward Arnold & Co., 1934, pp. vii + 194. 2nd Ed. 1949, pp. viii + 396.
Covers testing of bitumens, tars and oils, and other constituent road and building materials, and of finished mixtures.

O. W. Burke, Jr., C. E. Starr, Jr., and F. D. Tuemmler, *Light Hydrocarbon Analysis. Analytical Methods Compiled and Tested for The Office of Rubber Reserve, Reconstruction Finance Corporation, by the Butadiene Committee on Specifications and Methods of Analysis,* New York, Reinhold Publishing Corp., 1951, pp. xv + 639.
Review of synthetic rubber program, production processes for butadiene, specifications, tests, analytical methods.

John Reid Campbell, *Methods of Analysis of Fuels and Oils,* New York, Chemical Publishing Co., 1952, pp. xii + 216. (Constable, London, 1951.)
Laboratory guide to principal methods of examination of gaseous, liquid, and solid fuels and lubricating oils.

Cooperative Fuel Research Committee, *Test Procedures and General Information in Current Use in the Development and Utilization of Aviation, Motor, and Automotive Diesel Fuels,* New York, the Committee, 1941, pp. 157.
Test procedures in development stage, calibration curves, fuel specifications and other information in current use by fuel technologists; not adopted formally by appropriate standardization body.

Coordinating Research Council, *CRC Handbook,* New York, the Council, 1946, pp. 558.
Test procedures for motor, aviation, and diesel fuels, developed by Coordinating Fuel Research Committee, and for engine oils and general lubricants, developed by Coordinating Lubricating Research Committee. Coordinating Research Council, organized 1942, is continuation and expansion of Cooperative Fuel Research Committee initiated in 1922 by American Petroleum Institute and Society of Automotive Engineers.

J. H. Coste and E. R. Andrews, *The Examination and Thermal Value of Fuel: Gaseous, Liquid and Solid,* London, Charles Griffin & Co., 1914, pp. xiv + 278.
Methods and appliances useful in comparison and valuation of fuels, sampling and analysis, and calorimetry of gaseous and liquid fuels.

Carl John Engelder, *A Laboratory Manual of Gas, Oil and Fuel Analysis,* New York, John Wiley & Sons, 1931, pp. x + 236.
Methods of analysis, testing, and evaluation of gaseous, liquid, and solid fuels, gas mixtures, oils and lubricants. Outlines 34 experiments, with 20 devoted to analysis and evaluation of gases, 10 to testing of liquid fuels and lubricants, and 4 to coal.

Elliott A. Evans, *Lubricating and Allied Oils. A Handbook for Chemists, Engineers and Students,* London, Chapman & Hall, 1921, pp. xv + 128. 2nd Ed. 1933, pp. xv + 175. 3rd Ed. 1945, pp. ix + 210.
Aid to compilation of specifications and examination of lubricating oils, dealing largely with physical and chemical tests.

Fisher Scientific Co., *Fisher-Tag Manual for Inspectors of Petroleum,* 28th Edition, Chicago, Fisher Scientific Co., 1954, pp. vi + 218.
Essential details of basic tests for properties of petroleum and products most frequently used by analysts and inspectors. Original manual compiled by Charles J. Tagliabue. Last 3 editions under Fisher/Tag name.

Augustus Herman Gill, *Oil Analysis,* Boston, Heliotype Printing Co., 1897, pp. 29. 2nd Ed.: *A Short Hand-Book of Oil Analysis,* 1898, pp. 139. 2nd Ed. (Revised) 1900, pp. 143. 3rd Ed. 1903, pp. 159. 4th Ed. 1905, pp. 163. 5th Ed. 1909, pp. 179. 6th Ed. 1911, pp. 188. 7th Ed. 1913, pp. 188. 8th Ed. 1918, pp. 209. 9th Ed. 1919, pp. 215. 10th Ed. 1922, pp. 223. 11th Ed. 1927, pp. 293. 2nd through 11th Editions, published by J. B. Lippincott Co., Philadelphia. Written to meet needs of author's classes at Massachusetts Institute of Technology. Later enlarged for public distribution to meet demand for manual of physical and chemical tests for mineral, animal, and vegetable oils.

Augustus Herman Gill, *Gas and Fuel Analysis for Engineers: A Compend for Those Interested in the Economical Application of Fuel,* New York, John Wiley & Sons, 1896, pp. vii + 89. Additional copyrights 1902, 1908, 1911,
1913, 1917. 9th Ed. 1920, pp. vii + 160. 10th Ed. 1925, pp. 181.
Prepared especially for the use of students at Massachusetts Institute of Technology.

William Allen Hamor and Fred Warde Padgett, *The Technical Examination of Crude Petroleum, Petroleum Products and Natural Gas,* New York, McGraw-Hill Book Co., 1920, pp. ix + 591.
Treatise on methods in use for technical examination and evaluation of hydrocarbon complexes, natural gas, crude petroleum, oil shale, and their commercially important products.

James A. Hicks, *The Laboratory Book of Mineral Oil Testing,* London, Charles Griffin & Co., 1906, pp. 74. 2nd Ed. 1912. 3rd Ed. 1918, Revised by Arthur G. V. Berry, pp. xii + 81. 4th Ed. 1925, Revised by Arthur W. Cox, pp. vii + 128.
Details for working apparatus for testing of petroleum and its derivatives; physical tests. Author was chief chemist to Sir Boverton Redwood, who wrote Introduction.

David Holde, *The Examination of Hydrocarbon Oils and of Saponifiable Fats and Waxes,* trans. from German by Edward Mueller, New York, John Wiley & Sons (London, Chapman & Hall), 1915, pp. xv + 483. 2nd Ed. (English) 1922, John Wiley & Sons, pp. 572.
Laboratory investigations of petroleum and its manufactured products, natural asphalt and waxes; distillation of coal and other materials; saponifiable fats and waxes.

Erastus Hopkins, *The Oil Chemists' Handbook,* New York, John Wiley & Sons, 1900, pp. viii + 72.
Methods for testing and analyzing oils; data for identification of unknown oils and adulterants.

Prevost Hubbard, *Laboratory Manual of Bituminous Materials for the Use of Students in Highway Engineering,* New York, John Wiley & Sons, 1916, pp. xi + 153.
Laboratory guide to analyses and tests of bituminous materials; characteristics

of more important bituminous materials.

Edward Norton Hurlburt, *Tycos Gravity and Temperature Tables for Mineral Oils, from Determinations of the Bureau of Standards and Other Tables for General Testing and Refinery Practice,* Rochester, N.Y., Taylor Instrument Companies, 1918, pp. 204. 2nd Ed. 1921, pp. 215.

Institute of Petroleum, *Standard Methods for Testing Petroleum and Its Products,* London. Published annually by the Institute. 1924, pp. x + 100; 1929, pp. xiv + 137; 1935, pp. xi + 228; 1942, pp. xi + 390; 1944, pp. xxxiv + 477; 1945, pp. xxxvi + 539; 1946, pp. xl + 550; 1947, pp. xliii+ 576; 1948, pp. xlviii + 616; 1949, pp. lvi + 660; 1951, pp. xix + 724; 1952, pp. xix + 727; 1953, pp. xxiv + 765; 1955, pp. xxvii + 688; 1956, pp. xxiii + 748; 1957, pp. xxii + 772; 1958, pp. xxiv + 788; 1959, pp. 835.
Developed by Standardization Committee, appointed originally May 30, 1921, representing industry and government departments. Includes details of methods of tests of crude oil and petroleum products, covering every aspect of petroleum testing. 18th Ed. (1959) contains full details of 130 of 136 methods of test, also covering every aspect of petroleum testing.

Institute of Petroleum, *Dangerous Gases in the Petroleum and Allied Industries,* London, the Institute, 1939, pp. 177.
Papers on dangerous gases in distillation and refining processes, field operations, oil tanks, ships; vapor detection, gas indicators, protection.

Institute of Petroleum, *IP Engine Test Methods for Rating Fuels,* London, the Institute, 1955, pp. x + 84.
Engine test methods for anti-knock rating of motor and aviation fuels; ignition quality of diesel fuels.

Institute of Petroleum, *Petroleum Measurement Manual,* London, the Institute, 1952, pp. viii + 227.
Instructions and recommendations covering oil measurement from calibration of tanks to final calculation of quantities; tank calibration, gauging,

sampling, temperature measurement, specific gravity, units of measurement, calculations, tables, oil measurement apparatus.

Edwin Robert Littmann, *Methods of Analysis for Petrochemicals,* New York, Chemical Publishing Co., 1958, pp. 384.
Testing primary and secondary products derived from petroleum and used in manufacturing processes and syntheses. Covers 61 different methods assembled from American Society for Testing Materials and Enjay Co., listing reagents and preparation of samples; describes and illustrates apparatus.

Edward Molloy and Ernest Walter Knott, *Fuel and Oil Systems,* Brooklyn, N.Y., Chemical Publishing Co., 1941, pp. viii + 124.
Maintenance and repair of fuel supply and oil circulation systems on representative types of aircraft.

Ohio State University, *Analysis of Lubricating Oils,* Columbus, Engineering Experiment Station, 1953, pp. v + 49.
Testing of lubricating oil fractions of crude oil.

University of Oklahoma, *Proceedings of the Petroleum Fluid Metering Conference,* Norman, Okla., University of Oklahoma Press, 1938, pp. 78.
Papers reviewing experiences of oil companies in using various types of meters; problems pertaining to metering of crude oil and products in field, pipe lines, and refineries.

University of Oklahoma, *Progress Report of the Fluid Meters Research,* 1937, var. pag.; final report, Works Progress Administration, 1939, pp. 14.
Reports on project for accurate determination of meter coefficients for viscous fluids at commercial rates of flow.

University of Oklahoma, *Proceedings of the Petroleum Fluid Metering Conference,* Norman, Okla., the University, 1940, pp. 64.
Papers and discussions.

Samuel Wilson Parr, *The Analysis of Fuel, Gas, Water and Lubricants,* New York, McGraw-Hill Book Co., 1922, 3rd Ed.

pp. xii + 250. 4th Ed. 1932, pp. xv + 371. Preceded by *The Chemical Examination of Water, Fuel, Flue Gases, and Lubricants,* Urbana, Ill., University of Illinois, 1911, pp. 100. 2nd Ed. 1916, pp. 130.
Synopses of lectures and laboratory methods covering analysis of fuels, gases, water, and lubricants.

Orin Wainwright Rees, Paul Welland Henline, and Alfred Hannam Bell, *Chemical Characteristics of Illinois Crude Oils, with a Discussion of Their Geologic Occurrence,* Urbana, Ill., State Geological Survey, 1943, pp. 128.
Methods of analysis, correlation index, characteristics as related to geologic age of producing strata, chemical analyses of 100 Illinois crude oils.

William August Christian Schlueter, *General Testing Methods and Tables for Mineral Oils,* Wichita, Kan., the author, 1920, pp. 99.
Discussion and directions of methods of testing, and tables, in general use by oil laboratories.

Report from the Select Committee on Petroleum: Together with the Proceedings of the Committee, Minutes of Evidence, London, Her Majesty's Stationery Office (No. 311), 1896, pp. xii + 918, appendix.
Report, July 23, 1896, by Select Committee of House of Commons, appointed to inquire into sufficiency of law relating to keeping, selling, using, and conveying petroleum and other inflammable liquids. Contains report on testing of petroleum. Table, appendix No. 29, shows imports of petroleum into Great Britain, by years, 1842–94. Witnesses included Boverton Redwood, Charles Frederic Chandler, Frederick Augustus Abel, D. I. Mendeleeff, Carl Engler.

Reid F. Stearns, Robert M. Jackson, Russell R. Johnson, and Charles A. Larson, *Flow Measurement with Orifice Meters,* New York, D. Van Nostrand Co., 1951, pp. xviii + 350.
Applications of flow equations to metering problems, principles of operation of commercial meters, interpretation of meter records, orifice meter installations, testing and checking, special metering problems, and accuracy of orifice meter installations.

Thomas Bliss Stillman, *Examination of Lubricating Oils,* Easton, Penna., Chemical Publishing Co., 1914, pp. 125.
Manual for testing of lubricating oils.

Alexander Norman Tate, *The Examination of Petroleum and Other Mineral Oils according to the Petroleum Act, 1868,* London, Henry Greenwood, 1869, pp. 12.
Description of apparatus and procedure for testing flash point of mineral oils; discussion of imported oils.

Jocelyn Home Thomson and Boverton Redwood, *Handbook on Petroleum for Inspectors,* London, Charles Griffin & Co., 1901, pp. xix + 298. 2nd Ed. 1906, pp. xix + 324. 3rd Ed. Revised by Aston Cooper-Key, 1913, pp. xix + 340.
Characteristics of petroleum, origin, occurrence, production, refining; commercial products, with full description of testing and legislation relating to petroleum; necessary precautions in handling and use of petroleum products; petroleum oil lamps.

Jocelyn Home Thomson and Boverton Redwood, *The Petroleum Lamp. Its Choice and Use,* London, Charles Griffin & Co., 1902, pp. 104.
Historical review of development of oil-burning lamps, principles of construction, choice, care, and use of petroleum lamps.

United States Fuel Administration, Oil Division, *Report of Committee on Standardization of Petroleum Specifications,* Washington, Government Printing Office, 1918, pp. 10.
Report on first Federal specifications and testing procedure for export, fighting, and domestic grades of aviation gasoline, motor gasoline, Navy fuel oil, gas oil, and bunker oil.

Universal Oil Products Co., *U.O.P. Laboratory Test Methods for Petroleum and Its Products,* Des Plaines, Ill., the Company, 1937, pp. 250. 2nd Ed. 1940, var. pag. 3rd Ed. 1947, var. pag.
Test methods for small refiners with limited personnel and facilities.

Alfred Holmes White, *Technical Gas and Fuel Analysis,* New York, McGraw-Hill Book Co., 1913, pp. x + 276. 2nd. Ed. 1920, pp. xiii + 319.
Testing and analysis of fuels; chapters on natural gas, liquid fuels.

Arthur Columbine Wright, *The Analysis of Oils and Allied Substances,* London, Crosby Lockwood & Son, 1903, pp. x + 241.
Deals with chemistry of processes and methods employed in analysis of oil, including lubricating oils and greases.

C. PETROLEUM CHEMISTRY AND PETROCHEMICALS

Melvin J. Astle, *The Chemistry of Petrochemicals,* New York, Reinhold Publishing Corp., 1956, pp. v + 267.
Preparation and chemical reactions of industrial chemicals made directly or indirectly from petroleum hydrocarbons.

Benjamin T. Brooks, Steward S. Kurtz, Jr., Cecil E. Boord, and Louis Schmerling, *The Chemistry of Petroleum Hydrocarbons,* New York, Reinhold Publishing Corp., 1954–55, 3 vols., pp. xx + 1802.
Written by chemists employed by oil companies, research institutes, universities, governmental agencies, and those engaged as consultants; covers broad and specific subjects in chemistry of petroleum hydrocarbons and industrial processes involving hydrocarbon chemistry.

Benjamin Talbott Brooks, *The Chemistry of the Non-Benzenoid Hydrocarbons and their Simple Derivatives,* New York, Chemical Catalog Co., 1920, pp. 612. 2nd Ed. New York, Reinhold Publishing Corp., 1950, pp. xiv + 615.
Relationship of non-benzenoid hydrocarbons and comparison with chemical behavior of more complex hydrocarbons of paraffine series.

Albert Ernest Dunstan, *Chemistry and the Petroleum Industry,* London, Institute of Chemistry of Great Britain and Ireland, 1942, pp. 48.
Distillation, cracking, hydrogenation; refinery products; utilization of refinery gases; synthetics; part played by chemist in oil fields, refineries, research.

Carleton Ellis, *The Chemistry of Petroleum Derivatives,* (Marked Vol. I.), New York, Chemical Catalog Co., 1934, pp. 1285. 2nd Ed. New York, Reinhold Publishing Corp., (Marked Vol. II), 1937, pp. 1464.

Chemical derivatives of petroleum.

Adalbert Farkas, *Physical Chemistry of the Hydrocarbons,* New York, Academic press, 1950 and 1953, 2 vols., pp. xviii + 864.
Physico-chemical basis of new techniques and methods adopted by the hydrocarbons industry.

Richard Frank Goldstein, *The Petroleum Chemicals Industry,* London, E. & F. N. Spon, 1949, pp. xiii + 449. 2nd Ed. 1958, pp. xv + 458.
Surveys fields of industrial organic chemistry in which oil is most economic starting material; source materials, chemistry of paraffins, manufacture of hydrocarbons and chemical by-products.

William A. Gruse, *Petroleum and Its Products. A Chemical Discussion of the Properties, Refining, and Utilization of Petroleum,* New York, McGraw-Hill Book Co., 1928, pp. viii + 377.
Data on petroleum chemistry assembled from the standpoint of American industry. Includes composition of petroleum, refining methods and utilization.

William A. Gruse and Donald R. Stevens, *The Chemical Technology of Petroleum,* New York, McGraw-Hill Book Co., 1942, pp. xiii + 733.
Deals with chemical composition and physical properties of petroleum; distillation, refining by physical and chemical methods, cracking; chemical thermodynamics; products and by-products.

Lewis Frederic Hatch, *The Chemistry of Petrochemical Reactions,* Houston, Gulf Publishing Co., 1955, pp. vii + 182.
Chemical constitution of petroleum; chemical reactions in production of in-

termediate and finished petroleum chemicals; flow diagrams of industrial plants.

Vladimir Anatole Kalichevsky and Bert Allen Stagner, *Chemical Refining of Petroleum,* New York, The Chemical Catalog Co., 1933, pp. 451. Revised Ed., New York, Reinhold Publishing Corp., 1942, pp. xi + 550.
Theory and practice of chemical processes used in refining petroleum and its products; use of reagents for improvement of products.

Vladimir Anatole Kalichevsky, *The Amazing Petroleum Industry,* New York, Reinhold Publishing Corp., 1943, pp. 234.
Petroleum manufacturing processes, including hydrogenation, chemical treatment, and manufacture of chemicals from petroleum.

Vladimir Anatole Kalichevsky and Kenneth Albert Kobe, *Petroleum Refining with Chemicals,* Amsterdam, Netherlands, Elsevier Publishing Co., 1956, pp. xi + 780.
Use of chemicals and solvents in preparation of petroleum products.

Organisation for European Economic Co-operation, *Corrosion Problems and Prevention in the Chemical and Petro-Chemical Industries in the U.S.A.,* Paris, the Organisation, 1954, pp. 129.
Report of technical assistance mission from European countries to United States, 1953, to study problems of maintenance in chemical industry; contains section on anticorrosion practices.

Alexander Nicholas Sachanen and Matislav Dimitrievich Tilicheyev, *Chemistry and Technology of Cracking,* trans. from Russian by A. A. Boehtlingk, D. F. Brown, and K. T. Steik, New York, Chemical Catalog Co., 1932, pp. 389.
Experiments by authors at Petroleum Research Institute of Grozneft on physical and chemical laws governing petroleum cracking reactions.

James Edward Southcombe, *Chemistry of the Oil Industries,* London, Constable & Co., 1913, pp. ix + 204. 2nd Ed. 1920, pp. ix + 224.
Physical and organic chemistry of oil.

Charles Kenneth Tinkler and Frederick Challenger, *The Chemistry of Petroleum and Its Substitutes,* London, Crosby Lockwood & Son, 1915, pp. xvi + 352.
Handbook of petroleum chemistry in theoretical and practical aspects.

D. REFINING OF PETROLEUM, PROCESSING PATENTS

American Chemical Society, *Progress in Petroleum Technology,* n.p., the Society, 1951, pp. vi + 392.
Thirty-two papers dealing particularly with technological progress in refining processes.

American Petroleum Industries Committee, *Reply to the Deserted Village, No. 6,* New York, the Committee, 1943, pp. 5.
Regards assertion of imminent shortage of motor fuel and lubricants as claim made to gain support for idea of blending gasoline and alcohol.

Thomas Antisell, M.D., *The Manufacture of Photogenic, or Hydro-Carbon, Oils from Coal and Other Bituminous Substances,* New York, D. Appleton & Co., 1859, pp. 144. 2nd Ed. 1866, pp. 150.
Reviews technological achievements and advances in distillation of bituminous substances in United States and abroad, general principles involved, products derived, manufacturers then operating. Lists of patents and comments on main features of many. Revised edition contains appendix reviewing oil well drilling in Pennsylvania. Author was professor of chemistry in Medical Dept. of Georgetown College, Washington, D.C., and examiner of chemical patents for United States Patent Office. Previously had served as geologist of expedition to explore railroad route from Mississippi River to Pacific Ocean and wrote *Geological Report,* published 1856.

George Armistead, Jr., *Safety in Petroleum Refining and Related Industries,* New York, John G. Simmonds & Co., 1950, pp. 416.

Principles of safe plant layout, fire protection of structures, mechanical standards; operating, maintenance, and inspection practices; fire control.

George Armistead and Company, Comp., *Petroleum Refining Data Book,* Washington, the Company, 1952, var. pag.

Prepared for use by American Cyanamid Company as textbook. Data frequently used in design and economics calculation; description of main basic refining processes.

Harold Sill Bell, *American Petroleum Refining,* New York, D. Van Nostrand Co., 1923, pp. xiv + 456. 2nd Ed. 1930, pp. xiii + 631. 3rd Ed. 1945, pp. xii + 619. 4th Ed. 1959, pp. ix + 538.

Good overall survey of refining processes, equipment, plant protection, operation.

Allan Berne-Allen, Jr., *The Solubility of Refined Paraffin Waxes in Petroleum Fractions,* New York, the author, 1936, pp. 83.

Thesis for degree at Columbia University.

Robert E. Burk, Howard E. Thompson, Archie J. Weith, and Ira Williams, *Polymerization and Its Applications in the Fields of Rubber, Synthetic Resins, and Petroleum,* New York, Reinhold Publishing Corp., 1937, pp. 312.

General discussion of polymerization and its mechanisms, with section devoted to polymerization in the petroleum industry; appended list of references.

Andrew Campbell, *Petroleum Refining,* London, Charles Griffin & Co., 1918, pp. xvi + 297. 2nd Ed. 1922, pp. xvi + 297.

Methods for preparing marketable products from petroleum, based on author's experience, mostly with Burmah Oil Co. Limited to "ordinary methods of refining."

Harry M. Crain, *Petroleum Refining,* Golden, Colo., Colorado School of Mines (Vol. 45, No. 2A, Colorado School of Mines *Quarterly*), 1950, pp. xii + 162.

Papers on various aspects of petroleum refining, research, and instrumentation.

Marshall Perley Cram, *The Fractionation of Crude Petroleum by Capillary Filtration,* Easton, Penna., Eschenbach Printing Co., 1908, pp. 50.

Doctoral dissertation for degree at Johns Hopkins University. Deals with experiments in filtration of crude oil in tube packed with fuller's earth and resulting fractionation. Crude used was dark green oil from Venango County, Pennsylvania.

Roy Cross, *A Handbook of Petroleum, Asphalt, and Natural Gas,* Kansas City, Mo., Kansas City Testing Laboratory, 1918 (Bulletin 14), pp. vi + 248; 1919 (Bulletin 15), pp. 496; 1922 (Bulletin 16), pp. 622; 1924 (Bulletin 17), pp. 739; 1928 (Bulletin 25), pp. 832; 1931 (Rev. Bulletin 25), pp. 864; 1933 (Bulletin 26), pp. 865.

Excellent summaries of current state of refining art, as of publication date. Cross was a leading petroleum technologist, operator (with his brother) of the Kansas City Testing Laboratory, and co-inventor of the Cross cracking process, one of the most successful thermal cracking processes of the 1920's. These handbooks contain authoritative material on all main cracking methods, with drawings; lists of patents; tables; petroleum product specifications; bibliography.

Roy Cross, *Petroleum and Its Products,* Kansas City, Mo., Kansas City Testing Laboratory, 1915 (Bulletin 9), pp. 19.

Specifications, properties, tables.

Roy Cross, *From A Chemist's Diary,* Kansas City, Mo., Kansas City Testing Laboratory (Bulletin No. 29), 1943, pp. 315.

Collection of items from diary of author, who devoted forty years to work as industrial and research chemist. Discusses results of oil cracking, with particular attention to Cross cracking process, and tells of testing anti-knock qualities of gasoline.

Johannes Christianus Ludovicus Defize, *On the Edeleanu Process for the Selec-*

tive Extraction of Mineral Oils, Amsterdam, Netherlands, D. B. Centen, 1938, pp. viii + 310.
Describes nature and purpose of Edeleanu process (solvent extraction to remove impurities using as solvent liquid sulphur dioxide); design and operation of plants; physical and chemical principles involved; experiments and investigations relating to kerosene, lubricating oil, gasoline; bibliography; list of patents.

Albert Ernest Dunstan, *Scientific Foundations of the Refining of Petroleum,* London, Royal Society of Arts, 1928, pp. 95.
Progress of chemistry and refining processes; gas and gasoline distillation methods; refining of petroleum distillates; cracking.

Gustav Egloff and C. D. Lowry, Jr., *The Cracking Art in 1927,* Chicago, Universal Oil Products Co., 1928, pp. 79.
First of eleven annual reviews, continued through 1939, of notable advancements, patents issued in various countries, and literature dealing with mechanism of cracking, vapor-phase cracking, use of catalysts, corrosion, etc. Universal was owner of the Dubbs process. UOP booklets were started in July, 1926, with booklet No. 1, *Systematic Refining of Cracked Distillates,* by J. C. Morrell; booklet No. 266, *The Use of UOP Inhibitors* (1958) is latest in series.

Carleton Ellis, *The Hydrogenation of Oils, Catalyzers and Catalysts and the Generation of Hydrogen and Oxygen,* New York, D. Van Nostrand Co., 1914, pp. x + 340. 2nd Ed. 1919, pp. xvii + 767. 3rd Ed.: *Hydrogenation of Organic Substances, Including Fats and Fuels,* 1930, pp. xxiv + 986.
Methods of hydrogenation; catalyzers, especially base metals, hydrogenated products; production of hydrogen and hydrogenation of petroleum. Ellis was well-known consulting chemist in oil refining, inventor of cracking methods and pioneer process for producing alcohols from petroleum.

R. J. Forbes, *Short History of the Art of Distillation,* Leiden, Netherlands, E. J. Brill, 1948, pp. 405.
History of distillation beginning with work of Alexandrian chemists at opening of Christian era, followed by work of Arabs, through Middle Ages, through death of Cellier-Blumenthal in early 19th century; early work in distillation of crude oil.

Arch L. Foster, Maurice Bacon Cooke, Albert Gordon Peterkin, and James Edwin Latta, *Petroleum Cracking and Refining,* Scranton, Penna., International Textbook Co., 1939, pp. vi + 149.
Cracking processes and their operation; polymerization of hydrocarbons and commercial processes; chemistry of petroleum hydrogenation, process examples; treatment, filtration, blending and compounding of oils, waxes, lubricants and greases.

Foster Wheeler Corporation, *Petroleum Refining,* New York, the Corporation, 1946, pp. 59. (Loose-leaf). 2nd Ed 1949, pp. 59.
Shows examples of processing units designed and constructed by the Company; condensed statement of outstanding features, illustrations, flow-diagrams, and description of process-flow.

Foster Wheeler Corporation, *Petroleum Refining Processes. Flow Diagrams,* New York, the Corporation, 1955, pp. 69.
Shows flow diagrams of 41 processes in the petroleum refining industry, with text and illustration for each.

Halley Tansley Gaetz, *Water-White Hydrocarbons from Trinidad Asphalt,* Los Angeles, Grafton Publishing Corp. 1935, pp. 137. 2nd Ed. 1936, pp. 195 3rd Ed. 1937, pp. 284.
Fractionation and purification of hydrocarbons from commercially refined Trinidad Lake asphalt.

Abraham Gesner, M.D., *A Practical Treatise on Coal, Petroleum, and Other Distilled Oils,* New York, Baillière Bros. 1861, pp. 134. 2nd Ed., George Weltden Gesner, 1865, pp. 181.
Dr. Gesner was Canadian physician and geologist who made and named first kerosene, as early as 1846. Coming to New York in 1853, he was responsible for organization of New York Kerosene Co. (1854), first commercial plant in

United States making "coal oil" illuminants. Book is practical handbook covering distillation of oils from coals and other bituminous substances, testing, and treating; contains list of refineries. 2nd Ed. by son of Dr. Gesner contains much information on new Pennsylvania petroleum industry.

Gulf Research and Development Co., *A Source Book of Technical Literature on Fractional Distillation,* Pittsburgh, the Company, 1950, pp. 388.
Papers on distillation, general theory of vapor-liquid equilibria, batch distillation, binary mixture separation; summary of literature on hydrocarbon absorption and fractionation process design methods.

Leo Gurwitsch (Gurvich), *The Scientific Basis for Petroleum Refining,* trans. by Carl J. von Bibra, Paul D. Barton, and Rosetta A. Barton, n.p., n.pub., 1921, 2 vols, pp. 439, mimeographed.
English translation of work published 1913 in Berlin. Gives general view of scientific principles involved in oil refining. Standard work for years.

Leo Gurwitsch and Harold Moore, *The Scientific Principles of Petroleum Technology,* London, Chapman & Hall, 1926, pp. xvi + 470. Rev. Ed., New York, D. Van Nostrand Co., 1932, pp. 572.
Translation of 2nd German Ed. with additions by translator. Rev. Ed. devotes attention to American developments.

Jan Herman van der Have and C. G. Verver, *Petroleum and Its Products,* London, Sir Isaac Pitman & Sons, 1957, pp. viii + 421.
Crude petroleum, manufacture, properties, and application of its products. Written in Dutch during World War II primarily for technical school students. First published 1941. Text rewritten for English edition.

Samuel Dana Hayes, *On The History and Manufacture of Petroleum Products,* Boston, Rand, Avery & Co., 1872, pp. 33.
History of petroleum products manufacture, work of leaders in manufacture of coal oil, lubricating oils, and other products.

R. J. Hengstebeck, *Petroleum Processing. Principles and Applications,* New York, McGraw-Hill Book Co., 1959, pp. 348.
Technology of petroleum refining, uses and properties of principal petroleum products, distillation, absorption, other separation processes, refining processes, manufacture of lubricating oils, waxes, and asphalts, and hydrogenation processes.

International Correspondence Schools, *Petroleum and Products,* Scranton, Penna., 1902. 2nd Ed. 1918.
Instruction paper, with examination questions, in 3 parts, dealing with nature and composition of petroleum, and methods of testing petroleum and its products.

Horace Greeley James, *Petroleum Refining. Possibilities Through Federal Cooperation. Follies of 1916. Refining Efficiency,* Kansas City, Mo., Western Petroleum Refiners Assn., 1916, pp. 35.
Graphic portrait oil refining problems, work of Bureau of Mines, need for increased refinery efficiency, and distribution problems; author of *Refining Industry of the United States,* with List of Refineries, Capacity and Investment and Oil Jobbers of America. Published 1916 by Derrick Publishing Co., Oil City, Penna.

Horace Greeley James, *Petroleum Refiners Hand Book,* Kansas City, Mo., Western Petroleum Refiners Assn., 1921, pp. 123.
Variety of information on trade relations, tank car unloading rules, crude oil market fluctuations in Mid-Continent field, 1900–21, freight rates.

Maxcine J. Japour, *Petroleum Refining and Manufacturing Processes,* Los Angeles, Wetzel Publishing Co., 1939, pp. 310.
Author's ideas of fundamentals of refining industry.

James Kewley, *Petroleum and Allied Industries,* London, Baillière, Tindall and Cox, 1922, pp. x + 302.
Practical handbook of chemical side of oil business, refining, products specifications, conversion tables; by member of Royal Dutch-Shell staff.

Emil Kirschbaum, *Distillation and Rectification,* trans. by M. Wulfinghoff, Brook-

lyn, N.Y., Chemical Publishing Co., 1948, pp. xiii + 426.
Fundamentals and theory of fractional distillation and rectification; design of equipment.

Kenneth Albert Kobe and John J. McKetta, Jr., *Advances in Petroleum Chemistry and Refining,* New York, Interscience Publishers, 1958, Vol. I, pp. xv + 641.
Reports by 21 writers on petroleum economics and future trends, unit operations and design, refining processes, petrochemicals, and mechanical equipment.

James Edwin Latta and Harold L. Kauffman, *Petroleum Distillation and Testing,* Scranton, Penna., International Textbook Co., 1939, pp. 134.
Transportation, storage, and testing of petroleum, and petroleum distillation; text for International Correspondence School.

Allen Norton Leet, *Petroleum Distillation,* New York, Oil, Paint and Drug Publishing Co., 1884, pp. 114.
Extensive review of distillation and refining in United States during first quarter century of oil business, based largely upon author's own contacts and experiences in oil country. Deals with coal-oil stills, early experimental methods, early refining processes and subsequent developments; historical and technical aspects of distillation.

H. L. Lochte and E. R. Littmann, *The Petroleum Acids and Bases,* New York, Chemical Publishing Co., 1955, pp. 368.
Distribution and concentration of acids in petroleum; naphthenic acids, nitrogen compounds in petroleum.

Lummus Company, *Lummus Petroleum Horizons,* New York, the Company, 1947, pp. 62. 2nd Ed.: *Petroleum Horizons,* 1950, pp. 80. 3rd Ed.: *New Horizons,* 1954, pp. 106.
Engineering, construction, and other aspects of building modern petroleum refinery and placing it in operation; flow diagrams.

Alan S. Manne, *Scheduling of Petroleum Refinery Operations,* Cambridge, Mass., Harvard University Press, 1956, pp. xii + 186.
Application and use of mathematical economics in operation of petroleum refineries, with 4 case studies.

Charles Martindale, *Special Master's Report, U.S. v. Standard Oil Co. (Indiana),* U.S. District Court, Northern District of Illinois, Eastern Division, Indianapolis, 1927, pp. 384.
Summary of fact in famous "Patent Club" Suit of 1920's; all major patented cracking processes reviewed, with details of their technical operation and licensing. Concludes with finding that case against defendants be dismissed.

David McKnight, Jr., *A Study of Patents on Petroleum Cracking With Special Reference to Their Present Status,* Austin, University of Texas, 1938, pp. 627.
Authoritative discussion of cracking patents; historical summary and description of Burton, Dubbs, Cross, Holmes Manley, Tube and Tank, and other processes; detailed listing and description of several hundred patents, including application dates and names of assignees. Invaluable sourcebook for student of cracking art.

Edmund James Mills, *Destructive Distillation: A Manualette of the Paraffin, Coal Tar, Rosin Oil, Petroleum, and Kindred Industries,* 1877. 3rd Ed., London, John Van Vorst, 1886, pp. 126. 4th Ed., London, Gurney & Jackson, 1892, pp. 200.
Distillation of coal, bituminous shales, lignite, wood, peat, as well as petroleum.

Harold Moore, *Liquid Fuels for Internal Combustion Engines,* New York, D. Van Nostrand Co., 1918. 2nd Ed. 1920, pp. xv + 206.
Treatise on products derived from petroleum, shale oil, coal and lignite tars, animal and vegetable oils; methyl and ethyl alcohol; examination of liquid fuels, their use in engines of various types.

Alfred William Nash and Donald A. Howes, *The Principles of Motor Fuel Preparation and Application,* London, Chapman & Hall, 1934–1935, 2 vols., pp. xxviii + 1061. Vol. I. 2nd Ed. 1938, pp. xiv + 628.
Vol. I: Deals with production of motor fuels by distillation, cracking, etc.; Vol. II: Deals with properties of motor fuels,

analysis, specifications, and diesel engine fuels. 2nd Ed. valuable for descriptions of early aviation gasoline manufacture.

National Petroleum News, Technical Staff, *Refresher on Wartime Refining Technology,* Cleveland, National Petroleum Publishing Co., 1945, pp. 135.
Summary of most important new refining processes and methods, plant-operating techniques developed during World War II, with lists of plants; list of articles on wartime refinery technology and booklets reprinted from *National Petroleum News.*

W. L. Nelson, *Petroleum Refinery Engineering,* New York, McGraw-Hill Book Co., 1936, pp. viii + 647. 2nd Ed. 1941, pp. ix + 715. 3rd Ed. 1949, pp. xi + 830. 4th Ed. 1958, pp. xiii + 960.
Fundamentals of engineering design and processing, evaluation of crude petroleum for yield of products, cost of refinery equipment and its operation. Appendix lists characteristics and properties of 70 foreign and 90 domestic crudes. By refining editor of *Oil & Gas Journal.*

Charles H. Nielsen, *Distillation in Practice,* New York, Reinhold Publishing Corp., 1956, pp. vi + 133.
Papers on tower design, design of plate columns, techniques of petroleum fractionation, distillation control and operation, vacuum distillation.

Henry Martyn Noel, *Petroleum Refinery Manual,* New York, Reinhold Publishing Corporation, 1959, pp. x + 182.
Describes activities associated with design and construction of modern petroleum refineries, engineering, shop fabrication, field construction, and operations and equipment.

A. L. Nugey, *Oil Refinery Specifications,* Easton, Penna., Chemical Publishing Co., 1924, pp. x + 210.
American practice in design, construction, and renovation of petroleum refineries.

Organisation for European Economic Co-operation, *Oil Refining and Drilling in the U.S.A.,* Paris, the Organisation, 1952, pp. 262.
Report of technical assistance mission to study American oil refining, drilling, and production methods. Refining operations, utilities, laboratories, research and related operational control, drilling equipment and methods, developments in logging, production, oil well servicing, gas production and cycling, offshore drilling and production.

Winona Patton, *United States Petroleum Refining. War and Postwar,* Washington, Government Printing Office (Industrial Series No. 73, U.S. Dept. of Commerce), 1947, pp. vi + 137.
Basic economic data on, and analysis of, refining segment of petroleum industry, including trends in ownership, geographical location, and outlook.

Pennsylvania State College, *Petroleum Refining, Vol. II,* State College, Penna., School of Mineral Industries, 1937, pp. vi + 485. 2nd Ed. 1941, pp. x + 522. Reissued 1948.
Text for second of 3-year extension courses in petroleum refining. History and economics of petroleum industry, known commercial refining processes, products, specifications. *Petroleum Refining, Vol. III,* 1939, pp. x + 419. (Reprinted 1943.) 4th Ed. 1956, pp. 569.
Text for third year of 3-year extension course in petroleum refining. Covers unit processes and basic laws, design and operation, instrumentation, refinery control.

Petroleum Educational Institute, *Simplified Petroleum Chemistry and Physics As Applied to Lubricants and Fuels,* Los Angeles, the Institute, 1923, pp. 122.
Technical text for training of oil company salesmen and sales engineers.

Phillips Petroleum Company, *Hydrofluoric Acid Alkylation,* Bartlesville, Okla., the Company, 1946, pp. vi + 366.
Covers chemistry of HF alkylation, design and operation of units, based on Phillips' experience during World War II.

Clark Shove Robinson, *Elements of Fractional Distillation,* New York, McGraw-Hill Book Co., 1922, pp. ix + 205. 2nd Ed. 1930, pp. xii + 255. 3rd Ed., by C. S. Robinson and Edwin Richard Gilli-

land, 1939, pp. xii + 267. 4th Ed. 1950, pp. ix + 492.
Principles of fractional distillation, modern practice in distillation column design.

Clark Shove Robinson, *The Recovery of Volatile Solvents,* New York, Chemical Catalog Co., 1922, pp. 188.
Principles of solvent recovery, design of equipment, description of apparatus.

Clark Shove Robinson, *The Recovery of Vapors, with Special Reference to Volatile Solvents,* New York, Reinhold Publishing Corp., 1942, pp. 273.
Revision and updating of previous title.

Alexander Nicholas Sachanen, *Conversion of Petroleum. Production of Motor Fuels by Thermal and Catalytic Processes,* New York, Reinhold Publishing Corp., 1940, pp. 413. 2nd Ed. 1948, pp. xii + 602.
Principle and practice of converting petroleum stocks into gasoline and other fuels; thermal and catalytic reactions of hydrocarbons; cracking and hydrogenation; equipment.

Bruce Hornbrook Sage and William Noble Lacey, *Volumetric and Phase Behavior of Hydrocarbons,* Stanford University, Cal., Stanford University Press, 1939, pp. xii + 299.
Standard reference work. Hydrocarbon behavior other than chemical reactions and molecular changes, applicable to petroleum and natural gas production and transportation, and parts of petroleum refining.

Thomas Kilgore Sherwood, *Absorption and Extraction,* New York, McGraw-Hill Book Co., 1937, pp. viii + 278. 2nd Ed. Sherwood and Robert Lamar Pigford, 1952, pp. ix + 478.
Theoretical aspects and underlying theory of design of absorption equipment, performance data on various types of equipment, and basic principles of solvent extraction, including solvent refining of petroleum oils.

Standard Oil Co. (Ind.), *Brief of Defendant Standard Oil Company (Indiana) on the Validity of Patents.* United States of America vs. Standard Oil Company (Indiana) and others. In Equity No 4131, in the District Court of the United States, Northern District of Illinois Eastern Division, (c. 1925), pp. xi + 201.
Important document in famous "Patent Club" Suit of 1920's.

Technical Reference Book to Accompany Brief of Defendant Standard Oil Co. (Indiana) on the Validity of Patents, U.S. v. Standard Oil Co (Indiana) et al., Chicago, n.d. (prob. 1925), pp. 381.
Detailed discussion with diagrams of all important cracking patents then extant, submitted as defense document for edification of Court. Glossary of technical terms. Valuable for students of cracking in 1920's.

John Fleming Strachan, *Practical Inspection of Oil Refinery Equipment,* Anglo-Iranian Oil Co., 1947. 2nd Ed.: *Petroleum Refinery Engineer's Handbook,* New York, Philosophical Library, 1956, pp. xv + 168.
Methods of inspection and recording developed and used in modern oil refineries and latest aspects of plant corrosion and protective measures.

Gifford H. Symonds, *Application of Linear Programming to the Solution of Refinery Problems,* New York, Esso Standard Oil Co., 1954, loose-leaf, var. pag.
Linear programming applied to refinery problems, where many relationships between variables exist, such as blending components into products for maximum profit and optimum crude oil allocation to refineries.

Alexander Norman Tate, *Petroleum and Its Products,* London, John W. Davies, 1863, pp. lv + 116.
Competent early technical work by an analytical chemist employed in oil industry.

Vacuum Oil Company, *Petroleum and Its Commercial Products,* New York, the Company, 1930, pp. 37.
Origin of history of petroleum, oil refining, distillation, dewaxing, filtration, chemical treatment, blending and compounding, classification of refined products and testing.

ustin Federal Wait, *Purification of Petroleum by Treatment with Sodium,* New York, the author, 1932, pp. 34.
Thesis submitted to Columbia University.

. Albert Washer, *Fundamentals of General Refining Practices,* Engineering Extension Service, Texas A. & M. College, 1952, var. pag.
Instructor's guide covering most aspects of refinery processing.

Benjamin Henry Weil and John C. Lane, *Synthetic Petroleum from the Synthine Process,* Brooklyn, N.Y., Chemical Publishing Co., 1948, pp. x + 303. English Edition: *The Technology of the Fischer-Tropsch Process,* London, Constable & Co., 1949, pp. xii + 248.
Deals with synthine, or variations of Fischer-Tropsch, process for manufacture of products, by-products, and derivatives from coal, basic economics, and current work by oil companies and government agencies.

R. B. Werey, *Instrumentation and Automatic Control in the Oil Refining Industry,* Philadelphia, Brown Instrument Co., 1941, pp. ix + 182.
Instrumentation of oil refining industry, with illustrations from current refinery practice.

William Henry Whitmore, *The Results of the Destructive Distillation of Bituminous Substances,* pp. 14; **Frank H. Storer,** *An Essay on the History of the Manufacture of Paraffin Oils,* pp. 20.

Boston, Henry W. Dutton and Son, 1860.
Paper by Whitmore is largely summation of historical notations, together with copy of British patent granted Oct. 7, 1850, to James Young for making paraffin oil from coal and petroleum. Paper by Dr. Storer is review of book by Dr. Antisell (q.v.) on photogenic oils, with which considerable fault is found. Storer presents comprehensive review of distillation of bituminous substances, with footnote references to sources of specific data.

Robert Erastus Wilson, *Pioneers in Oil Cracking,* Chicago, Newcomen Society address, Oct. 29, 1946, pp. 27.
Discussion of work of William M. Burton and Robert E. Humphreys in developing Burton cracking process. Prepared with benefit of Burton's and Humphreys' recollections.

Sydney Young, *Fractional Distillation,* London, Macmillan & Co., 1903, pp. xii + 284.
Process of fractional distillation; devising of new laboratory methods and apparatus; fractionation of American and Galician crude oils.

Sydney Young, *Distillation Principles and Processes,* London, Macmillan & Co., 1922, pp. xiii + 495.
Published in lieu of 2nd edition of *Fractional Distillation;* deals with wartime importance of acetone, toluene, petrol, and glycerine, which involved distillation on a large scale.

XI.

Petroleum Products:
Their Manufacture and Use

A. MOTOR FUELS INCLUDING AVIATION GASOLINE

Frank W. Abrams, *What's In A Gallon of Gasoline?,* New York, American Petroleum Institute, 1953, pp. 7.
Background Information Bulletin. The research and competition behind today's gasoline.

American Society for Testing Materials, *ASTM Manual for Rating Aviation Fuels by Supercharge and Aviation Methods,* Philadelphia, the Society, 1958, pp. xxiii + 310.
Revises methods and provides information on operation and maintenance of knock-testing equipment for aviation fuels.

American Society for Testing Materials, *Petroleum Products as Related to Automotive Equipment,* Philadelphia, the Society, 1948, pp. 52.
Papers from technical meeting.

American Society for Testing Materials, *Symposium on Tractor Fuels,* Philadelphia, the Society, 1948, pp. 37.
Five papers on fuel requirements of tractors, standardization of tractor fuels, clarification of state tax regulations, specifications.

American Society for Testing Materials, *Symposium on Vapor Phase Oxidation of Gasoline,* Philadelphia, the Society, 1957, pp. 68.
Four papers on gasoline oxidation in automotive fuel induction systems.

Edgar Lee Barger, *Tractor Fuels,* Manhattan, Kan., Kansas State College, 1939, pp. 76.
Selection and use of tractor fuels, including fuel tests and their significance, fuel classification and specifications, brake and plowing tests.

Thomas Alvin Boyd, *Gasoline: What Everyone Should Know About It,* New York, Frederick A. Stokes Co., 1925, pp. xii + 211.
"Romantic story of petroleum and its valuable products, of which gasoline is first, to the automobile driving public."

George Granger Brown, *The Relation of Motor Fuel Characteristics to Engine Performance,* Ann Arbor, Mich., University of Michigan, 1927, pp. 129.
Volatility and anti-knock properties of motor fuels, including engine and laboratory tests.

George Granger Brown, *The Volatility of Motor Fuels,* Ann Arbor, Mich., University of Michigan, 1930, pp. vii + 299.
Relationships between volatility of motor and aviation fuels, ease of starting, atmospheric temperature, acceleration, vapor pressure, vapor lock.

George Arthur Burrell, *Gasoline and How to Use It,* Boston, Oil Statistical Society, 1916, pp. 281.
Handbook for gasoline users, covering hazards of handling, proper methods of use for automotive fuel, domestic and

industrial applications, manufacture of gasoline, its analysis and testing.

arleton Ellis and Joseph V. Meigs, *Gasoline and Other Motor Fuels,* New York, D. Van Nostrand Co., 1921, pp. xix + 709.
Outstanding treatise on gasoline, covering testing, refinery practices and methods, distillation, cracking and other processes, natural gasoline, substitute fuels. Mr. Ellis was leading chemist of the day and inventor of cracking process.

thyl Corporation, *A New Concept of Gasoline Progress,* New York, American Petroleum Institute, 1958, pages unnumbered.
Background Information Bulletin. Presents new yardstick for measuring value of modern gasoline. Reprint from *Ethyl News.*

thyl Corporation, *Aviation Fuels and Their Effects on Engine Performance,* New York, the Company, 1951, pp. 145. 2nd Ed.
Properties of aviation fuel, their effects on engine performance; effects of engine design and operating conditions on fuel behavior; turbine (jet) fuels.

thyl Corporation, *Collected Technical Papers of the Ethyl Corporation Research Laboratories,* annually 1950–1958.
Papers presented before technical societies by members of Research and Engineering Department of Ethyl Corporation, primarily on qualities and characteristics, manufacture, and performance of motor fuels.

thyl Corporation, *Tetraethyl Lead: Its Effectiveness in Today's Fuels and Engines,* New York, the Company, 1951, pp. 55.
Changes from 1923 to 1951 in composition and characteristics of motor gasoline and in automobile engines; evaluation of anti-knock quality; advances in octane numbers; contribution of tetraethyl lead to fuel performance.

thyl Corporation, *Six Lectures on the Basic Combustion Process,* Detroit, the Company, 1954, pp. ix + 155.
Collection of lectures presented in fall

of 1952 by group of foreign scientists dealing with flame speed and propagation, carbon formation, hydrocarbon combustion; chemical and physical studies of engine knock.

Ethyl Corporation, *The Story of Gasoline,* New York, the Company, 1957, pp. 87.
Physical and chemical characteristics of petroleum; manufacture of gasoline, including distillation, cracking, reforming; combustion and detonation; testing, anti-knock quality.

Ethyl Corporation, *Annual Review of Gasoline Quality,* New York, the Corporation, 1956, pp. 47. Yearly editions thereafter.
Comprehensive review of gasoline quality based on samples obtained at service stations in United States, at refineries in Canada, and comparable information on gasoline quality in 22 other principal countries, with trend charts reviewing gasoline quality trends over past 25 years. Octane number of premium and regular grade gasoline by months for principal cities, hydrocarbon analyses for selected cities, vapor pressure, gum and sulfur content, etc.

Augustus H. Gill, *Automobile Gasoline; Its Dangers and Tests,* Philadelphia, J. B. Lippincott Co., 1923, pp. 54.
Handbook dealing with gasolines and their manufacture, dangers, tests, and substitutes.

Arthur Hugh Goldingham, *The Design and Construction of Oil Engines,* London, E. & F. N. Spon, 1900, 1st Ed. 2nd Ed. 1904, pp. xviii + 255. 3rd Ed. New York, Spon & Chamberlain, 1910, pp. xx + 260.
British and American kerosene and distillate engines and their operation on American and Russian crude oils.

Frederick Grover, *A Practical Treatise on Modern Gas and Oil Engines,* Manchester, Eng., Technical Publishing Co., Ltd., 1897, pp. vi + 256. 3rd Ed. 1902, pp. vi + 372. 5th Ed. 1909, pp. 373.
Gas and oil engines, properties of appropriate fuels.

Wilfred Emil Guttentag, *Petrol and Petroleum Spirits,* London, Edward Arnold, 1918, pp. xi + 135.

Manufacture, treatment, and testing of gasoline; general background information on oil business.

S. D. Heron, *Development of Aviation Fuels,* (Part II of two-part volume, *Development of Aircraft Engines and Fuels,* by Robert Schlaifer and S. D. Heron), Boston, Harvard University Graduate School of Business Administration, 1950, pp. xviii + 754.
Authoritative history of aviation gasoline development from the "front-row" seat of a fuel technologist whose career embraced two World Wars, the Twenties, and years following 1945 in military aviation both in Britain and America as well as with private firms in both countries. Very full coverage of military aviation fuel prior to and during World War II.

Wilfred Hermann Hoffert and G. Claxton, *Motor Benzole: Its Production and Use,* London, National Benzole Association, 1931, pp. xxi + 689. 2nd Ed. 1938, pp. xxv + 933.
Techniques of extracting benzene from coke-oven gases and adding it to motor fuel to improve performance characteristics, a practice formerly very common in England.

Institution of Petroleum Technologists, *Report of the Empire Motor Fuels Committee,* London, the Institution, 1924, pp. vii + 352.
Theoretical work on suitability of various fuels for internal combustion engines, influence of various fuels on engine performance, data on detonation, etc.

Eugene Hendricks Leslie, *Motor Fuels: Their Production and Technology,* New York, Chemical Catalog Co., 1923, pp. 681.
Handbook of motor fuel technology.

Lion Oil Company, *You Can't Buy Gas Any More,* New York, American Petroleum Institute, 1955, pp. 11.
Background Information Bulletin. Reprinted from *Lion Oil News.*
Composition of modern gasoline.

H. G. Mendelson, *Gasoline Facts,* Brad-

ford, Penna., National Tank Auditing Service, 1926, pp. 163.
Compendium of useful information on gasoline, supply of oil, refining, testing, distribution, economics, relations with government, history of petroleum.

Natural Gasoline Association of America, *Fuels and Fuel Systems,* Tulsa, the Association, 1955, pp. 108.
Papers by technologists of Phillips Petroleum Co. on motor fuel characteristics and problems of vapor lock in fuel systems.

Petroleum Educational Institute, *Fundamentals and Application of Fuels and Lubricants,* Los Angeles, the Institute, 1948, 2 parts, var. pag.
Instruction course textbook on production of petroleum, manufacture, utilization, and testing of fuels and lubricants.

Milosh Nicholas Popovich and Carl Hering, *Fuels and Lubricants,* New York, John Wiley & Sons, Inc., 1959, pp. vi + 312.
Boiler, internal-combustion-engine, and jet-engine fuels; properties of fuels and lubricants; synthetic lubricating oils and correlation between properties of fuels and lubricants and performance in engine or machine.

John Lewis Thomas, *Petroleum Law,* London, Police Review Publishing Co., 1950, pp. 84. 2nd Ed. 1951, pp. 84.
Laws and regulations relating to storage and conveyance of petroleum spirit and other highly inflammable substances.

Jacob Vanderdoes, Lacey Harvey Morrison, and Charles Thomas Baker, *Combustion Engine Fuels and Heat,* Scranton, Penna., International Textbook Co., 1935, pp. 177.
Correspondence school texts covering heat, combustion and fuels, and principles of internal combustion engines.

Matthew Van Winkle, *Aviation Gasoline Manufacture,* New York, McGraw-Hill Book Co., 1944, pp. ix + 275.
History and development of aviation fuel, specifications, testing, production of base stocks, manufacture of high anti-knock hydrocarbons, production of finished aviation gasoline.

B. KEROSENE

(See also "Refining of Petroleum" for other works on Kerosene)

Charles Frederick Chandler, *Report on the Quality of the Kerosene Oil Sold in the Metropolitan District,* (Extract from the 4th Annual Report of Metropolitan Board of Health), New York, D. Appleton & Co., 1870, pp. 23.
Reports on "dangerous kerosene," listing 21 oils found safe for sale and 280 found unsafe, with additional list of 335 oils reported as "highly dangerous."

Charles Frederick Chandler, *Report on Petroleum As An Illuminator,* (Extract from Annual Report of the Board of Health of the City of New York for 1870), New York, New York Printing Co., 1871, pp. 110.
Reviews oil refining at close of first decade of oil industry, manufacture of illuminating oils, testing; compilation of laws and ordinances pertaining to safety of such oils. Relates allegations pertaining to dangerous kerosene.

William Sydney Gibbons, *Kerosene Oil: What It is; With Causes and Prevention of Accidents In Its Use,* Melbourne, F. Baillière, 1862, pp. 25.
Brief history of manufacture of oils from bituminous substances, oil discoveries in America, their effect on trade, author's analyses of sample oils sold in Melbourne.

Pethuel Millspaugh, *Kerosene Accidents: How to Prevent Them,* New York, McDonald, Dillont & Co., 1874, pp. iv + 35.
Brief treatise on illuminating oils and other burning fluids, pointing to vapor as "true cause of danger."

William H. Wahl, *Report on the Light Petroleum Oils,* New York, National Board of Fire Underwriters, 1873, pp. 29.
Conflagrations from use of oil in homes and methods of prevention.

C. FUEL AND HEATING OILS

Julius Walker Adams, *Petroleum as Fuel,* New York, the author, 1865, pp. 7.
Report to trustees of Petroleum Light Company on daily experiments, begun May, 1865, on use of crude petroleum as fuel under marine boiler.

American Society for Testing Materials, *Forum on Diesel Fuel Oils,* Philadelphia, the Society, 1947, pp. v + 38.
Standardization and research work on diesel fuels, with 7 papers on military needs, diesel fuel in railroad and bus operation, and distillate fuel-oil production.

American Society for Testing Materials, *Symposium on Industrial Fuels,* Philadelphia, the Society, 1936, pp. iii + 70.
Papers on boiler fuel problems.

American Society for Testing Materials, *Symposium on Diesel Fuels,* Philadelphia, the Society, 1954, pp. 50.

Eight papers on diesel fuel supply and demand outlook, problems of procurement and use, diesel fuel specifications.

American Society of Mechanical Engineers, *Latest Technology in Oil and Gas Power,* New York, the Society, 1958, var. pag.
Twenty-six papers on Diesel engine development, fuels, and various aspects of lubrication, lubricating oils and greases.

American Society of Mechanical Engineers, *Proceedings of the 1st and 2nd Oil Power Conferences and the 1st National Meeting of the Oil and Gas Power Division,* State College, Penna., Pennsylvania State College, 1929, pp. 216. *3rd Conference,* 1929, pp. 208. *4th Conference,* 1930, pp. 307. *5th Conference,* 1932, pp. 105. *6th Conference,* 1933, pp. 171. *7th Conference,* 1933, pp. 173. *8th Conference,* 1934, pp. 143.

Papers devoted mainly to fuel and diesel oils and their combustion.

American Society of Mechanical Engineers, *Proceedings, 27th Conference of the Oil and Gas Power Division,* New York, the Society, 1955, var. pag.
Diesel engines, gas turbines and their fuels; preparation of residual fuel for motive power; additives for diesel fuels, etc.

American Society of Mechanical Engineers, *Diesel Fuel Oils: Production, Characteristics, and Combustion,* New York, the Society, 1948, pp. 128.
Lectures on diesel oil.

George William Andrew, *Fuel,* London, Ernest Benn, 1924, pp. 208.
Section III: *Fuel-Oils,* by Arthur W. Eastlake, covers all petroleum products used for production of heat and power; production, imports, exports, and consumption of fuel oils in British Empire.

Stephen Osgood Andros, *Fuel Oil in Industry,* Chicago, Shaw Publishing Co., 1920, pp. 274. 2nd Ed. Fort Wayne, Indiana, Petroleum Extension University, 1922, pp. 198.
Principles of fuel oil combustion, physical and chemical properties of fuel oil, comparisons with coal, colloidal fuel, distribution, storage, handling, furnaces, burners, discussion of uses.

Anglo-Mexican Petroleum Products Co., Ltd., *Mexican Fuel Oil,* London, the Company, 1914, pp. viii + 150. 2nd Ed. 1921, pp. xv + 210.
Published by company (subsidiary of Mexican Eagle) in promotion of oil fuel for marine, railway, power generation, and heating uses. Equipment described and illustrated; tables.

Associated Factory Mutual Fire Insurance Companies, *Fuel Oil: Industrial Storage and Use,* Boston, the Company, 1935, pp. v + 82.
Characteristics of fuel oils; indoor and outdoor storage; descriptions of tanks, fittings; fire protection; oil distribution; piping, valves, oil burners.

Raymond Foss Bacon and William Allen Hamor, *American Fuels,* New York,

McGraw-Hill Book Co., 1922, 2 vols pp. 1257.
Vol. I: Devoted to solid fuels, the gasification and distillation.
Vol. II: Deals with fuel oil, natura gas, other gases, stokers, finely divide fuel, conservation, and economics.

William Newton Best, *The Science of Burr ing Liquid Fuel,* New York, the autho 1913, pp. 159. 2nd Ed., *Burning Liqui Fuel,* New York, U.P.C. Book Co 1922, pp. 341.
"A practical book for practical mer covering origin, production, and analy sis of liquid fuel, atomization, o systems, refractory material, equipmen and combustion practices.

Clayton O. Billow, *Application of Fuel O to Steam Generators,* Chicago, Electr cal Engineering Magazine, 1894, pp. 2
Applications of oil fuel for steam generation, with drawings of variou oil-fired furnaces.

William Henry Booth, *Liquid Fuel and I Combustion,* London, Archibald Co stable & Co., 1903, pp. xx + 410. 2n Ed., *Liquid Fuel and Its Apparatu* New York, E. P. Dutton & Co., 191 pp. 308. 3rd Ed. New York, E. P. Du ton & Co., 1922, pp. 308.
Principle and practice of burning c liquid fuel in steam raising and in sta tionary engines to drive power genera tors.

Edward Cyril Bowden-Smith, *Oil Firin for Kitchen Ranges and Steam Boiler* London, Archibald Constable & Co 1920, pp. ix + 102.
Deals with burning of heavy residues c fuel oil for culinary purposes and unde steam boilers; oil-burning installation in Cairo, Egypt.

J. S. S. Brame, *Fuel: Solid, Liquid, an Gaseous,* London, Edward Arnold 1914. 2nd Ed. 1917. 3rd Ed. 1924. 4t Ed. (with J. G. King) 1935. 5th Ed (rewritten by King) 1955, pp. xii + 551.
Comprehensive review of all commo fuels; oil for burning, motor fuels, kero sene for aviation turbines; production refining, properties; shale oils; alcohol fuel mixtures; combustion characteris tics.

dward Butler, *Oil Fuel: Its Supply, Composition, and Application,* London, Charles Griffin & Co., 1921, pp. xvi + 319.
Fourth edition of work originally begun by Sidney North (q.v.). Characteristics and analysis of fuel oils, methods of combustion, types of burners, application of oil fuel to marine, locomotive, vehicular, metallurgical, lighting, and heating purposes.

Domestic Engineering Co., *Oil Burner Heating,* Chicago, the Company, 1934, pp. viii + 174.
Specific information on costs, oil analyses, installations, testing, and other operational data related to oil burner heating.

. B. Dunn, *Industrial Uses of Fuel Oil,* San Francisco, Technical Publishing Co., 1916, pp. 235.
Fuel oil in naval, domestic, and gas-making applications; descriptions of burners, oil storage, pumping, tests.

Esso Marketers, *Marine Fuel Oils and Lubricants,* New York, the Company, 1936, pp. 141.
Esso bunkering installations throughout world; tables; product descriptions.

Arthur F. Evans, *The History of the Oil Engine, A Review in Detail,* 1680–1930, London, Sampson Low, Marston & Co., 1932, pp. xviii + 318.
Summary of development of internal combustion engine and direct-injection oil engine.

Percival Elliott Fansler, *House Heating with Oil Fuel,* New York, *Heating & Ventilating Magazine,* 1925, 2nd Ed. 3rd Ed. 1927, pp. xii + 354.
Liquid fuels for home heating; theory and practice of combustion; oil burners and accessories.

James Sandford Gander, *Oil Fuel Burning At Sea and On Land,* Glasgow, James Munro & Co., 1923, pp. xi + 356.
Installation and maintenance of principal British and American oil-burning systems and auxiliaries; instructions on use of oil for fuel at sea and in land installations.

Alfred H. Gibbings, *Oil Fuel Equipment for Locomotives and Principles of Ap-*

plication, New York, D. Van Nostrand Co., 1915, pp. x + 125.
Methods of burning fuel oil, types of oil-burning apparatus, tests, and auxiliary appliances.

E. M. Goodger, *Petroleum and Performance in Internal-Combustion Engineering,* London, Butterworth Scientific Publications, 1953, pp. xiii + 295.
Petroleum-based fuels from gasoline to fuel oil. Describes techniques employed in producing and refining petroleum; significant properties related to types of engines; testing.

Frank Duncan Graham, *Audel's Oil Burner Guide,* New York, Theo. Audel & Co., 1946, pp. 384. 2nd Ed. 1947, pp. 384. 3rd Ed. 1955, pp. 416. 4th Ed. 1958, pp. 432.
Theory, construction, installation, operation, testing, servicing, and repair of all types of burners; fuel oils and their combustion.

Ernest Greenwood, *Prometheus, U.S.A.,* New York, Harper & Bros., 1929, pp. xvi + 213.
Legends and history of fire, chapters on wood, coal, gas, petroleum; history, future prospects, oil heating, development of house heating, competition between fuels.

John Griswold, *Fuels, Combustion and Furnaces,* New York, McGraw-Hill Book Co., 1946, pp. vii + 496.
Chemical engineering text in field of fuel technology, combustion mechanism, and furnace practice.

A. T. Henly, *Oil Fuel Applications,* London, Crosby Lockwood & Sons, 1956, pp. ix + 250.
Problems encountered in application of liquid fuels; standards for fuel oils and oil-firing installations; oil storage; oil pipe lines; heating oil for combustion and flow; oil-burning systems, equipment, instruments; diesel power; heating plants.

James Dodds Henry, *Oil Fuel and The Empire,* London, Bradbury, Agnew & Co., 1908, pp. xvi + 286.
Imperial and naval aspects of fuel oil, history of oil-burning experience in United States, France, and Italy; safety

aspects of naval use; oil burner development; work of Royal Commission on Coal Supplies.

E. A. Brayley Hodgetts, *Liquid Fuel for Mechanical and Industrial Purposes,* London, E. & F. N. Spon, 1890, pp. viii + 134.
History of oil burning; oil fuel for steam raising; types of burners; use as locomotive and naval fuel.

Marshall Monroe Kirkman, *How Oil Is Used for Fuel on Locomotives,* New York and Chicago, World Railway Publishing Co., 1903, pp. 71.
Oil used as locomotive fuel by Southern Pacific and Santa Fe railroads; descriptions of tankage, burners, other equipment; firing and operating rules.

Han A. Kunitz, *Oil Heating Handbook,* Philadelphia, J. B. Lippincott Co., 1936, pp. viii + 456. 2nd Ed. 1937, pp. x + 464. 3rd Ed. 1947, pp. x + 464.
Manual of theoretical and practical; manufacture and installation, and use of oil burners in moderate size heaters; petroleum fuels; testing; combustion.

John Lamb, *Petroleum and Its Combustion in Diesel Engines,* London, Charles Griffin & Co., 1955, pp. viii + 264.
History of compression-ignition engine; characteristics of petroleum fuels; combustion, atomization and ignition of residual fuels; low-speed and high-speed engines.

Claude C. Levin, *The Blue Book of Oil Burning and Burners,* New York, Ocean Publishing Co., 1920, pp. 114.
Handbook for operators of oil burners.

Vivian Byam Lewes, *Liquid and Gaseous Fuels and the Part They Play in Modern Power Production,* London, Archibald Constable & Co., 1907, pp. xiv + 334. 2nd Ed., Revised by J. B. C. Kershaw, 1922, pp. 353.
Covers fuel in liquid and gaseous forms, dealing with combustion, production, properties and use of liquid fuels and their adoption in European navies, and production and use of water and fuel gas.

Raymond Little and Fluvius B. Jones, *Oil and Gas Burning Under Boilers,*

Scranton, Penna., International Text book Co., 1933, pp. v + 70.
Correspondence school text on oil-burning methods.

Herbert Victor Mitchell, *Fuel Oils and Their Applications,* London, Sir Isaac Pitman & Sons, 1924, pp. xii + 171.
Treatise on fuel oils for power and heating applications.

Harold Moore, *Liquid Fuels: Their Manufacture, Properties, Utilization, and Analysis,* London, Technical Press 1935, pp. viii + 263.
Chemistry and preparation of liquid fuels from petroleum, oil shale, etc relation between chemical and physical properties and engine efficiency; fuel for internal and external combustion testing and analytical methods.

Harold Moore, *Liquid Fuels for Internal Combustion Engines,* London, C. Lockwood and Son, 1918, pp. xv + 200. 2nd Ed. 1920, pp. 206.
Practical treatise for engineers.

James Ambrose Moyer, *Oil Fuels and Burners,* New York, McGraw-Hill Book Co., 1937, pp. ix + 375.
Atomization and combustion; burners and equipment—particularly automatic types intended for domestic heating.

National Industrial Conference Board, Inc. *Oil Conservation and Fuel Oil Supply,* New York, the Board, 1930, pp. xiv + 165.
Sources of world energy, world supply and consumption of fuel oil; detailed discussion of fuel oil consumption. Conservation aspect virtually limited to obtaining more gasoline from crude oil through cracking, with less fuel oil.

Sydney H. North, *Oil Fuel. Its Supply Composition, and Application,* London Charles Griffin & Co., 1905, pp. viii + 151. 2nd Ed.: Revised and enlarged by Edward Butler, 1911, pp. xi + 238. 3rd Ed.: by Edward Butler, 1914, pp. xiv + 328. 4th Ed. published under Butler's name (q.v.).
Evolution of burners; combustion problems; economic and mechanical advantages of oil fuel.

dney H. North, *Oil Power*, London, Sir Isaac Pitman & Sons, 1922, pp. ix + 122.
Oil for power generation; supply available to United Kingdom; methods of use; employment in industry, ships, railways, internal combustion engine, heating; storage and distribution.

l Heat Institute of America, *Handbooks*, New York, the Institute.
Frank H. Faust and G. Theodore Kaufman, *Handbook of Oil Burning*, 1951, pp. x + 978.
Floyd Olmstead, *Handbook of Domestic Oil Burning*, 1926, pp. 224.
Harry F. Tapp, *Handbook of Domestic Oil Heating*, 1928, pp. 383.
Harry F. Tapp, *Handbook of Oil Burning*, 1931, pp. 629.
G. Theodore Kaufman, *Basic Service Test: High Pressure Type Burners*, 1945, pp. 216.
Oil burning; combustion principles; atomization; vaporization; types of burners; heating systems; automatic control; installation and maintenance.

enjamin H. Paul, *On Liquid Fuel*, London, E. & F. N. Spon, 1868, pp. 31.
Liquid fuels for steam vessels, operation and combustion problems. Paper read before Society of Arts, April, 1868.

rnest H. Peabody, *Oil Fuel*, Reprinted from *Transactions* of International Engineering Congress, San Francisco, 1915, pp. 134.
Burners, furnaces, and other apparatus employed in oil burning, testing of fuels. By a pioneer inventor of marine oil-burning equipment.

rnest H. Peabody, *Oil Fuel. A World-Wide Adventure*, New York, American Newcomen Society, 1942, pp. 96.
Reviews history of oil burning and development of oil burners.

Villiam Battle Phillips and Steve Howard Worrell, *The Fuels Used in Texas*, Austin, University of Texas, 1913, pp. x + 287.
Fuels available in Texas; discussion of natural gas and crude petroleum as fuel.

ortland Cement Association, *Concrete Tanks for Fuel Oil Storage*, Chicago, the Association, n.d., pp. 19.

Concrete tanks for storing fuel oil, with list of 394 plants having them.

Cuthbert Coulson Pounder, *Oil Burning Installations*, London, Emmott & Co., 1924, pp. xiv + 366.
Liquid fuel for steam raising; properties and combustion of liquid fuels; burners, apparatus, auxiliary equipment.

Solomon Ayer Raboy, *A Digest of Law and Cases on Heating Systems and Devices, Etc.*, New York, American Oil Burner Association, 1932, pp. 361.
Reviews principles of law applicable to oil-burning devices and equipment; digest of cases.

Winfield Scott Rogers and Nellie S. Rogers, *Oil Heating the Home*, Montclair, N.J., the author, 1930, pp. 47.
Reports on private investigation of oil burning in home, using different types of burners variously equipped.

H. A. Romp, *Oil Burning*, The Hague, Martinus Nijhoff, 1937, pp. xxiii + 336.
Definitive work on principles of combustion as applied to oil fuels, calculations, charts, tables; detailed history of evolution of oil burner, with individual makes described and illustrated. Prime sourcebook on subject.

Owen Charles Dalhousie Ross, *Air as Fuel; or, Petroleum and Other Mineral Oils Utilized by Carburetting Air and Rendering It Inflammable*, 1874. 2nd Ed. London, E. & F. N. Spon, 1875, pp. xi + 76.
Progress in utilization of liquid fuel; conversion of mineral oils into gas; superiority over coal; applications of carburetted air; petroleum for illuminating oils. 2nd Ed. contains added chapter on practical application of carburetted air.

Owen Charles Dalhousie Ross, *Petroleum and Other Mineral Oils Applied to the Manufacture of Gas*, London, W. Clowes & Sons, 1875, pp. 15.
Making gas from gas-oil.

Paul Frank Schmidt, *Fuel Oil Manual*, New York, Industrial Press, 1951, pp. 160. 2nd Ed. 1958, pp. 168.
Handbook for fuel purchasers.

George Sell, Ed., *Modern Applications of Liquid Fuels*, London, Institute of Fuel

and Institute of Petroleum, 1950, pp. viii + 495.
Nineteen papers on industrial uses of liquid fuel and its place in British economy; fuel oil in steel making, metals, glass and ceramics, gas manufacture, domestic heating.

Shell Petroleum Co., Ltd., *Fuel Oil,* London, the Company, 1946, pp. 159.
Manual of fuel oil specifications, burning principles, equipment. Glossary; conversion tables.

Robert Sibley and Charles Henry Delaney, *Elements of Fuel Oil and Steam Engineering,* San Francisco, Technical Publishing Co., 1918, pp. xiv + 320. 2nd Ed. New York, McGraw-Hill Book Co., 1921, pp. xix + 466.
Power plant operation using oil fuel.

Albert Sommer, *Petroleum As a Source of Power on Ships,* London, General Oil Publishing Co., 1913, pp. 63.
Written during period when British and American Navies were introducing use of oil as fuel under boilers; advocates direct combustion of liquid fuel in cylinders of internal combustion or Diesel engines. Characteristics of various oils and their possible applications in internal combustion engines.

John William Major Sothern, *Oil Fuel Burning in Marine Practice,* Glasgow, James Munro & Co., 1920, pp. xii + 186.
Systems of oil burning for marine purposes; properties and combustion of fuel oil; tests; notes on oil fuel burning.

Standard Oil Company (New Jersey), *Fuel Oil Installations for Industrial, Railways, and Marine Uses,* New York, the Company, 1919, pp. 112.
Production, supply, and properties of fuel oil; advantages in use; burners and methods of atomization; equipment; oil-burning steam plants; tests and tables.

Kalman Steiner, *Oil Burners,* New York, McGraw-Hill Book Co., 1937, pp. xvi + 436. 2nd Ed. 1950, pp. xx + 502.
Properties of fuel oils; combustion; oil-burner design; types of domestic, commercial, and industrial burners; electric motors and controls; ignition; pumps; storage; service.

Kalman Steiner and Fred Ravnsbeck, *Oil Burner Service Manual,* New York, McGraw-Hill Book Co., 1942, pp. ix + 365.
Handbook for training.

Chester K. Sterrett, *Fuel Oil Requirements of Oregon and Southern Washington,* Corvallis, Ore., Oregon State College, 1950, pp. 20.
Circular on fuel requirements of manufacturing plants, fuels consumed, and water movements of fuel oil into area.

Rufus Tracy Strohm, *Oil Fuel for Steam Boilers,* New York, McGraw-Hill Book Co., 1914, pp. x + 145.
Oil as fuel in stationary steam boilers; types of burners; arrangement of furnaces, accessories; storage.

The Texas Company, *Oil-Fuel,* New York, the Company, 1912, pp. 149.
Advantages of oil; types of heaters, furnaces, and burners.

Benjamin Howarth Thwaite, *Liquid Fuel, Its Advantages for Firing Steam Generators,* London, E. & F. N. Spon, 1887, pp. 15.
Burning oil under boilers.

Edgar Pierce Trask, *Oil Burning Under Marine Boilers,* Scranton, Penna., International Textbook Co., 1942, pp. 96.
Correspondence school text on fuel oil; oil-burning methods, equipment.

United States Navy, *Report of the U.S. Naval "Liquid Fuel" Board of Test Conducted on the Hohenstein Water Tube Boiler, made under Direction of Rear Admiral George W. Melville,* Washington, Government Printing Office, 1904, pp. v + 450.
Fuel oil tests made aboard merchant and naval vessels with California and Texas oils and various types of burners.

J. H. Vosskuehler, *Burning Crude Oil, Handbook for Architects and Heating Engineers,* Oakland, Cal., American Heat & Power Co., 1914, pp. 102.
Unrefined heavy crude oil as fuel, analyses of crude oils.

H. C. Wilson, *Liquid Fuel and How to Burn It,* London, Institute of Marine Engineers, 1896, pp. 16.

Paper on liquid fuel and conditions affecting combustion.

Edwin Chester Wright and Herbert Frank Percy Purday, *Diesel Engine Fuels and Lubricants,* London, Archibald Constable & Co., 1950, pp. viii + 152.
Diesel fuels and lubricants, physical properties, methods of analysis, testing.

D. LUBRICATING OILS AND GREASES, WAXES

Edward Goodrich Acheson, *Conservation,* Port Huron, Mich., Acheson Oildag Co., 1919, pp. 56.
Lubrication and potential fuel and power savings from selection and use of lubricant "of the lowest viscosity capable of carrying the load thrown on it." Reprinted from series in *The Forum,* 1919.

American Society for Testing Materials, *Symposium on Motor Lubricants,* Philadelphia, the Society, 1933, pp. 121.
Seven papers on requirements and performance of lubricating oils for motor car and aircraft engines.

American Society for Testing Materials, *Symposium on High Additive Content Oils,* Philadelphia, the Society, 1950, pp. 63.
Four papers on high-additive lubricating oils, special heavy-duty oils, possible future military engine oils.

American Society for Testing Materials, *Symposium on Turbine Oils,* Philadelphia, the Society, 1950, pp. 52.
Four papers dealing with lubrication of turbine equipment.

American Society for Testing Materials, *Symposium on Steam Turbine Oils,* Philadelphia, the Society, 1957, pp. 106.
Eight papers dealing with evaluation and performance of turbine oils, antiwear requirements, rust-preventive additives.

American Society for Testing Materials, *Symposium on Industrial Gear Lubricants,* Philadelphia, the Society, 1949, pp. 19.
Three papers on heavy-duty gear oils and gear lubricants.

Leonard Archbutt and Richard Mountford Deeley, *Lubrication and Lubricants,* London, Charles Griffin & Co., 1900, pp. xxiv + 451. 2nd Ed. 1907, 3rd Ed. 1912. 4th Ed. 1920, 5th Ed. 1922, pp. xxxv + 599.
Friction, viscosity of liquids, lubrication from theoretical viewpoint; nature, properties, and testing of lubricants; practical application of lubricants to machinery.

Arthur Alan Ashworth, *Analysis of Oil for the Production of Lubricants,* London, Ernest Benn, 1933, pp. 63.
Determination of maximum yield of lubricants obtainable from various raw stocks, design of apparatus, etc.

E. L. H. Bastian, *Metalworking Lubricants, Their Selection, Application, and Maintenance,* New York, McGraw-Hill Book Co., 1951, pp. vii + 357.
Complete textbook of petroleum materials used in metalworking—cutting fluids, coating, drawing and rolling oils; machine tool press, and forge lubricants; application, tests, specifications, quality control.

John Rome Battle, *Lubricating Engineer's Handbook,* Philadelphia, J. B. Lippincott Co., 1916, pp. 333.
Historical notes on lubrication, theory, manufacture and compounding of lubricating oils and greases, description of types, tests, applications, costs, specifications.

John Rome Battle, *The Handbook of Industrial Oil Engineering,* Philadelphia, J. B. Lippincott Co., 1920. 2nd Ed. 1923, pp. viii + 1141. 3rd Ed. 1926.
General review of oil industry, refining, testing, manufacture of lubricants; specific discussion of applications and uses.

Harry Bennett, *Commercial Waxes,* Brooklyn, N.Y., Chemical Publishing Co., 1944, pp. xvii + 583. 2nd Ed. 1956, pp. 688.
Natural, manufactured, and synthetic waxes; paraffin and other petroleum de-

rivatives; physical properties, composition, technology, uses, wax formulary, glossary.

Arnold Aaron Bondi, *Physical Chemistry of Lubricating Oils,* New York, Reinhold Publishing Co., 1951, pp. vii + 380.
Physical properties of liquid lubricants, flow properties of liquids, surface phenomena, optical and electrical properties, hydrocarbon analysis of lubricating oils, etc.

C. J. Boner, *Manufacture and Application of Lubricating Greases,* New York, Reinhold Publishing Co., 1954, pp. v + 977.
Comprehensive treatise on lubricating greases, processing, equipment, theory of structure and application of lubricating greases; trends.

Arthur Warner Burwell, *Oiliness: Importance of Oiliness in Lubricating Oils and How It May be Improved,* Niagara Falls, N.Y., Alex Chemical Corp., 1934, 2nd Ed. 1935, pp. iv + 128. 3rd Ed. 1942, pp. vi + 92.
Oiliness defined as "that property which an oil must possess to a sufficient degree to enable the oil to lubricate adequately under all conditions imposed by the machine for which the oil is designed."

James Ira Clower, *Lubricants and Lubrication,* New York, McGraw-Hill Book Co., 1939, pp. viii + 464.
General principles and fundamentals of lubricants and lubrication; application to specific types of machinery.

Claude Ettele, *Lubricating Oil Salesman's Primer,* New York, Chemical Publishing Co., 1926, pp. 118. 2nd and 3rd Ed. n.d.
Theories of friction and lubrication; manufacture of lubricating oils; tests; lubrication of machinery and prime movers.

Carl W. Georgi, *Motor Oils and Engine Lubrication,* New York, Reinhold Publishing Corp., 1950, pp. xii + 514.
Manufacture, chemical and physical properties, testing and performance characteristics of motor oils; application to internal combustion engines; reclaiming, refining.

George Henry Hurst, *Lubricating Oils, Fats and Greases,* London, Scott, Greenwood

& Son, 1896, pp. 313. 2nd Ed. 1902, p viii + 317. 3rd Ed. 1911, pp. 400. 4 Ed. (Revised and enlarged by Herbe Birtwhistle Stocks) 1925, pp. xi + 41 Oils used for lubricating machiner testing and adulteration of oils, lubr cating greases; lubrication.

Institute of Petroleum, *Symposium on L brication,* London, the Institute, 195 pp. 46.
Six papers on lubrication.

Vladimir Anatole Kalichevsky, *Moder Methods of Refining Lubricating Oil* New York, Reinhold Publishing Corp 1938, pp. 235.
Methods of refining; classification processes.

Edwin Neal Klemgard, *Lubricating Grease* New York, Chemical Catalog Co., 192 pp. 198.
Covers manufacture of cup, soda bas lead base, and other greases; compoun ing oils; trend of grease research.

Edwin Neal Klemgard, *Lubricating Grease Their Manufacture and Use,* New Yor Chemical Catalog Co., 1937, pp. 873.
Enlargement and revision of earlier titl above. Chemical and physical chara teristics and specifications of greas making material; design and manage ment of grease plants; fundament theories underlying manufacture greases; costs; individual greases separately discussed.

Luther Bynum Lockhart, *American Lubr cants From the Standpoint of the Cor sumer,* Easton, Penna., Chemical Pub lishing Co., 1918, pp. ix + 236. 2nd Ec 1920, pp. xi + 341. 3rd Ed. 1927, pp. + 408.
Refining, lubrication, physical and chem ical methods of testing; specification and testing of other oils. Prepared a aid to purchaser of lubricants.

David McKnight, Jr., and Robert Elm Price, *A Study of Motor Oils Sold i Texas and Review of Motor Oil Spec fications,* Austin, University of Texas 1936, pp. 43.
Study of all motor oils sold in Austi and Houston, Texas, 1935–36, with de scription of laboratory procedure, dis cussion of significance and interrelation of tests, comments.

rich Meyer, *White Mineral Oil and Petrolatum,* Brooklyn, N.Y., Chemical Publishing Co., 1950, pp. vi + 135.
Chemical and physical characteristics and uses of white mineral oil and petrolatum; technical aspects, applications, testing, shipping, handling.

Alfred William Nash and Arthur Riley Brown, *The Principles and Practice of Lubrication,* London, Chapman & Hall, 1929, pp. xi + 315. 2nd Ed. 1937, pp. xi + 345.
Chemistry of lubricants; chemical and physical tests for lubricating oils.

Arthur Edwin Norton, *Lubrication,* New York, McGraw-Hill Book Co., 1942, pp. xi + 244.
Lubrication and properties of lubricants; various types of bearings.

Boyd I. Redwood, *Lubricants, Oils and Greases,* London, E. & F. N. Spon, 1897, pp. xi + 54.
Properties and manufacture of lubricants and greases; theory and general requirements governing manufacture.

Walter Schenker, *Fuel and Lubricating Oils for Diesel Engines,* New York, D. Van Nostrand Co., 1922, pp. xii + 114. (Published originally in German, 1919.)
Origin, composition, and preparation of Diesel engine fuels, lubricating oils; testing of fuel and lubricants.

Shell Oil Company, *Panorama of Lubrication,* New York, the Company, 1953, pp. xx + 352.

Collection of booklets originally published separately 1944–52 under same title. Designed to explain to nontechnical readers history and fundamentals of friction and lubrication; bearings; Diesel, automotive, aviation, steam engine, and turbine lubrication; tests and specifications; hydraulic oils; greases.

Louis Simpson, *The Manual of Lubrication,* New York, Oil, Paint, and Drug Publishing Co., 1887, pp. xiv + 111.
Variety and characteristics of lubricating oils; adulterations and tests; use in locomotives and steamships.

Thomas Christian Thomsen, *The Practice of Lubrication,* New York, McGraw-Hill Book Co., 1920, pp. 607. 2nd Ed. 1926, pp. 616, 3rd Ed. 1937, pp. xiv + 638.
Manufacture of lubricating oils and greases; testing; applications.

Albin Henry Warth, *The Chemistry and Technology of Waxes,* New York, Reinhold Publishing Corp., 1947, pp. viii + 519. 2nd Ed. 1956, pp. vii + 940.
Handbook of wax industry; wax technology and wax uses in industry; solvent and other processes for dewaxing oils; treating, properties, and characteristics.

Hilbert Harry Zuidema, *The Performance of Lubricating Oils,* New York, Reinhold Publishing Corp., 1952, pp. vi + 179. 2nd Ed. 1959, pp. 205.
Performance characteristics of lubricating oils in variety of applications and conditions.

E. ASPHALTS

Herbert Abraham, *Asphalts and Allied Substances,* New York, D. Van Nostrand Co., 1918, pp. xxv + 606. 2nd Ed. 1920, pp. xxv + 608. 3rd Ed. 1929, pp. xviii + 891. 4th Ed. 1938, pp. xxiv + 1491. 5th Ed. 2 vols. 1945, pp. xxvi + 2142.
Standard work on asphalt, of rare scholarship and thoroughness. Historical review of asphalt in ancient, medieval, and modern times, chemistry of bituminous substances, geology and occurrence of bitumens, production, methods of processing, native asphalts, tars, pitches, and petroleum asphalt, products and

their uses, applications, and testing. Vol. I of 5th Ed. covers raw materials and manufactured products. Vol. II deals with methods of testing. Extensive bibliography; comprehensive list of patents in asphalt field; detailed index.

Asphalt Association, *Asphalt: Pocket Reference for Engineers,* New York, the Association, 1923, pp. 71. (Subsequent editions without material change published at intervals, last appearing 1929.)
Engineer's handbook.

Asphalt Institute, *Asphalt Handbook,* New York, the Institute, 1947, pp. 304.

Facts about asphalt, terms used, tests and specifications, construction of pavements, other applications of asphalts and tars.

Arthur Beckwith, *Report on Asphalt and Bitumen, as Applied to Construction,* (Paris Universal Exposition, Reports of the United States Commissioners), Washington, Government Printing Office, 1868, pp. 31.

History and description of use of asphalt and bitumen in construction of roads and streets; asphalt products in Exhibition of 1867.

Thomas Hugh Boorman, *Asphalts: Their Sources and Utilizations,* New York, William T. Comstock Co., 1908, pp. 168. 2nd Ed. 1914, pp. 191.

Discovery and early uses of asphalt deposits; development of industry; applications to road construction, surface roofing, waterproofing; rock asphalts.

Arthur Danby, *Natural Rock Asphalts and Bitumens,* London, Archibald Constable & Co., 1913, pp. viii + 244.

Geology, history, properties, and commercial uses of asphalt.

W. H. Delano, *Twenty Years' Practical Experience of Natural Asphalt and Mineral Bitumen,* London, E. & F. N. Spon, 1893, pp. viii + 73.

Nomenclature of asphalt; list of asphalt mines of world; uses and applications of natural asphalt.

Abraham Gesner vs. William Cairns, *Report of a Case, Tried at Albert Circuit, 1852, Before His Honor, Judge Wilmot and a Special Jury, Copied from Judge's Notes,* St. John, New Brunswick, William L. Avery, 1853, pp. 167.

Suit involved question of whether material disputed was coal or asphaltum; if coal, deposits belonged to Cairns, if asphalt, to Gesner. Outstanding chemists and geologists testified and volume is of particular interest because of accounts of examination and tests of bitumen from Cuba, Trinidad, Egypt, etc., and of the special importance of Gesner as earliest kerosene manufacturer; this was his raw material. Gesner lost case, al-

though mineral was in truth asphalt and not coal.

H. Wager Halleck, *Bitumen: Its Varietie, Properties, and Uses,* Washington, Pete Force, 1841, pp. 206.

Abstract on properties and uses of bitumen; discussion of naphtha and petroleum, listed as first and second varietie of bitumen. Was No. 1 of Series on Practical Engineering published for use of United States Corps of Engineer, Author was Lieutenant with Army Engineers, later advanced to General-in-Chief and Chief of Staff.

Prevost Hubbard and Bernard Elbert Gray *Asphalt: Pocket Reference for Highway Engineers,* New York, Asphalt Institute, 1937, pp. 237. 2nd Ed. 1941, pp. 254. 3rd Ed. 1943, pp. 253.

George W. Le Maire, *A Study of Asphalt and Asphaltic Materials,* Golden, Colorado, Colorado School of Mines, 1953, pp. 89.

Manufacture and testing of asphalts, physical and chemical tests and their significance.

Stephen Farnum Peckham, *Solid Bitumens,* New York, Myron C. Clark Publishing Co., 1909, pp. viii + 324.

Natural history of bitumens, origin classification and derivation; chemical and physical methods of analysis; properties of solid bitumens; technology of bituminous streets. Author began experimenting on bitumens while student in Brown University in 1859 and later continued work on Pacific Coast.

Johan Philip Pfeiffer, *The Properties of Asphaltic Bitumen, with Reference to Its Technical Application,* New York and Amsterdam, Elsevier Publishing Co., 1950, pp. xvi + 285.

Technical treatise on asphalt and its properties.

Clifford Richardson, *On the Nature and Origin of Asphalt,* Long Island City, N.Y., Barber Asphalt Paving Co., 1898, pp. 63.

Principal asphalt deposits of North and South America, their characteristics and suggestions as to nature and origin of asphalt. Firm was pioneer in asphalt street-paving.

XII.

Transportation and Storage

A. GENERAL

Patrick Barry, *Over the Atlantic and Great Western Railway,* London, Sampson Low, Son & Marston, 1866, pp. xiv + 146.
Contains 12 letters by special commissioner appointed to report on position and prospects of the railway. First letter, written Meadville, Penna., May 8, 1866, includes description of plant manufacturing barrels. Third, written Pithole, May 22, 1866, describes oil fields and traffic on railroads and rivers.

Rolland Harper Maybee, *Railroad Competition and the Oil Trade, 1855–1873,* Mount Pleasant, Mich., Extension Press, 1940, pp. x + 451.
History of railroad competition among Atlantic trunk lines and relation of those railroads and competitive system to development of oil trade, during formative period of industry.

Philip Harvey Middleton, *Oil Industry and Transportation—Prewar and Postwar,* Chicago, Railway Business Association, 1943, pp. v + 60.
Development of petroleum industry in United States and services rendered to it by various forms of competition.

James Lawson Nesbitt, *Inspection of Petroleum Products. Digest of Statutes in*
the Several States and Canada. New York, *Evening Post* Job Printing Office, 1914, pp. 97. 2nd Ed. by James Lawson Nesbitt and Louis Broido, 1920, pp. 115.
Laws governing inspection of tests of petroleum products, and marking of containers; Canadian customs tariff on petroleum products.

Petroleum Administration for Defense, *Transportation of Oil,* Washington, Government Printing Office, 1952, pp. viii + 118.
Evaluation of adequacy of petroleum transportation facilities to meet industry needs during period of active mobilization; demand forecasts, study of tank trucks, pipe lines, railway tank cars, barges, ocean tankers, and storage facilities.

Royal Dutch-Shell Research Laboratory, *Electrostatics in the Petroleum Industry. The Prevention of Explosion Hazards,* Amsterdam, Netherlands, Elsevier Publishing Co., 1958, pp. 191.
Study of electrostatic phenomena accompanying flow of liquids, covering general aspects of static electricity and its relation to hydrocarbons, explosions, safety recommendations, theory and experiments.

B. TANK CARS

R. E. Buffington, *Petroleum,* Washington, Assn. of American Railroads, 1945, pp. xxi + 192.
Third report of Group 7, Sub-Committee for Economic Study, Railroad
Committee for Study of Transportation. Postwar developments in petroleum industry and potential traffic for railroads; review of industry and future demand and supply.

Defense Transport Administration, *The Tank Car Story,* Washington, the Administration, 1951, pp. ii + 48.
Appraisal of present, future, and emergency requirements for tank cars, covering construction, operations, and traffic.

General American Tank Car Corporation, *General American Tank Car Journeys, Where Industrial Liquids Come From and Where They Go,* Chicago, the Corporation, 1931, pp. 189. (Marked Vol. I, but no subsequent publication.)
Describes tank car as "the most versatile of all the vehicles of transportation" and devotes chapter to each of 14 classes of liquid products transported in tank cars, with chapter on tank cars in Europe. One chapter devoted to petroleum and petroleum products, including liquefied gases.

Francis Ogden, *Railway Wagon and Tank Construction and Repair,* London, Sir Isaac Pitman & Sons, 1948, pp. xiv + 174.

Contains chapter, pp. 84–116, dealing with construction, rebuilding, and repair of railway tank wagons.

Pennsylvania Tank Car Company, *The Tank Car,* Sharon, Penna., the Company, 1920, pp. 143.
Types, specifications, heating, cleaning, and other operating practices, regulation, accounting records and forms, gauge tables.

William M. Spencer, "*X*", *Symbol of Independence and Progress,* Newcomen Society address, Jan. 3, 1956, pp. 28.
Deals with private car line industry, with brief history of four leading companies.

Standard Car Equipment Company, *All About Tank Cars,* Sharon, Penna., the Company, 1917, pp. 325. 2nd Ed., Philadelphia, 1919, pp. 657.
Reference book for users and operators of tank cars, with information on construction, leasing, cleaning, repairing, specifications, and accounting.

C. PIPE LINES

American Institute of Aerological Research, *A Preliminary Study of the Relationship of Winter Weather to Fuel Oil (Distillate) Deliveries at Pipe Line Terminals,* prepared for Great Lakes Pipe Line Co., by Institute, Denver, 1953, pp. 21, with charts.
Reports on weather relationships to oil deliveries on daily, weekly, monthly, and seasonal bases, forecasting deliveries.

William Beard, *Regulation of Pipe Lines as Common Carriers,* New York, Columbia University Press, 1941, pp. vi + 184.
Discusses 2 basic concepts of pipe line transportation; horizontal aspect, that of being a public transportation agency moving freight in competition with rail and water; and vertical aspect, that of being primarily a major plant facility.

E. P. Bly, *Oil Pipe Lines in California. A Review of Oil Pipe Line Development and of Some of the Special Features*

that Characterize Oil Pipe Line Systems in California, (Reprinted from Aug., Sept., and Oct., 1926, issues of *Oil Bulletin*), Los Angeles.
Authoritative information on history and construction of pipe lines in California, with data on facilities, character of oil handled, equipment, corrosion, welding.

Leslie Cookenboo, Jr., *Costs of Operating Crude Oil Pipe Lines,* Houston, Rice Institute, 1954, pp. 78.
Methods and findings of empirical cost study of crude oil pipe line industry.

Leslie Cookenboo, Jr., *Crude Oil Pipe Lines and Competition in the Oil Industry,* Cambridge, Mass., Harvard University Press, 1955, pp. vi + 177.
Costs of operation of crude oil trunk lines; petroleum industry's structure, pipe lines, refining, and production; views of other writers; suggests public policy toward crude oil pipe lines.

R. S. Danforth, *Oil Flow in Pipe Lines*, San Francisco, King Knight Co., 1921, pp. 12. 2nd Ed. 1927.
Charts showing pressure loss in different-sized pipe lines, conversion of viscometer readings, horsepower required for pumping.

Federal Trade Commission, *Report on Pipe-Line Transportation of Petroleum*, Washington, Government Printing Office, 1916, pp. xxxii + 467.
Submitted in response to Senate Resolution No. 109, 63rd Congress, 1st Session, June 18, 1913, calling for investigation into field price of crude oil in Oklahoma and whether pipe line companies were keeping price below market levels elsewhere in United States. Review of pipe line costs, details of investments, earnings of 5 principal interstate carriers.

Richard Finnie, *Canol, The Sub-Arctic Pipeline and Refinery Project Constructed by Bechtel-Price-Callahan for the Corps of Engineers, U.S. Army, 1942–44*, Ryden & Ingram, 1945, pp. 210.
Problems, difficulties, and achievements by Canadian and American men and women who built Canol project; description of project.

Iraq Petroleum Company, Ltd., *The Construction of the Iraq-Mediterranean Pipe-Line*, London, the Company, 1934, pp. xvii + 125.
Account of construction, 1932–34, of pipe line of Iraq Petroleum Co., Ltd., from oilfields at Kirkuk, Iraq, to Mediterranean ports of Haifa and Tripoli, from design and organization to completion.

W. C. Kinsolving, *Underground Rivers of Oil*, New York, American Petroleum Institute, 1954, pp. 7.
Background Information Bulletin. History, costs, economics, defense aspects of oil pipe lines.

Ronald Van Auken Mills, *The Pipe Line's Place in the Oil Industry*, New York, the author, 1935, pp. vii + 138.
Development of pipes lines in petroleum industry, pipe line practice, rates and earnings, tariff regulations, proposals for divorcement of pipe lines.

John Henry Peper, *Factor Tables on Data for the Calculation of Pipe Line Pumpings, Based on Formula of F. M. Towl*, New York, the author, 1918, pp. 64.
Tables for calculation of pipe line pumpings, taking account of size of pipe, viscosity, net head, and mileage factors.

Pipe Line Contractors Association, *A Primer of Pipe Line Construction*, Dallas, Petroleum Extension Service, University of Texas, 1952, pp. 92.
Text and illustrations covering all phases of pipe line construction, from original planning to completion. Includes glossary.

Joseph E. Pogue, *Economics of Pipe-Line Transportation in the Petroleum Industry*, New York, the author, 1932. pp. 34.
Economic role, legal status, and social aspects of oil pipe lines; examines proposals for divorcing pipe lines from oil company ownership, with appraisal of economic consequences.

S. S. Smith and R. K. Shulze, *Interfacial Mixing Characteristics of Products in Pipe Lines*, Los Angeles, American Recording Chart Co., 1948, pp. 12. (Reprinted from *The Petroleum Engineer*, September and October, 1948.)
Pioneer study of turbulence in flow and how it affects the mixing of various petroleum products as they are pumped through pipe lines.

C. Stribling Snodgrass, *Sui Gas Pipeline*, n.p., the author, 1953, pp. 30; *Sui-Lahore Gas Pipeline*, 1955, pp. 22.
Piping natural gas from Sui, in Pakistan, to Karachi and Lahore; review of costs, capacities, requirements.

Walter M. Splawn, *Report on Pipe Lines*, Washington, Government Printing Office (House of Representatives, Document No. 2192, 72nd Congress, 2nd Session), 1933, Parts I and II, pp. lxxxi + 969.
Report and conclusions addressed to Committee on Interstate and Foreign Commerce, House of Representatives, by Walter M. Splawn, Special Counsel. Control and operation of oil and gasoline pipe lines, transportation of natural gas by pipe line; summaries of reports

submitted by companies; examination of accounts and records of certain holding companies.

Agricultural and Mechanical College of Texas, *Oceanographic Analysis of Marine Pipe Line Problems,* College Station, Tex., the College, 1951, var. pag.
Report of research conducted by Dept. of Oceanography, Texas A. & M. College, sponsored by and prepared for United Gas Pipe Line Co., outlining factors encountered in constructing and maintaining offshore pipe lines, with sections covering geology, waves, engineering, biology, and instrumentation.

University of Texas, Petroleum Extension Service, *Oil Pipe Line Transportation Practices,* Austin, the Service and Committee on Personnel Training, American Petroleum Institute, 1953 to 1956, 4 vols., pp. 537.
(Replacement for 1944 manual.) Vol. I: A Primer of Oil Pipe Line Operation. Vol. II: Oil Pipe Line Construction and Maintenance. Vol. III: Oil Pipe Line Measurement and Storage Practices. Vol. IV: Oil Pipe Line Pumping Station Operation and Maintenance.

Forrest Milton Towl, *Special Slide Rule for Rapid and Accurate Calculation of Flow of Crude Petroleum and Natural Gas Through Long Lines of Pipes, with Formulae and Explanation,* New York, the author, 1889, pp. 7.

Forrest Milton Towl, *The Pipe Line Flow Factor in the "Hydraulic" Flow Formula and Its Relation to Density and Viscosity,* New York, the author, in 2 parts, first published 1934 and second 1935, pp. vii + 70.
Report of work done in plotting and tabulating flow factor in reference to volume flowing. Towl also author of

The Pipe Line Flow Constant 0.0288, the Pipe Line Flow Factor; Their Relation to Density, Gravity, Velocity, Viscosity, and Reynolds Number, Cornwall, N.Y., Cornwall Press, 1943, pp. viii + 99.

Trans-Arabian Pipe Line Company, *Tapline, The Story of the World's Biggest Oil Pipe Line,* New York, the Company, 1951, pp. 40.
Account of construction of 1000-mile oil pipe line from oil fields of Saudi Arabia to Mediterranean at Sidon; details of pipe, valves, tankage.

Charles Morrow Wilson, *Oil Across the World, The American Saga of Pipelines,* New York, Longmans, Green & Co., 1946, pp. 318.
Popularly done historical account of pipe line transportation in United States and abroad.

Neill Compton Wilson and Frank J. Taylor, *The Building of Trans Mountain, Canada's First Oil Pipeline Across the Rockies,* Vancouver, B.C., Trans Mountain Oil Pipe Line Co., 1954, pp. 107.
Account of building oil pipe line from Edmonton, Alberta, to Vancouver from original planning to first oil delivery; organization, financing, and operating details.

George S. Wolbert, Jr., *American Pipe Lines, Their Industrial Structure, Economic Status, and Legal Implications,* Norman, Okla., University of Oklahoma Press, 1952, pp. xi + 179.
Authoritative review of development of pipe lines with particular attention to complaints lodged against pipe lines and analysis of proposed remedial devices such as divorcement. Pipe line regulation under the Interstate Commerce Act, and the Consent Decree under the Elkins Act.

D. TANK SHIPS AND TANKERS

American Bureau of Shipping, *Guidance Manual for Loading T2 Tankers,* New York, the Bureau, 1952, pages unnumbered.
Prepared jointly by American Bureau of Shipping and United States Coast Guard. Deals with proper distribution

of cargo or ballast; conditions encountered at sea, with attention to hogging and sagging.

L. R. Anderson and Lacey Harvey Harrison, *The Tanker in Practice,* Liverpool, Charles Birchall & Sons, 1935, pp. 245.

Arrangement, management, and maintenance of liquid-in-bulk carriers; loading and discharging.

Baptist, *Tanker Handbook for Deck Officers,* Glasgow, Brown, Son & Ferguson, 1954, pp. 69. 2nd Ed. 1956, pp. vii + 124.
History of oil transportation at sea; development of tanker types; pumps and pumping equipment; loading, discharging, and other operational information.

Bes, *Tanker Chartering and Management,* Amsterdam, Netherlands, C. De Boer, Jr., 1956, pp. iv + 176.
Design, construction, and operation of modern tankers; world oil movements by sea; rate structures; types of chartering; comparison of movements through Suez Canal and via Cape of Good Hope.

R. H. Bonn, *The Oil Tanker,* London, Association of Engineering and Shipbuilding Draughtsmen, 1922, pp. 135.
History of tankers and development of modern type; hull design and construction; tank testing; pumping arrangement and design; tank heating, ventilating; gauging.

Irving Crump, *Our Tanker Fleet,* New York, Dodd, Mead & Co., 1952, pp. 244.
Development of ships that carry oil; their crews, experiences, ports of call, accomplishments, hazards, and enemy encounters during World War II.

William Davies, *Petroleum Tables,* London, Dunn, Collin & Co., 5th Ed. 1912, pp. 57. 7th Ed. 1925, pp. 58.
Tables for calculating cargo weights and volumes, distances between ports of call, etc.

Laurence Dunn, *The World's Tankers,* London, Adlard Coles, 1956, pp. 176.
Development of oil tanker, emergence of present basic tanker design, growth of tanker fleets, entry of giant tanker. Well illustrated with numerous drawings and photographs of prototypes.

Esso Shipping Company, *Register of Tank Vessels of the World,* New York, the Company, 1957, pp. 43 + 229.
Lists owners, managers, names and flags of self-propelled tank vessels of 300 gross tons or over, with data on tonnage, draught, dimensions, and related items. First published as *Register of Tank Vessels Built for Carrying Petroleum Products, Etc.,* New York, Philip Ruprecht, 1904, pp. 27. Rev. Ed. 1909, pp. 15. Under same or similar titles, published subsequently by Foreign Shipping or Marine Departments, Standard Oil Company (New Jersey), Standard Shipping Company or Esso Shipping Company, 1915 Ed., pp. 37; 1917 Ed., pp. 46; 1920 Ed., pp. 59; 1922 Ed., pp. 86; 1925 Ed., pp. 76; 1928 Ed., 87; 1932 Ed., pp. 83; 1934 Ed., pp. 90; 1936 Ed., pp. 93; 1939 Ed., pp. 107; 1946 Ed., pp. 152; 1949 Ed., pp. 169; 1952 Ed., pp. 206.

Leonard G. Fay, *Tanker Directory of the World,* London, Terminus Publications, Ltd., 1959, pp. 308.
Compendium of articles on tanker fleets, tanker construction, operation, and maintenance; list of tankers by name, with names of owners or managers.

A. C. Hardy, *Oil Ships and Sea Transport: A Story of Oil in Relation to its Effect on Sea Transportation,* London, George Routledge & Sons, 1931, pp. xii + 159.
The change from coal to oil, effect of oil transportation on shipping and economic effects on industry, particularly British.

James Dodds Henry, *Thirty Five Years of Oil Transport: The Evolution of the Tank Steamer,* London, Bradbury, Agnew & Co., 1907, pp. 175.
History of world's oil-carrying fleets; companies and vessels engaged in tanker trade; passage of first tank steamers through Suez Canal; tanker design; description of oil ports with special reference to Baku and Port Arthur; tables, rules, regulations.

H. Hyams, *Sampling and Measurement of Petroleum Cargoes,* London, Anglo-Saxon Petroleum Co., 1939, pp. 165. 2nd Ed. 1949.
For use in countries employing imperial and metric systems of measurement.

H. Hyams, *Oil Measurement Tables,* London, Asiatic Petroleum Co., 1941, pp. 80.

Tables of volume and weight for oil cargoes.

H. Hyams, *Petroleum Cargoes,* Glasgow, Brown, Son & Ferguson, 1957, pp. xi + 379.
Technical material on crude oil and petroleum products for use in tanker operations, including standardized procedures and apparatus used in measuring cargoes.

International Correspondence School, *Tanker Mate's Manual. Special Edition for the United States Maritime Service Institute,* Scranton, Penna., International Textbook Co., 1946, pp. 144.
Correspondence school text. Tank-vessel operation from seaman's point of view, particularly deck officers of T2 tankers; glossary.

P. Jansen, *Petroleum Products and Its Transport, and Petroleum Tables,* South Shields, England, T. L. Ainsley, 1925, pp. 107.
Techniques of loading, discharging, etc.

P. Jansen, *Sea Transport of Petroleum,* **H. Hyams,** *Sampling and Measurement of Petroleum Cargoes,* South Shields, England, T. L. Ainsley, 1938, pp. 185. (Single volume in 2 parts.)
First part deals with transport of petroleum description of tank steamers, loading, discharge and gas-freeing of tankers, transport of various types of oil and precautions against fires. Second part deals with principal laboratory tests, sampling, and measurement, and furnishes miscellaneous tables.

J. A. Janssens, *Practical Petroleum Tables for Ship's Use,* Antwerp, Belgium, G. Dirix, n.d., pp. 143.
Contains sets of tables for determination of cargo quantities, converting weight to volume, converting cubic feet to tons, etc.

Philip Jenkins, *Stability of Oil-Carrying Steamers,* Glasgow, the author, 1889, pp. 29.
Written during period of transition from barrels to bulk oil-carrying. Reviews problems involved in building vessels to carry oil in bulk, including stability. List of oil-carrying vesels then built or building.

G. A. B. King, *Tanker Practice: The Construction, Operation and Maintenance of Tankers,* New York, Edward W. Sweetman, 1956, pp. 148.
Design of tankers, their operation and maintenance; oil measurement; loading, discharge, ballasting; tank cleaning and pollution problems; hazards of fire and explosion.

Louis William Koenig, *The Sale of the Tankers,* Washington, Committee on Public Administration Cases, 1950, pp. iv + 184.
How United States Government sold 83 ocean-going tankers to thirteen nations, 1947–1948, with chronology of principal events.

John Lamb, *Oil Tanker Cargoes, Their Safe and Efficient Handling,* London, Charles Griffin & Co., 1954, pp. viii + 208.
Leading contemporary authority on tanker design and operation describes oil cargo handling, cargo pipe systems and pumps, bulk loading and discharging, heating of viscous cargoes, tank venting, gas-freeing, cleaning; butane and propane; safety.

H. M. Le Fleming, *ABC of Ocean Tankers,* Surrey, England, Ian Allen, 1955, pp. 64.
Lists tankers of companies, mostly British, with tankers of 3000 gross tons upwards; associated fleets, identifying marks, tonnage, speed, and other details; plan adopted by each fleet for naming tankers. Does not include all fleets.

B. Orchard Lisle, *Tanker Technique, 1700–1936,* London, World Tankship Publications, 1936, pp. 83.
Development of tanker design and construction technique from earliest vessels.

George Herbert Little, *The Marine Transport of Petroleum.* London, E. & F. N. Spon, 1890, pp. xii + 251.
Handbook of ship design; loading, discharging, and other operational techniques; explosion hazards and famous accidents; glossary.

Dimitri Anthony Manthos, *The Future of the Tanker,* Bremen, Germany, Insti-

tute for Shipping Research Bureau, 1957, pp. 200.
Probable tanker requirements of Free World by 1965. Supply and demand forecasts for 130 individual countries, oil movements and shipping capacity, tanker requirements. (German and English text on alternate pages.)

Robert W. Morrell, *Oil Tankers,* New York, Simmons-Boardman Publishing Co., 1927, pp. viii + 284. 2nd Ed. 1931, pp. xii + 342.
Design and construction of tankers, trade requirements, tonnage measurement, fire protection, piping, propelling machinery, operation.

Robert S. Nielson, *Oil Tanker Economics,* Bremen, Germany, Institute for Shipping Research, 1959, pp. 303.
Excellent study of tanker economics with a section devoted to its history and development.

Standard Oil Company (New Jersey), *Instructions for Measuring, Sampling and Testing Bulk Oil Cargoes,* New York, the Company, 1926, pp. 139.
Procedures for measuring, sampling, and testing bulk oil shipments, based on methods in use by company and affiliates.

Standard-Vacuum Oil Company, *Tanker Manual for the Guidance of Officers and Department Heads,* New York, the Company, 1947, pp. 221.
Practice and procedure of tanker operation; designed for masters and officers on ocean-going vessels.

John F. Summerill, *Tanker Manual,* New York, Cornell Maritime Press, 1947, pp. viii + 150.
Textbook for sea-going mates, engineers, and crews. Development, design, and construction of tankers; loading

and unloading of cargoes; ballasting, tank cleaning and maintenance; review questions and tables of conversion factors.

Sun Oil Company, *Analysis of World Tank Ship Fleet, December 31, 1957,* Philadelphia, the Company, 16th Ed. 1958, pp. 50. (1st Ed. 1945, pp. 56.) Since 1954, editions dated close of each year and published midway of succeeding year.
Data on tank ship fleets of major flags, average deadweight tonnage and speed, carrying capacities, age, dimensions, ownership, control, etc.

B. Tunnard, *Tunnard's Tanker Tables,* Glasgow, Brown, Son & Ferguson, 2nd Ed. 1932, pp. vi + 78. 3rd Ed. 1954, pp. 80.
Comprehensive discussion of measurement, tables for conversion and handling of oil cargoes.

Leo Walmsley, *Invisible Cargo,* London, Michael Joseph, 1952, pp. 302.
Account of voyage by author aboard tanker from England to Maracaibo and return. Historical data and commentary.

Herbert John White, *Oil Tank Steamers,* Glasgow, Brown, Son & Ferguson, 1917, pp. 51. 2nd Ed. 1920, pp. 150. 4th Ed. 1927. 5th Ed.: *Oil Tank Steamers and Modern Motor Tankers,* 1935, pp. viii + 277.
Describes numerous types of tankers, carriage of various grades of petroleum; submarine and floating pipe lines.

Richard G. Wooler, *Tankerman's Handbook,* New York, Edward W. Sweetman, 1946, pp. xxi + 230. 2nd Ed. 1950, pp. xxi + 254. 3rd Ed. 1956, pp. 278.
Safe handling of oil cargoes, loading and discharging, gas-freeing and cleaning, pump operation, safety measures.

E. STORAGE

A. Cooper-Key, *A Primer on the Storage of Petroleum Spirit and Carbide of Calcium for the Use of Local Inspectors and Motorists,* London, Charles Griffin & Co., 1914, pp. viii + 128, 2nd Ed. n.d., pp. x + 133.

Safe storage of gasoline; local ordinances and safety regulations.

West Dodd, *Lightning and Petroleum Storage Tanks,* Des Moines, the author, 1920, pp. 48.

Principles relative to petroleum storage tanks and hazards of lightning, with recommended safeguards.

Great Britain. Home Department. Committee on Petroleum Spirit, *Final Report of the Departmental Committee on Petroleum Spirit, Minutes of Evidence and Appendices,* London, His Majesty's Stationery Office, 1913, pp. 29.
Report of committee appointed 1908 to inquire into sufficiency of regulations relating to storage, use, and conveyance of petroleum spirit, including tank steamers in harbors or docks.

Interstate Oil Compact Commission, *Underground Storage of Liquid Petroleum Hydrocarbons in the United States,* Oklahoma City, the Commission, 1956, pp. xiii + 104.
Aspects of underground storage of petroleum and products, with 43 state reports dealing with specific underground storage operations and possibilities.

Hubbert L. O'Brien, *Petroleum Tankage and Transmission,* East Chicago, Ind., Graver Tank & Mfg. Co., 1951, pp. 170.

Formulae, charts, tables, and discussion on storage of petroleum and derivatives, tankage, flow of fluids through pipe lines, selection of pumps, and other problems.

Hugh Edmund Watts, *Storage of Petroleum-Spirit,* London, Charles Griffin & Co., 1951, pp. 320.
Handbook for local authorities concerned with storage and trucking of gasoline, loading and unloading in harbors and on canals; pumps and equipment; accidents and safeguards. Appendices of acts, codes, and orders in British Isles relating to petroleum and gasoline.

Hugh Edmund Watts, *The Law Relating to Petroleum Mixtures, Acetylene, Calcium Carbide, and to the Transport of Carbon Bisulphide and Certain Compressed Gases,* London, Charles Griffin & Co., 1956, pp. 179.
Petroleum (Consolidation) Act of 1928 as it relates to properties, storage, and transport of petroleum mixtures, regulations for road transport of compressed gases; accidents in connection with petroleum mixtures; lists of inflammable substances in petroleum mixtures.

XIII.

Commercial, Financial, and Economic Matters

A. MARKETING METHODS AND PRACTICES

American Petroleum Institute, *National Code of Practices for Marketing Refined Petroleum Products,* New York, the Institute, 1929, pp. 31.
Code of 21 rules, outlining practices for marketing refined petroleum products, as recommended by board of directors, American Petroleum Institute, and approved July 25, 1929, by Federal Trade Commission and July 30, 1929, by board of directors, American Petroleum Institute. Short-lived attempt to cure alleged marketing evils under legal authority of Federal Trade Commission to call trade practice conferences.

American Petroleum Institute, *Marketing Research in the Petroleum Industry,* New York, the Institute, 1957, pp. 176.
Reviews history of marketing research in oil industry; its place in company organization; scope of activities and marketing research procedures.

Harvey P. Bishop, *Retail Marketing of Furnace Oil,* Boston, Graduate School of Business Administration, Harvard University, 1946, pp. 42.
Development of oil heating, 1920–45, market for furnace oil, channels of distribution, suggestions for independent retailers. Covers New England and Middle Atlantic States.

Richard E. Chaddock, *Chemical Market Research in Practice,* New York, Reinhold Publishing Corp., 1956, pp. x + 196.
Chapter on petrochemical industry.

Harry Wing Chinn, *Some Factors that Affect Marketing,* Golden, Colo., Colorado School of Mines, 1940, pp. 39.
Discussion from refiner's viewpoint of factors affecting marketing of petroleum products; effect of railroad tariffs upon marketing areas and in determining points at which competition arises for similar products from other sources.

Andrew Milton Cross, *Outline of the Oil Industry and Filling Station Sales and Operations,* Weems, Va., the author, 1935, pp. 71.
General background information on petroleum, petroleum products, oil industry; operation of service stations, sales of products and accessories.

Leonard M. Fanning, *Petroleum Code Handbook, 1933,* Bayonne, N.J., Oildom Publishing Co., 1933, var. pag.
Petroleum facts and figures for 1932; taxes; specifications; problems of bulk depot and service station operation; truck and trailer truck hauling.

Independent Oil Men's Association, *Petroleum Annual: Handbook of the Petroleum Industry,* Chicago, the Association, 1921, pp. 430. (I.O.M.A. Blue Book, 1918–1919, pp. 354.)
Association formed 1909 by group of jobbers and marketers as Independent Petroleum Marketers Association, changed 1915 to Independent Oil Men's Association. Annual volumes contain list of jobbers, refineries, dealers in petroleum products in foreign countries,

information on traffic and transportation, tables and other data, together with papers presented at annual meetings.

Charles Landon Jones, *Service Station Management, Its Principles and Practice,* New York, D. Van Nostrand Co., 1922, pp. v + 171.
Handbook of merchandising and record-keeping methods.

James O. Kemm, *Let's Talk Petroleum,* Springfield, Mo., Mycroft Press, 1958, pp. vi + 170.
Background of information on oil to assist marketing men in answering questions; suggestions for sales promotion by jobbers and retailers.

La Salle Extension University, *Service Station Salesmanship,* Chicago, the School, 1930, pp. 68.
Correspondence school text on lubrication service and other aspects of service station operation.

La Salle Extension University, *Service Station Selling and Management, The Sale of Gasoline,* Chicago, the School, 1934, pp. 103.
Correspondence course text.

Ministry of Transport, *Petrol Stations,* London, His Majesty's Stationery Office, 1949, pp. 52.
Survey of service stations in England; history; wartime and postwar conditions; licensing and control; layout and site choosing.

National Association of Petroleum Retailers, *A Manual of Service Station Merchandising and Management,* Milwaukee, the Association, 1938, pp. xxiii + 213.
Handbook for service station owners; methods and routines for building sales of gasoline, motor oil, tires, etc., operating procedures, record keeping.

National Cash Register Company, *Toward Successful Service Station Management,* Dayton, Ohio, the Company, 1958, pp. 56.
Service station operating methods, planning, location, merchandising, record keeping.

National Tax Equality Association, *Cooperative Expansion in the Petroleum Industry,* Chicago, the Association, 1944, pp. 49.
Discusses growth of petroleum cooperatives and their tax privileges.

State of New York, *Report of Joint Legislative Committee to Study and Investigate the Subject of Gasoline, Motor Fuels and Oil, with Particular Reference to the Cost Price Thereof to the Public,* Document No. 90, 1937, Albany, New York, 1937, pp. 55. 2nd Report, Document No. 93, 1938, pp. 64. 3rd Report, Document No. 93, 1939, pp. 162.
Reports describe work of Committee and legislation recommended. Committee inquired into many phases of gasoline distribution, including price structure, dealer organizations, retailers practices, and trade journals.

Clayton D. Nielson, *Service Station Management,* Lincoln, University of Nebraska Press, 1957, pp. 229.
Nature of service station business; opportunities and risks; sales, advertising training and supervision of personnel inventories, housekeeping, handling of merchandise; records and controls; case histories.

Petroleum Administrative Board, *Final Report of the Marketing Division,* Washington, Government Printing Office, 1936, pp. iv + 190.
Competitive practices in marketing branch of petroleum industry, including early history of marketing. Marketing section of Petroleum Code and effect of its abandonment on trade practices, with attention to Pacific Coast and survey of retail outlets in Allen County, Indiana.

Petroleum Industry Research Foundation, *Cooperatives in the Petroleum Industry,* New York, Empire State Petroleum Assn. and Illinois Petroleum Marketers Assn., 1947, 4 Parts, pp. xiv + 391.
Part 1: Origin, principles, objectives, and methods of cooperatives. Part 2: Operation of petroleum cooperatives, including international cooperatives Part 3: Tax laws governing cooperatives. Part 4: Results of surveys and interviews covering public attitude toward cooperatives.

Phillips Petroleum Co., *Service Station Operation and Selling,* Bartlesville, Okla., the Company, 1955, pp. 138.
Handbook for management and training of driveway salesmen.

Warren C. Platt, *The Future for the Independent Oil Jobber,* Cleveland, National Petroleum Publishing Co., 1941, pp. 71.
Historical and economic story of oil jobbers and discusses functions and opportunities.

Shell Oil Company, Inc., *Service Station Retailing,* New York, the Company, 1946, pp. 202.
Similar to textbook compiled by Shell and published by Department of Commerce. Opportunities in service station business, requirements, procedure for servicing, merchandising, advertising, maintenance, personnel selection and training, business controls and records.

Earl W. Sinclair, *Petroleum Marketing,* New York, the author, 1932, pp. 21.
Address at Princeton University on distribution patterns in oil marketing; company-owned, individual-owned, and super-service stations; overexpansion and overdevelopment of marketing facilities; wasteful practices; gasoline taxation.

John C. Spurr, *The Market for Industrial Lubricating Oils and Greases In the Manufacturing Industries,* New York, McGraw-Hill Book Co., 1955, pp. 61.
Survey covering 121 cities in 48 states on purchases of industrial lubricating oils and greases, cutting and soluble oils, process oils, paraffin and other waxes.

A. A. Stambaugh, *The Petroleum Industry and Competition,* New York, American Petroleum Institute, 1952, var. pag.
Background Information Bulletin. Competition in the oil industry.

Standard Oil Company of New York, *Socony Information,* New York, the Company, 1921, pp. vi + 165.
To assist service station employees in care and maintenance of property and in transactions with customers.

Henry C. Stevenson, *A Hand-Book for the Use of Oil Dealers and Others,* Philadel-

phia, the author, 1894, pp. 114. 2nd Ed. 1895, pp. 110.
Rules regulating trade on New York Produce Exchange, list of independent petroleum refiners, tables and information on viscosity, tests, commercial data for oil dealers.

Richard H. Thomas, *The Merchandising of Petroleum Products,* Des Moines, Homestead Co., 1929, pp. 231.
From salesman to division manager; the duties of agents, service station salesmen, and others engaged in selling.

Grady Triplett, *Service Station Selling,* Houston, Texas, Gulf Publishing Co., 1932, pp. 79.
Successful selling habits for service station salesmen; fundamentals of service; study of customers; understanding products and accessories.

United States Department of Commerce, *Establishing and Operating a Service Station,* Industrial (Small Business) Series No. 22, Bureau of Foreign and Domestic Commerce, Washington, Government Printing Office, 1945, pp. vi + 198.
Prepared by members of the petroleum industry and reviewed by Petroleum Industry War Council and Petroleum Administration for War. Summary of business of service station operation, including opportunities and risks, location, layout, products and accessories, advertising, credit, record keeping, selection and training of personnel.

Roland S. Vaile, Alvin L. Nordstrom, and Ralph E. Brewer, *Gasoline Distribution in the Twin Cities,* Minneapolis, University of Minnesota Press, 1933, pp. 89.
Gasoline retailing in St. Paul and Minneapolis; economy of methods and opportunities for improvement. Marketing structure and methods of distribution; retail market; prices and margins; qualities of representative brands.

Western Petroleum Refiners Association, *Digest of State Inspection Laws Relating to Petroleum Products; United States Government Specifications for Gasoline, Kerosene, Diesel Fuel and Fuel Oils, Jan. 1, 1957,* Tulsa, the Association, 1957, pp. 151. Earlier editions with title variations, *July 1, 1952,* 1952, pp. xxvii + 175. *Jan. 1, 1948,* 1948, pp.

xlvii + 187. *Oct. 1943,* 1944, pp. lvi + 186, 1st Ed. 1939, pp. 161.
Inspection laws and specifications.

B. PRICES AND PRICING OF PETROLEUM AND ITS PRODUCTS

American Petroleum Institute, *The Recent Increases in the Prices of Petroleum and Its Products,* Memorandum submitted to the Federal Trade Commission by the Secretary of the American Petroleum Institute, New York, 1920, pp. 24.
Report, May 18, 1920, with factual presentation of petroleum production and consumption during period covered by Federal Trade Commission investigation of petroleum prices.

Warren L. Baker and Cecil W. Smith, *The Facts About Oil Prices,* New York, American Petroleum Institute, 1957, pp. 10.
Background Information Bulletin. Factors that determine petroleum prices.

Ralph Cassady, Jr., *Price Making and Price Behaviour in the Petroleum Industry,* New Haven, Conn., Yale University Press, 1954, pp. xx + 353.
Sourcebook on nature of oil price determination in United States.

Ralph Cassady, Jr., and Wylie L. Jones, *The Nature of Competition in Gasoline Distribution at the Retail Level,* Berkeley and Los Angeles, University of California Press, 1951, pp. xii + 220.
Competition in petroleum industry in retail sale of gasoline in Los Angeles area, 1949–50; demand, supply, quality of gasoline; supplier policies; nature of competitive rivalries; retail dealer margins, retail gasoline pricing and price behavior.

E. H. Davenport, *The Price of Petrol,* London, London General Press, n.d. (c. 1928–29), pp. 23.
How supply and demand affect price of gasoline in England.

Federal Trade Commission, *Report on the Price of Gasoline in 1915,* Washington, Government Printing Office, 1917, pp. xv + 224.
Investigation by FTC resulting from

complaints of unreasonably high prices of gasoline and allegation of discriminations in price. Covers demand and supply, costs and margins, methods of computing gasoline costs, earnings and dividends of representative refining and marketing companies, alleged inequalities in competition and price, position of Standard Oil companies.

Federal Trade Commission, *Advance in the Price of Petroleum Products,* Washington, Government Printing Office (H. R. Doc. 801. 66th Congress, 2nd Session), 1920, pp. 57.
Inquiry into advances in price of fuel oil, kerosene, gasoline, and other petroleum products. Oil prices during latter part of World War I and in postwar period, Jan. 1, 1918, to April 30, 1920: oil developments abroad.

Harold Fleming, *Gasoline Prices in Michigan,* New York, American Petroleum Institute, 1956, pp. 7.
Background Information Bulletin. Analysis of gasoline pricing mechanism in Michigan, dealer's prices and profits, definition of many oil-marketing terms. Reprinted from *Inside Michigan Magazine,* December, 1955.

Harold Fleming, *Montana Gasoline Prices and Competition,* Helena, Montana, Record Publishing Co., 1958, pp. 104.
Structure of gasoline marketing in Montana; survey of Montana gasoline prices, how established, comparison with other states; costs, profits; history of price regulation in two Canadian provinces. Publication sponsored by Continental Oil Co. as contribution to better understanding of oil pricing.

Harold Fleming, *Oil Prices and Competition,* New York, American Petroleum Institute, 1953, pp. iv + 62.
Report on inquiry made "at first hand from oil men in all segments of the industry, how petroleum prices are de-

termined—not in theory—but as they are in actual practice." Recommended for readers seeking a clear statement of the oil-pricing mechanism.

Great Britain, Parliament, *Prices of Petrol Products. Statement by the Oil Companies Concerned,* London, His Majesty's Stationery Office (Cmd 3296), 1929, pp. 16.
Statement, dated March 18, 1929, to Parliament by 3 companies supplying petroleum products to British consumers responding to invitation to give reasons for price increases in gasoline and kerosene.

Daniel Corning Hamilton, *Competition in Oil: The Gulf Coast Refinery Market,* Cambridge, Mass., Harvard University Press, 1958, pp. xiv + 233.
Economic study of Gulf Coast refinery market, refiners, market performance, price competition.

Samuel P. Irvin, *The Oil Bubble,* author, Franklin, Penna., 1868.
Account of high and low prices for crude oil, reasons for their rise and fall.

A. D. H. Kaplan, Joel B. Dirlam, Robert F. Lanzillotti, *Pricing in Big Business,* Washington, Brookings Institution, 1958, pp. xiv + 344.
Study of posted dealer tank wagon prices of Esso Standard Oil Co., 1946–1956, p. 84 ff.; Esso pricing policy, p. 156 ff.

Thomas M. Kavanaugh, Attorney General of Michigan (prepared by Stanton S. Faville), *A Report to the Governor by the Attorney General on the Gasoline Price Investigation, 1955–1956,* Lansing, 1956, pp. 271.
Report by Asst. Attorney General on investigation of gasoline pricing in Michigan, with attention to factors that produce price changes. Investigation, made at direction of Governor Williams, followed attempt by legislature to put gasoline under public utility price controls; industry exonerated of charges then current, and controls not recommended.

Robert M. La Follette, Sr., Chairman, Senate Manufacturing Subcommittee, *The High Cost of Gasoline and Other Pe-troleum Products,* Washington, Government Printing Office, 1923, 2 vols., pp. 1769.
Report of Senate Subcommittee inquiring into gasoline prices and oil marketing prices during early 1920's. One-sided tenor of report evident from title; also remarkable for prediction "the people of this country must be prepared before long to pay at least $1 a gallon for gasoline."

Edmund P. Learned, *Pricing of Gasoline: A Case Study,* Boston, Harvard Graduate School of Business Administration, 1948, pp. 34.
Reprinted from *Harvard Business Review.* Analysis of pricing of gasoline, based on examination of records of Standard Oil Co. (Ohio), to ascertain how prices to dealers and consumers at company-owned stations were made for regular-grade gasoline during period, 1937–47. Particular attention to Sohio's role as a so-called "market leader."

Edmund P. Learned and Catherine C. Ellsworth, *Gasoline Pricing in Ohio,* Boston, Graduate School of Business Administration, Harvard University, 1959, pp. xx + 258.
Study of "price leadership" in gasoline pricing based on thousands of specific prices obtained from companies operating in Ohio market. Valuable tables.

A. G. Maguire, *Prices and Marketing Practices Covering the Distribution of Gasoline and Kerosene Throughout the United States,* Washington, Government Printing Office, 1919, pp. 24.
Report of investigation by Bureau of Prices and Licenses, Oil Division, Fuel Administration, regarding trade practices in distribution and marketing of gasoline and kerosene. Alleges failure of Standard Oil dissolution decree to give desired results in certain directions, wide variations in marketing practices, suggestions.

McGraw-Hill Book Company, Comp., *Platt's Oil Price Handbook and Oilmanac,* 35th Edition, New York, the Company, 1959, pp. iv + 295.
Refinery and tank wagon prices for gasoline, kerosene, etc., crude oil prices in United States, Canada, Venezuela, and Middle East; tanker rates, statistics,

gasoline and kerosene price in 55 countries, refinery directory published through 1946 edition, Federal specifications, list of cycling plants, etc., during various periods of series. Volume is 35th of annual series initiated with *Oil Price Handbook for 1924 and Refinery Directory,* Cleveland, National Petroleum Publishing Co., 1925, pp. 116. Compiled by Staff of *National Petroleum News.* Name changed to *Platt's Oil Price Handbook,* 1940, and to present title 1952. McGraw-Hill, purchaser of Platt organization, assumed publication 1953.

National Bureau of Economic Research, Conference on Price Research, *Price Research in the Steel and Petroleum Industries,* New York, the Bureau, 1939, pp. xiii + 170.
Petroleum industry and its price problems; survey of available statistics; analysis and appraisal of price and other data; suggested program of price-cost research.

State of New Hampshire, Senate, *Report of Joint Committee to Study Gasoline and Fuel Oil Prices,* Concord, *Journal of the Senate,* June 24, 1959, pp. 687–693.
Report of interim legislative committee on how gasoline and fuel oil prices are established in New Hampshire, their fairness compared to surrounding states, why prices differ within the state, etc. Committee found indications of strong competition within oil industry and that price levels were not exorbitant. Reprint from official *Journal.*

State of New Jersey, *Report of the State of New Jersey Gasoline Study Commission,* Trenton, MacCrellish & Quigley Co., 1953, pp. 43.
Study of gasoline industry in New Jersey by Commission appointed Feb., 1952, to study factors governing gasoline prices.

Archibald Jamieson Nichol, *Partial Monopoly and Price Leadership. A Study in Economic Theory,* Philadelphia, the author, 1930, pp. 71.
Doctoral thesis submitted to Columbia University. Chapter on price leadership in petroleum industry; tabulation of gasoline price changes in New York,

Newark, and Philadelphia during 10 years ended June 30, 1929.

Alirio Antonio Parra, *Some Aspects of the International Price Structure of Crude Oil,* Washington, the author, 1957, pp. 124.
Thesis at George Washington University. Crude oil price structure of international petroleum industry in terms of observed behavior, 1920–44 and 1945–56; particular attention to United States, Middle East, and Venezuela; single-basing and multiple-basing points.

Commonwealth of Pennsylvania, *Report of the Oil Industry Investigation Commission,* Harrisburg, the Commission, 1939, pp. 46.
Pennsylvania oil industry in all functions, mostly with markets, distribution, and pricing of gasoline. History of investigation, 1937–39, by first and second oil industry investigation commissions, this being report of second commission, established Nov. 29, 1938. Report based on 67-page summary of evidence presented to first commission.

Warren Milton Persons, *Consequences of Price Fixing in Competitive Industries, with special reference to the Proposed Fixed Minimum Prices of Petroleum Products,* New York, the author, 1933, pp. 73.
Registers strong opposition to price-fixing order of Oct. 16, 1933, by Petroleum Administrator under petroleum code of National Recovery Administration.

Platt's Oilgram, *The Tank Car Market for Petroleum and Its Products, A Study of the Key Market of the Oil Industry,* Cleveland, Platt's Oilgram and National Petroleum News, 1928, pp. 41.
Tank car market and how pricing systems developed; discussion of spot-market contracts.

John Ponton, *A Crisis in the Oil Regions, A Few Words in Behalf of the Producer,* author, Titusville, Penna., 1867.
First known booklet dealing with overproduction and prices. Author was staff writer for *Titusville Herald.*

United States Attorneys General, *Proceedings of the Conference of Attorneys*

General on the Subject of Gasoline Prices, n.p., n.pub., 1923, pp. 39.
Minutes of meeting, Oct. 15–17, 1923, Chicago, Ill.

United States Chamber of Commerce, *The Robinson-Patman Act and S. 11,* New York, American Petroleum Institute, 1958, pp. 7.
Background Information Bulletin. United States Chamber of Commerce membership referendum on subject.

State of Vermont, House of Representatives, *Report of the Committee on Study of Gasoline Prices,* Montpelier, *Journal of the House,* April 23, 1957, pp. 541–546.
Report of legislative committee which had inquired into charges of artificially high gasoline prices, collusion, etc. Committee found charges without substance, presented reasons why Vermont gasoline prices somewhat higher than neighboring states. Reprinted from official *Journal.*

C. TAXATION AND EVALUATION

Arthur Anderson & Co., *Oil and Gas Federal Income Tax Manual,* Houston, Arthur Anderson & Co., 1939, pp. 30, includes 17 headings. 2nd Ed. includes 85 cases, 1942, pp. 77. 3rd Ed. includes 98 cases, 1944, pp. v + 97. 4th Ed. includes 130 cases, 1946, pp. vi + 131. 5th Ed. includes 143 cases, 1948, pp. vi + 197. 6th Ed. includes 147 cases, 1950, pp. vi + 231. 7th Ed. includes 154 cases, 1953, pp. v + 251. 8th Ed. in preparation.
Case method in dealing with tax problems associated with acquisition and development of properties, depreciation and depletion, grants or assignments of rights, adjustments resulting from percentage depletion allowance, tax planning; glossary; citation of cases.

Ralph Arnold, J. L. Darnell, and others, *Manual for the Oil and Gas Industry under the Revenue Act of 1918,* New York, John Wiley & Sons, 1920, pp. xiv + 190.
Income Tax law and regulations as amended, depreciation of equipment, depletion, methods of estimating recoverable underground reserves of oil. Based on manual issued by Bureau of Internal Revenue, Feb., 1919.

John Wendell Beveridge, *Federal Taxation of Income from Oil and Gas Leases, Etc.,* Chicago, Callaghan & Co., 1948, pp. xiii + 312.
Federal income tax problems of oil and gas producing industry, taxable income from leases, capital gain and loss rules, depletion, depreciation, intangible drilling costs.

F. J. Blaise, *The Case for Percentage Depletion for Oil and Gas Wells,*

Chicago, Pure Oil Co., 1959, pp. 60. 1st Ed., 1957.
History and explanation of percentage depletion.

Clark W. Breeding and A. Gordon Burton, *Taxation of Oil and Gas Income,* New York, Prentice-Hall, 1954, pp. xii + 340.
Principles of income taxation that control transactions common to producer of oil and gas to permit reasonable prediction of tax impact. Reviews essentials of petroleum production, property interests and conveyances, ownership and operation, costs, depletion, joint operations, unitization agreements and special problems. One chapter on corresponding tax concepts in Canada.

Robert Wesley Brown, *Valuation of Oil and Gas Lands,* New York, McGraw-Hill Book Co., 1924, pp. viii + 215.
Determination of value, estimation of oil reserves, prices, equipment value, costs, interest, depletion, depreciation; methods of valuation for oil and gas lands; Federal Income Tax law.

John M. Campbell, *Oil Property Evaluation,* Englewood Cliffs, N.J., Prentice-Hall, Inc., 1959, pp. x + 523.
Recent factors affecting valuation of oil properties, general economics of petroleum industry, calculation of reserves, prediction of future reservoir performance, preparation of evaluations.

David L. Cohn, *Oil Depletion Allowance,* New York, American Petroleum Institute, 1953, pp. 7.
Background Information Bulletin. The 27½ per cent depletion allowance.

Leland E. Fiske, *Federal Taxation of Oil and Gas Transactions,* Albany, Matthew Bender & Co., 1958, var. pag.
Principles of taxation with special application to oil and gas industry and related problems; treatment of exploration and development expenditures, depletion, oil payments, etc.

Dale H. Flagg (Consulting Editor), *Oil and Gas Taxes Report,* Englewood Cliffs, N.J., Prentice-Hall, 1956, Vol. 1, No. 1.
Supplements *Taxation of Oil and Gas Income.* Analyses of tax aspects and problems of property interests, ownership and operation, organization; with monthly report bulletin.

Paul Forasté, *Depletion in the Oil Industry,* New York, Graduate School of Business Administration, New York University, 1943, pp. 73.
Thesis based on survey questionnaire sent to financial officers of 100 large and small oil companies. Methods of accounting for wasting assets in oil industry, characteristics of depletable property and elements of cost, intangible development costs, depletion for income tax purposes.

Simon Moritz Frank, C. W. Wellen, and Owen Lipscomb, *Oil and Gas Taxation. Cases and Materials,* Englewood Cliffs, N.J., Prentice-Hall, 1956, pp. xv + 314.
For advanced level of legal education in oil and gas income taxation; covers types of property interests, payments incident to acquisition and operation, intangible drilling and development costs, depletion, depreciation and obsolescence, transfers of interest and other property aspects, capital gains, joint operations and associations, etc.

Richard J. Gonzalez, *Land of the Big Risk,* New York, American Petroleum Institute, 1956, pp. 7.
Background Information Bulletin. Percentage depletion deduction, its role in providing incentive to oil exploration.

Richard J. Gonzalez, *Percentage Depletion for Petroleum Production,* Houston, Humble Oil & Refg. Co., 1959, pp. 36.
Testimony delivered to House Ways and Means Committee, December 1, 1959.

S. S. Hayes, *Petroleum As A Source of National Revenue,* Washington, Treasury Department, 1866, pp. 52. (Special Report No. 7, United States Revenue Commission. Also Executive Document No. 61, U.S. House of Representatives, 39th Congress, 1st Session.)
First Government report on oil business. Reviews tax on oils, history of American oil, foreign developments, exports, profits, prices and values, lists of wells and average yields, refining, trade, future supply. Recommends abolition of tax on crude oil production.

Institute on Federal Taxation, *Oil and Gas Negotiation and Taxation in "Slow Motion," or Black Gold and the Silent Partner,* New York, Fallon Law Book Co., 1954, pp. xviii + 213.
Proceedings of Third Annual Institute on Federal Taxation. A play.

J. K. Lasser Tax Institute and Francis L. Durand, *How to Get Tax Protected Income and Capital from Oil and Gas Investments,* Larchmont, New York, Business Report, 1956, pp. 136.
Oil investments, taxes, protection given investors; case histories.

John H. Lichtblau and Dillard P. Spriggs, *The Oil Depletion Issue,* New York, Petroleum Industry Research Foundation, Inc., 1959, pp. x + 148.
Well rounded coverage of mineral depletion, tax law applicable to oil, related economics. Authors do not seek to "grind axe" on either side of subject.

McMurry College, School of Business Administration, *Petroleum Conference on Oil and Gas Taxation,* Abilene, Tex., the College, 1957, pp. iv + 112.
First conference held April 23–25, 1957. Six papers on tax problems of oil and gas developments.

McMurry College, School of Business Administration, *Second Annual Conference on Oil and Gas Taxation and Estate and Gift Tax Planning,* Abilene, Tex., the College, 1958, var. pag.
Held May 14–16, 1958. Six papers on valuation of oil and gas properties for Federal estate tax purposes, financing, unitization.

Kenneth G. Miller, *Oil and Gas. Federal Income Taxation,* Chicago, Commerce Clearing House, 1948, pp. 251. 2nd Ed. 1951, pp. 284. 3rd Ed. 1957, pp. 350.

Correlates law, regulations, rulings, decisions. Covers depletion, royalty and working interests, leases, costs, rentals, etc.

Albert L. Nickerson, *Oil, Taxes, and Progress,* New York, American Petroleum Institute, 1958, pp. 7.
Background Information Bulletin. Tax depletion deduction as applied to oil industry.

Paul Paine, *Oil Property Valuation,* New York, John Wiley & Sons, 1942, pp. viii + 204.
Authoritative text by well-known valuation engineer of meaning and scope of valuation in oil business; factors which enter into valuation; methods of application.

Roland D. Parks, *Examination and Valuation of Mineral Property,* Reading, Mass., Addison-Wesley Publishing Co., 1957, pp. xvi + 507, 4th Ed. 2nd Ed.: *Mine Examination and Valuation,* by Parks and Charles Homer Baxter, Houghton, Mich., Michigan College of Mining and Technology, 1939. 1st Ed. 1933.
Contains section on valuation of oil property.

South Texas Geological Society (Corpus Christi Branch), *Notes on Valuation of Oil and Gas Properties,* Corpus Christi, Tex., the Society, 1939, pp. 47.
Determination of assets and liabilities associated with developed and partly developed properties; prospects, protection leases, spreads, and trend plays. Bibliography.

Standard Oil Co. (N.J.), *The Depletion Provision in Taxing Natural Resources: How and Why It Was Created,* New York, the Company, 1958, pp. 15.
History of percentage depletion.

Standard Oil Co. (N.J.), *An Analysis of the Depletion Provision as It Applies to the Petroleum Industry,* New York, the Company, 1958, pp. 24.
Main arguments advanced against percentage depletion, with answers.

Lowell Stanley, *Percentage Depletion,* New York, American Petroleum Institute, 1957, pp. 11.

Background Information Bulletin. Discussion of oil depletion tax provision.

Truman Glenn Tracy, *Valuation of Illinois Oil Producing Properties for Tax Assessment,* State of Illinois, Department of Revenue, 1948, pp. 75.
Variables involved in estimating total recoverable oil; formula for assigning values to various types of production.

James Irwin Tucker, *Oil Valuation,* Houston, Tex., Gulf Publishing Co., 1923, pp. 332.
Federal income tax as applied to producers of oil and gas, including appraisal of oil properties for depletion purposes.

Tulane University, College of Law and College of Business Administration, *First Annual Tulane Tax Institute,* New Orleans, the University, 1952, pp. 325. *Second Annual Tulane Tax Institute,* 1953, pp. 318. *Third Annual Tulane Tax Institute,* Albany, Matthew Bender & Co., 1954, pp. x + 588. *Fourth Annual Tulane Tax Institute,* Albany, Matthew Bender & Co., 1955, pp. xiv + 561. *Fifth Annual Tulane Tax Institute,* Indianapolis, Bobbs-Merrill Co., 1956, pp. xvi + 820. *Sixth Annual Tulane Tax Institute,* Indianapolis, Bobbs-Merrill Co., 1957, pp. xv + 830. *Seventh Annual Tulane Tax Institute,* Indianapolis, Bobbs-Merrill Co., 1958, pp. xiv + 678. *Eighth Annual Tulane Tax Institute,* Indianapolis, Bobbs-Merrill Co., 1959, pp. xi + 835.
Papers on tax law with many references to oil and gas taxes.

United States Treasury Department, Bureau of Internal Revenue, *Manual for the Oil and Gas Industry under the Revenue Act of 1918,* Washington, Government Printing Office, 1921, pp. vi + 245. 1st Ed. 1919, pp. 136.
Government instructions on methods for claiming discovery-value depletion.

Harold Vance, *Oil Field Evaluation,* Houston, the author, 1959, pp. 80.
Methods for estimating recoverable oil

and gas, valuation of oil and gas properties.

Western Petroleum Refiners Association, *Digest of State Gasoline Tax Laws, Jan.*

1, 1957, Tulsa, the Association, 1957 pp. 180. Earlier editions *Dec. 1, 1947,* 1948, pp. 173. *July 1, 1952,* 1952, pp. 183.
Gasoline tax laws, and their history.

D. ACCOUNTING, AUDITING, COSTING

American Association of Oilwell Drilling Contractors, Accounting Committee, *Accounting Manual for the Oilwell Drilling Industry,* Dallas, the Association, 1945, pp. 116. 2nd Ed. 1950, pp. 144. 3rd Ed. 1957, pp. 225.
Procedure for determining and interpreting costs of drilling wells; urges use of standardized, practical accounting procedures for use in drilling.

American Petroleum Institute, Accounts and Accounting Procedures Subcommittee of Financial and Accounting Committee, *Outline of Petroleum-Industry Accounting,* New York, the Institute, 1954, pp. 165.
Accounting procedures suggested for 9 major departments or functions of industry: producing, natural-gas processing and cycling, pipe line, crude purchasing and storage, refining, tank car, marine, marketing, and administrative. Chart of accounts, coding system, description of departmental activity and accounts, alternative methods, proforma financial statements.

American Petroleum Institute, *Uniform System of Accounts for the Oil Industry,* first published 1926 in *Annual Proceedings of American Petroleum Institute* and then as separate pamphlet with revisions to Dec. 31, 1928, with later revisions to Dec. 31, 1929 and to June 30, 1936.

American Petroleum Institute, *Uniform System of Accounts for Pipe Lines Prescribed by The Interstate Commerce Commission in Accordance with Section 20 of the Interstate Commerce Act* (Revised to May 1, 1948), New York, the Institute, 1948, pp. 79.
Regulations of Interstate Commerce Commission on pipe line accounting.

R. W. Cobb, *Costs for Oil Producers,* New York, National Association of Cost Accountants, 1925, pp. 12.

Outlines, itemizes, and discusses investment and production costs in oil production.

Paul J. Graber, *Common Carrier Pipe Line Operations and Accounting,* Tulsa, Ross-Martin Co., 1951, pp. 220.
Eleven articles by pipe line executives on background and nature of accounting problems of common-carrier pipe lines; manner in which such problems are handled; appendix with uniform system of accounts for pipe lines.

H. G. Humphreys, *The Accounts of an Oil Company,* New York, American Institute Publishing Co., 1934, pp. xiii + 138.
Problems of accounting in petroleum industry; changes in accounting methods.

Robert H. Irving, Jr. and Verden R. Draper, *Accounting Practices in the Petroleum Industry,* New York, Ronald Press Co., 1958, pp. viii + 247.
Basic operations of oil industry and accounting practices peculiar to industry; accepted alternative methods of accounting for frequently encountered transactions. Covers crude oil production, refining, transportation, and marketing, with model forms for unit operations. Glossary.

Joseph Johnson, *Petroleum Distribution Accounts,* London, Gee & Co., 1932, pp. xiv + 126.
System of accounting suitable for oil marketing company.

Roswell H. Johnson, L. G. Huntley, and R. E. Somers, *The Business of Oil Production,* New York, John Wiley & Sons, 1922, pp. v + 264.
Business management of oil and gas production: leasing, financing, organization, cost accounting, depreciation, depletion, taxation, drilling methods, Mexican situation, prices, outlook.

Raymond Walter McKee, *Handbook of Petroleum Accounting,* New York, Harper & Bros., 1938, pp. xi + 496.
Oil company structure and significant aspects of each functional unit. Appropriate systems for producing, pipe line, refining, natural gas and natural gasoline, marketing, and marine divisions, with sample forms commonly used.

David F. Morland and Raymond Walter McKee, *Accounting for the Petroleum Industry,* New York, McGraw-Hill Book Co., 1925, pp. viii + 304.
Accounting principles and procedures applicable to petroleum; technical practices of industry, with separate treatment for production, transportation and storage, refining, and marketing functions; section on federal taxes.

Robert M. Pitcher, *Practical Accounting for Oil Producers,* Tulsa, Mid-West Printing Co., 1938, pp. xiii + 370. 2nd Ed. 1947, pp. ix + 645. 10th Printing, Tulsa, the author, 1957.
Chart of accounts for use in oil production accounting, discussion of various accounts and forms and records employed, extracts from American Petroleum Institute's *Uniform System of Accounts for the Oil Industry.*

Charles Aubrey Smith and Horace R. Brock, Jr., *Accounting for Oil and Gas Producers. Principles, Procedures, and Controls,* Englewood Cliffs, N.J., Prentice-Hall, Inc., 1959, pp. xvi + 536.
Present-day accounting procedures for large and small oil operators, variations in accounting practices currently in use, arguments for and against each.

Collis Porter Thompson, *An Introduction to Gas Utility Accounting,* Ann Arbor, Mich., Edward Brothers, 1935, pp. xv + 135.
Departmental organization of operating gas utilities, State regulation, uniform classification of accounts, accounting problems peculiar to gas utility industry, principles evolved, comparisons with general accounting.

Robert E. Waller, *Oil Accounting: Principles of Oil Exploration and Production Accounting in Canada,* University of Toronto Press for the Canadian Institute of Chartered Accountants, Toronto, 1956, pp. 90.
Exploration and production accounting practices, with objective some degree of standardization appropriate to Canadian conditions of ownership, taxation, and other variations from practice in United States. Glossary.

E. OIL STATISTICS

American Institute of Mining Engineers, *Statistics of Oil and Gas Development and Production. (Vol. 12. Covering 1957),* Dallas, American Institute of Mining, Metallurgical, and Petroleum Engineers, 1958, pp. viii + 596.
Annual statistical review of domestic and foreign production and drilling activity. Series initiated with *Statistics of Oil and Gas Development and Production,* New York, American Institute of Mining Engineers, 1946, pp. x + 444.

American Petroleum Institute, *Petroleum Facts and Figures,* New York, the Institute, 13th Ed. 1959, pp. 472.
Exhaustive statistical data on all aspects of petroleum; the prime sourcebook for oil statistics. First published 1928, pp. xv + 264. First four editions, published annually through 1931, contained text

and tables. Subsequent editions, 1937 through 1956, generally without text. 9th and 12th editions together give complete runs of oil industry statistics through 1955.

Gordon H. Barrows, Ed., *World Petroleum Report, 1958,* New York, Mona Palmer Publishing Co., 1958, pp. 242. Vol. V, 1959. Annual series initiated with *World Petroleum Statistical Year Book, 1953–1954 Edition,* 1954.
World review of exploration, development, production, refining, legislation.

Robert J. Bradley, *Twentieth Century Petroleum Statistics,* Washington, Office of Director, Naval Petroleum Reserves, 1945, pp. xix + 60, with equal number of charts. Publication continued 1946 by Robert J. Bradley, Dallas, DeGolyer

& MacNaughton, 1946, and each subsequent year, pp. xix + 60. Issue for 1958, data through 1957, pp. x + 87.
Pertinent records to date of production, consumption, reserves, drilling, United States and foreign.

William B. Harper, Ed., *The Petroleum Almanac. A Statistical Record, etc.,* New York, National Industrial Conference Board, 1946, pp. 420.
Major statistical sourcebook covering all departments of the oil industry, with runs of figures as complete as possible to obtain. Like American Petroleum Institute's *Petroleum Facts and Figures,* a prime sourcebook.

National Petroleum News, *NPN Fact Book,* New York, McGraw-Hill Book Co., 1959, pp. 274.
Issued annually since 1955 as supplement to May issue of *National Petroleum News.*
Tables of oil marketing statistics; details of individual companies, their areas of operation, advertising expenditure, etc.; directories of oil company sales personnel, manufacturers and suppliers of equipment.

Sydney H. North, Comp., *The Petroleum Year Book,* London, Wilkinson Bros., 1914, pp. 104. Subsequent editions: St. James' Press and The Petroleum Press, London. 1923 Ed., pp. 466.
Tables of oil producton; geological review of oil fields; chemical composition and properties of crude oils; oil fuel; oil burners, diagrams and description, regu-

lations, specifications; import duties gravity tables. Later editions contain data on individual companies, or bunkering stations, refining, oil shales.

Petroleum Information, *Resumé, Rock Mountain Oil and Gas Operations fo. 1958. 29th Annual Review,* Denver, Pe troleum Information, 1959, var. pag.
Reviews drilling, well completions, dis coveries, production, and other petro leum activities in Rocky Mountain States, including Four Corners area Series of yearly reports, begun in 1927 published originally in mimeographed form.

Rinehart Oil News Company, *Abe Rine hart's Yearbook, 1959,* Dallas, the Com pany, 1959, 2 vols., var. pag. Publishe annually since 1938.
Statistical and graphical review an summary of oil exploration and de velopment in Mid-Continent area southeast New Mexico, Texas, an Interstate Panhandle area in Vol. I Arkansas, Louisiana, Southeaster States, Rocky Mountains, and Canad in Vol. II.

H. J. Struth and J. P. Love, Eds., *The Petro leum Data Book,* Dallas, Petroleum Engineer Publishing Co., 1947, var. pag 2nd Ed. 1948.
Operational information and statistic on world oil development, exploration drilling, production, refining, gas proc essing, transportation, utilization; direc tories of governmental agencies; bibliog raphy.

F. OIL INVESTMENTS AND ROYALTIES

B. L. Abicht, *Explanation of Oil and Gas Royalties,* Tulsa, the author, 1935, pp. 19.
Account of nature of oil and gas royalties and factors affecting status as investments.

American News Company, *Guide-Book for Investors in Petroleum Stocks,* New York, the Company, 1865, pp. 80.
Oil stocks; advice to investors; advice against issuance of large number of low-priced shares; mining laws of Pennsyl-

vania, Ohio, West Virginia, and New York; list of oil companies.

George S. Anderson, *Romance of Royalty* Fort Worth, Tanner-Williams Co., 1928 pp. 62. (2nd Edition of earlier book *Royalty.*)
Suggestions for buying of royalties; de fines terms, and illustrates profit pos sibilities.

Charles E. Bowles, *Oil Royalties: An In dustrial Analysis,* New York, Urquhar Press, 1927, pp. 47.

Basis and amount of royalty contracts; common practice.

Ray C. Capes, *The Oil Royalty Analyzed,* Tulsa, the author, 1929, pp. 31.
Origin and kinds of royalties, transactions, and relation to development and production.

George Evert Condra, *Blue Sky vs. Square Dealing in Land and Oil,* Lincoln, University of Nebraska, 1919, pp. 14.
Guide to prospective investors in land and oil properties.

F. W. Freeborn, *Producing Oil Royalties, From the Engineer's Viewpoint,* Tulsa, the author, 1933, pp. 40.
Kinds and nature of oil royalties, methods of appraising oil properties, oil prices, proration, and data on production, potentials, and proration in various fields.

Samuel Haven Glassmire, *Oil and Gas Royalties,* New York, Urquhart Press, 1927, pp. 40. 2nd Ed.: *Oil and Gas Royalties; A Practical Legal Treatise on Petroleum Rights,* St. Louis, Mo., Thomas Law Book Co., 1930, pp. 160. 3rd Ed.: (rev.) *Law of Oil and Gas Leases and Royalties; A Practical Legal Treatise on Petroleum Rights Accruing by Virtue of Mineral Deeds and Oil and Gas Leases,* St. Louis, Mo., Thomas Law Book Co., 1935, pp. 400. 1938, pp. ix + 467.
The law of oil and gas royalties and leases.

David D. Leven and Harold Johnson, *Petroleum Royalty Handbook,* New York, Nevell Publishing Co., 1934, pp. 64.

Oil royalty interests, business, investments, buying and selling, factors affecting royalties; related information on oil leases, royalties, regulations.

Forest R. Rees, *The Oil Men's Scrapbook,* Tulsa, the author, n.d. (c. 1930), pages unnumbered.
Descriptive material on petroleum royalties, maps of oil fields; questions and answers on geological matters.

Edwin Isherwood Reeser, *Oil Royalties: A Handbook on Petroleum for the Layman,* Tulsa, Dexter Publishing Co., 1929, pp. 190.
Oil royalties and investments, including historical basis.

Andrew M. Rowley, *Oil Royalties. Worth Much More Under New Methods,* Tulsa, the author, 1937, pp. 27.
Nontechnical discussion of policies and production practices which affect income from and investment in petroleum royalties, including unit operation, deeper drilling, acid treatment, repressuring, water flooding, and well spacing.

Francis Maurice Van Tuyl and J. William Smallwood, *Oil Securities,* Boston, American Institute of Finance, 1922, pp. 56.
Review of oil industry; oil finding and production, future supply, and means of determining values in selection of oil securities.

Taft Welch, *Oil Royalty, "A Business Without Operating Cost,"* Tulsa, Scott-Rice Co., 1933, pp. 32.
Main features and operational aspects of oil royalties.

G. ECONOMICS, FORECASTS, ENERGY STUDIES

American Petroleum Institute, *American Petroleum Supply and Demand,* New York, McGraw-Hill Book Co., 1925, pp. 269.
Report to board of directors, American Petroleum Institute, by committee of 11 board members on future supply and demand. In response to establishment of Federal Oil Conservation Board.

American Petroleum Institute, *American Petroleum Industry,* New York, the Institute, 1935, pp. xiv + 229.
1925 report of above committee brought up to 1935.

American Petroleum Institute, *Petroleum-Industry Hearings Before the Temporary National Economic Committee,*

New York, the Institute, 1942, pp. xii + 590.

Description of hearings; texts of prepared testimony by industry witnesses covering all phases of petroleum industry; list of investigations of oil industry, 1906–39. Prime source material for historian or economist interested in oil industry of the 1930's.

American Petroleum Institute, Department of Information Staff, *Oil's Expanding Job Market,* New York, the Institute, 1955, pp. 7.

Background Information Bulletin. Growth in employment stability and employee benefits in petroleum industry.

Eugene Ayres and Charles A. Scarlott, *Energy Sources—The Wealth of the World,* New York, McGraw-Hill Book Co., 1952, pp. vii + 344.

Broad discussion of future energy sources, including oil and gas.

Joe S. Bain, *The Economics of the Pacific Coast Petroleum Industry,* Berkeley, Cal., University of California Press, 1944–45–47, 3 vols., pp. xxxix + 789.

Vol. I: Market structure of Pacific Coast petroleum industry, description of principal market characteristics. Vol. II: Price behavior and competition, history of competition and cooperation, analysis of price behavior, competition of the 1929–40 period. Vol. III: Public policy toward competition and pricing.

Joe S. Bain, *War and Postwar Developments in the Southern California Petroleum Industry,* Los Angeles, Haynes Foundation, 1944, pp. 49.

Petroleum in economy of Southern California; prewar situation, effect of war, postwar prospects.

John W. Boatwright, *Petroleum and Economic Progress,* New York, American Petroleum Institute, 1954, pp. 7.

Background Information Bulletin. Contributions of oil and gas industries to national economic progress.

Chase National Bank, *Financial Analysis of Thirty Oil Companies,* New York, the Bank.

Annual Series initiated 1945 by the Chase National Bank. Joseph E. Pogue and Frederick G. Coqueron, *Financial Analysis of Thirty Oil Companies,* 1945, pp. 46. This was the first of the series it surveyed 30 oil companies for the years 1934–44. Beginning 1953 the number of oil companies included in the survey increased to 35, but was reduced to 33 by subsequent mergers. Frederick G. Coqueron, Norma J. Anderson, and Richard C. Sparling, *Petroleum Industry, 1957,* New York, Chase Manhattan Bank, 1958, pp. 44. This is the latest in the Series, begun 1945; it surveys financial and operating aspects of group of 33 oil companies, including capital expenditures by departments, investments, return, production, well completions, and competent analysis of relationships.

Columbia University, Graduate School of Business, *Energy and Man: A Symposium,* New York, Appleton-Century Crofts, 1960, pp. xiii + 113.

Papers delivered by Allan Nevins, Robert G. Dunlop, Edward Teller, Edward S. Mason, and Herbert Hoover, Jr., at Columbia Symposium honoring oil centennial, October, 1959.

Roy Clyde Cook, *Control of the Petroleum Industry By Major Oil Companies* (Monograph No. 39, Investigation of Concentration of Economic Power, 76th Congress, 3rd Session), Washington, Government Printing Office, 1941, pp. xi + 101.

Object of study was "to examine the more important monopolistic conditions which prevail in the petroleum industry. Study originated and completed as research project in Department of Economics, George Washington University, Washington, D.C.

Frederick G. Coqueron and Joseph E. Pogue, *Investment Patterns in the World Petroleum Industry,* New York, Chase National Bank, 1956, pp. 55.

Financial data on Free World Petroleum industry: capital expenditures 1946–1955; data on production, consumption, capacities.

Frederick G. Coqueron, Harold D. Hammar, and John G. Winger, *Future Growth of the World Petroleum Industry,* New York, Chase Manhattan Bank, 1958, pp. 48.

Anticipated energy requirements and

supplies, United States and foreign, 1967 compared with 1957; role of crude oil and natural gas; forecasts of drilling requirements, oil and gas production.

Melvin G. De Chazeau and Alfred E. Kahn, *Integration and Competition in the Petroleum Industry,* New Haven, Conn., Yale University Press, 1959, pp. xviii + 598.
Volume III of Petroleum Monograph Series. Deals with economic and historical setting of integration in oil industry, pricing of crude oil, regulation of production, conservation, national defense, public policy, and integration and competition in products markets.

ohn A. Dodge & Co., *Petroleum: Its Past, Present and Future in Commerce and Speculation,* New York, the Company, 1884, pp. 20.
Brief oil history, operation of oil exchanges, description of trading methods and tables of oil prices.

conomic Commission for Europe, *The Price of Oil in Western Europe,* prepared by the Secretariat (Gunnar Myrdal), Geneva, Switzerland, United Nations, 1955, pp. iv + 50, plus annexes.
Presented as working paper to Coal Committee of Economic Commission for Europe. Discusses structure of oil industry, price of Middle East crude oil and of refined product prices in Western Europe, and strains which have been observed in system.

V. S. Farish and J. Howard Pew, *Review and Criticism on Behalf of Standard Oil Co. (N.J.) and Sun Oil Co. of Monograph No. 39, With Rejoinder by Monograph Author,* Washington, Government Printing Office, 1941, pp. vi + 96. (Monograph 39-A)
Temporary National Economic Committee hearings in 1939 resulted in series of monographs by Committee staff. Here presidents of two major oil companies refute an author's contentions.

H. Frankel, *Essentials of Petroleum. A Key to Oil Economics,* London, Chapman & Hall, 1946, pp. xv + 173.
Analytical appraisal of pertinent economic factors which underlie structure of oil industry, including prices and policies. Translated into French, 1948,

with additional part dealing with French petroleum industry.

Walter M. Fuchs, *When The Oil Wells Run Dry,* Dover, N.H., Industrial Research Service, 1946, pp. xiv + 447.
The oil industry in its social, political, and scientific aspects, with section on synthetic oil.

Chester G. Gilbert and Joseph E. Pogue, *America's Power Resources. The Economic Significance of Coal, Oil and Water-Power,* New York, Century Co., 1921, pp. xiv + 326.
Interprets importance attaching to energy resources and notes shortcomings in handling, indicating avenues of advance in administration.

Chester G. Gilbert and Joseph E. Pogue, *Petroleum: A Resource Interpretation,* Washington, Government Printing Office (Bulletin 102, Part 6, The Mineral Industries of the United States, Smithsonian Institution), 1918, pp. v + 76.
Economic study of oil industry, maladjustments, suggested economc policy.

John E. Hodges and Leslie Cookenboo, Jr., *The Oil Well Drilling Contractor Industry. A Case Study in Pure Competition,* Houston, Rice Institute, 1953, pp. vi + 98.
Study of "one of the few purely competitive industries in the United States today." Structure of industry, costs, prices, and profits.

John E. Hodges and Henry B. Steele, *An Investigation of the Problems of Cost Determination for the Discovery, Development, and Production of Liquid Hydrocarbon and Natural Gas Resources,* Houston, Rice Institute, 1959, pp. 156.
Recent cost studies, recommendations for studies of crude oil and natural gas costs, trends in cost of finding oil and gas reserves in United States.

Columban A. Johnson, *Coal, Oil, Gas and Electricity,* Pittsburgh, Charles W. Swope, 1921, pp. 107.
General review and discussion of our natural resources, with chapters on formation of oil, natural gas.

Arthur Knapp, *The Use of Graphic Charts in the Petroleum Industry,* New York, Codex Book Co., 1927, pp. 33.
Types of charts necessary for general study of petroleum industry, with illustration and discussion of 11 typical charts.

Harry E. McAllister, *The Elasticity of Demand for Gasoline in the State of Washington,* Pullman, Wash., State College of Washington, 1956, pp. xiv + 80.
Study undertaken following investigation for legislature of State of Washington, 1948, which included analysis of tax yields from gasoline. Concludes inelasticity of demand applies to generic product gasoline, but demand among various brands is highly elastic.

John G. McLean and Robert William Haigh, *The Growth of Integrated Oil Companies,* Boston, Graduate School of Business Administration, Harvard University, 1954, pp. xxiv + 728.
Authoritative study of emergence of large, integrated companies in oil industry, based on case studies of a half dozen leading firms. Oil industry structure in 1950; technological, economic, and business circumstances which have encouraged vertical integration; discussion of selected group of oil companies; participation of small business in refining segment of industry, 1920–50.

Horst Mendershausen, *Dollar Shortage and Oil Surplus in 1949–1950,* Princeton, N.J., Princeton University Press, 1950, pp. 34.
Postwar conflict between needs for oil and shortage of dollars abroad; controversy over oil imports into United States; difficulties of more effective economic integration of United States, Western Europe, and areas of new development.

National Crude Oil Industry Advisory Committee, *Report on the Cost of Finding, Developing and Producing Crude Petroleum,* Washington, the Committee, submitted to Office of Price Administration, 1946, pages unnumbered.
Study, analysis, and interpretation of data obtained by Office of Price Administration in national survey of crude petroleum costs; numerous appendices.

National Refiners' Industry Advisory Committee, *Memorandum Regarding Refining Operations and Earnings,* Tulsa, Western Petroleum Refiners Association, 1945, pages unnumbered.
Conclusion that "any upward adjustment of crude oil prices would have to be accompanied by a commensurate and simultaneous increase in refined product prices." Refinery margin index for Mid-Continent and Gulf Coast refiners; special study covering 14 Michigan refineries.

Organisation for European Economic Co-operation, *First Report on Co-Ordination of Oil Refinery Expansion in the O.E.E.C. Countries,* Paris, the Organisation, 1949, pp. 87.
Forecasts of oil consumption and refinery plans; separate studies for each of 14 countries involved.
Second Report on Co-Ordination of Oil Refinery Expansion in the O.E.E.C. Countries,, 1951, pp. 97.
Historical background, oil requirements, development of refinery programs, balance of payments, economic and technical consequences, contribution of oil to recovery; 15 countries studied.
Third Report on Co-Ordination of Oil Refinery Expansion in the O.E.E.C. Countries, 1953, pp. 85.
Trends of consumption; expansion of refineries; technical, currency, and economic questions.

Campbell Osborn, *Oil Economics,* New York, McGraw-Hill Book Co., 1932, pp. 402.
Review of principal economic facts relating to oil; methods of analyzing and forecasting price movements and profits.

Eduardo Ospina-Racines, *The Economics of United States and World Oil,* Bogotá, Colombia, (loose-leaf binder), the author, 1950.
Economic factors governing oil supply, demand, price; time lag of United States oil industry; future development of world oil industry.

Petroleum Administrative Board, *Preliminary Report on a Survey of Crude Petroleum Cost of Production for the Years 1931–33 and Comparison with 1927–30,* Washington, Government Printing Office, 1934, pp. 74.

Depression year cost surveys.

Petroleum Administrative Board, *Report on Cost of Producing Crude Petroleum,* Washington, Government Printing Office, 1936, pp. iv + 137.
1931–34 costs of production of crude petroleum by areas and states, output at various cost levels, factors bearing on costs, estimated reserves.

Petroleum Industry War Council, *Report of Committee on Cost and Price Adjustment to the Petroleum Industry War Council,* Washington, the Council, 1943, var. pag.
Crude oil price structures which can be expected to stimulate and increase search for new crude oil reserves; recommendations.

Edward Clarence Petty, *Developments in the Petroleum Industry as Related to Overproduction of Crude Oil,* Norman, Okla., University of Oklahoma Press, 1931, pp. 31. Rev. Ed. 1932.
Deals with overexpansion of petroleum refining industry, pointing to gasoline demand and overproduction of crude oil as causes, discusses changes in size, type, and location of refining plants, pointing to gasoline pipe lines as offset to poor refinery location.

Joseph E. Pogue, *The Economics of Petroleum,* New York, John Wiley & Sons, 1921, pp. ix + 375.
First major work in field of petroleum economics by author who became recognized authority in field and long-time head of Chase Bank petroleum department.

Joseph E. Pogue, *Economics of the Petroleum Industry* (Advance printing of chapter in *The Elements of the Petroleum Industry,* edited by E. DeGolyer), New York, Chase National Bank, 1939, pp. 60.
Economic discussion of all aspects of petroleum industry; production control, suggestions for more effective proration.

Joseph E. Pogue and Kenneth E. Hill, *Future Growth and Financial Requirements of the World Petroleum Industry,* New York, Chase Manhattan Bank, 1956, pp. 39.

Projection to 1965 of oil demand and supply; capital required.

Eugene V. Rostow, *A National Policy for the Oil Industry,* New Haven, Conn., Yale University Press, 1948, pp. 173.
Investigates forces affecting prices and output in oil industry and examines functioning of system of law which defines public policy towards industry, and alternative courses which might serve national interest.

George Sell, Ed., *Competitive Aspects of Oil Operations,* London, Institute of Petroleum, 1958, pp. vii + 203.
Seven papers covering structure of oil industry; crude oil prices; competition in search for oil, research and development, quality and marketing.

George Sell, Ed., *Essential Factors in the Future Development of the Oil Industry,* London, Institute of Petroleum, 1956, pp. vii + 176.
Eight papers presented by various authors, dealing with world outlook for energy requirements, oil demand, resources, world oil movements, refining techniques, petrochemicals, and financial factors, with summary of discussions.

John E. Shatford, *Can The Non-Integrated Refiner Survive?* Washington, National Independent Refiners Association, 1934, pp. 29.
Position of nonintegrated petroleum refiner in relation to crude oil supply, refinery markets, and pipe lines, from viewpoint of conditions prevailing during period of National Recovery Administration.

Ronald B. Shuman, *The Petroleum Industry, An Economic Survey,* Norman, Okla., University of Oklahoma Press, 1940, pp. 297.
Survey of petroleum demands, development, production, refining, manufacturing, transportation, storage, marketing, taxation, personnel management, world situation, natural gas, conservation, and control.

John E. Swearingen and John W. Boatwright, *Meeting Future Petroleum Requirements,* New York, American

Petroleum Institute, 1952, pp. 17. Background Information Bulletin. Covers probable demand for oil and availability of supply.

William Taylor Thom, *Petroleum and Coal; The Keys to the Future,* Princeton, N.J., Princeton University Press, 1929, pp. xviii + 223.
Influence of petroleum and coal upon national policies; discussion of remaining reserves and their bearing upon future civilization.

United States Tariff Commission, *Report to The Congress on the Cost of Crude Petroleum* (Report No. 4., 2nd Series), Washington, Government Printing Office, 1931, pp. viii + 90.
Information for 1927, 1928, and 1929 on costs of production of crude petroleum in Mid-Continent-Gulf area and Venezuela, including delivery to Atlantic seaboard refineries; factors affecting comparative costs and prices.

United States Tariff Commission, *Production Costs of Crude Petroleum and of Refined Petroleum Products* (Report No. 30., 2nd Series; also, House Document No. 195, 72nd Congress, 1st Session), Washington, Government Printing Office, 1932, pp. xi + 205.
Crude oil costs, 1927–1930, for Mexico, Colombia, Peru, Ecuador, Trinidad, eastern Venezuela, and Maracaibo Basin; costs, 1929–1930, for products derived from domestic crude in comparison with products from foreign crude by refineries in United States and in Netherlands West Indies, Mexico, Colombia, Peru, Venezuela, Trinidad.

United States Tariff Commission, *Crude Petroleum: Report on the Cost of Producing Crude Petroleum in the United States,* by Tariff Commission for Office of Price Administration, 1942, pp. vii + 248.
Statistics by principal pools or fields for 1939, 1940, and first nine months of 1941; preliminary summaries for selected pools or fields to June, 1942.
Supplementary Report, covering period Oct., 1941, to July, 1942, published 1943, pp. 27. Sampling procedure to determine trends in costs.
Supplementary Report on the Cost of Producing Crude Petroleum in California, 1943, pp. iv + 77. Special investigation of costs of production of low-gravity crudes in California, resulting from exceptionally heavy demand for such crudes to meet war requirements for fuel oil.

Walter Henry Voskuil, *Postwar Issues in the Petroleum Industry,* Urbana, Ill., University of Illinois, 1946, pp. 32.
United States interests in world oil resources; adequacy of domestic supply, alternative sources of supply; cost levels; imports of foreign oil and attitudes of various groups; postwar requirements of armed forces, etc.

H. ANTI-TRUST

William J. Kemnitzer, *Rebirth of Monopoly, A Critical Analysis of Economic Conduct in the Petroleum Industry of the United States,* New York, Harper & Bros., 1938, pp. 261.
Views on developments in petroleum industry subsequent to dissolution of Standard Oil Co., indicating return of monopoly through industry control.

Simon N. Whitney, *Antitrust Policies: American Experience in Twenty Industries,* New York, Twentieth Century Fund, 1958, 2 vols., pp. xxxiii + 1101.

Chapter 3 (Vol. I, pp. 95–187) affords comprehensive survey of main oil-industry prosecutions under Sherman and Clayton Anti-Trust Acts: Standard Oil case, cracking patent pool, Madison trial, Elkins Act consent decree, Cartel Suit; Federal Trade Commission proceedings, price discrimination actions under Robinson-Patman Act, Detroit case, etc. Author former Professor of Economics, New York University; later chief economist, Federal Trade Commission.

XIV.

History and Biography

A. OIL INDUSTRY

1. GENERAL

(See also specific areas and subjects, such as "Pennsylvania," "Refining of Petroleum," etc.)

Frederick Lewis Allen, *Only Yesterday,* New York, Harper & Bros., 1931, pp. xiv + 370.
Discusses Teapot Dome and Elk Hills: events associated with leasing of naval petroleum reserves.

American Petroleum Institute, *California's Oil,* New York, the Institute, 1948, pp. 28.
Early oil industry in California compiled by Petroleum Production Pioneers Association; chronology of oil "firsts"; addendum relating to George S. Gilbert, refiner of 1860's.

Herbert Asbury, *The Golden Flood. An Informal History of America's First Oil Field,* New York, Alfred A. Knopf, 1952, pp. xv + 324.
Well-written account of happenings leading up to Drake Well and developments which followed; early fields and pioneers. Good account of "Coal Oil Johnny" Steele.

Robert L. Baker, *Oil, Blood, and Sand,* New York, D. Appleton-Century Co., 1942, pp. 300.
Hitler's needs for oil; Axis plans for Middle East; conditions in Italy, Turkey, Iran, and other countries; general military, economic strategy; Allied defense of Middle East.

Donald Banks, *Flame Over Britain, etc.,* London, Sampson, Low, Marston & Co., 1946, pp. xiv + 207.

Development and application of flame-defenses; Pipe Line Under The Ocean (PLUTO), the land and underwater pipe lines under English Channel; fog investigations; dispersal operations.

Kendall Beaton, *Dr. Gesner's Kerosene: The Start of American Oil Refining,* Boston, Harvard Graduate School of Business Administration, 1955. Reprint from *The Business History Review,* March, 1955, pp. 28–53.
Thorough and well-documented account of work of Abraham Gesner, including legal controversy involved in mining of "Albert Coal," first manufacture of kerosene by North American Gas Light Company, and discussion of origin of word, "kerosene."

Kendall Beaton, *The High Cost of Whale Oil—and What It Led To,* New York, World Petroleum, 1959. Reprint from *World Petroleum,* June 1959, pp. 62–67.
How rising cost of whale oil fostered new industry making "artificial" illuminants in 1850's; brief accounts of Gesner's New York Kerosene Co., Downer's Boston and Portland Works, James Young and beginning of Scottish shale oil industry, Jenney Mfg. Co. of Boston.

A. Cotton Bedford, *War Organization of the Petroleum Industry,* New York, the author, 1918, pp. 31.
Discusses appointment and work of Oil Division of Fuel Administration, and functions of Petroleum War Service Committee, of which author was chairman. Address delivered at convention, Western Jobbers' Association, March 28, 1918, Chicago.

Harry Botsford, *The Valley of Oil,* New York, Hastings House, 1946, pp. viii + 278.
Events leading to drilling and completion of Drake Well, excitement which followed, special attention to Pithole, individuals, transportation difficulties, early refining.

Arch Bristow, *Old Time Tales of Warren County,* Meadville, Penna., Tribune Publishing Co., 1933, pp. 389.
Petroleum in days before Drake; Drake's visit to Warren Aug. 14, 1859, to have drilling tools drawn out; first news of Drake Well being received at Tidioute Aug. 30, 1859; first oil well in Warren County, Pennsylvania, and other items.

George Washington Brown, *Old Times in Oildom,* Youngsville, Penna., printed by author, pp. 79; 2nd Ed. 1910, pp. 172; 3rd Ed. 1910, pp. 196; 4th Ed. 1912, pp. 251.
Author states he saw Drake Well on second day of its production; also, first flowing well. Many incidents of early oil excitement, with varying number of biographical sketches.

Bureau of Standards, *War Work of the Bureau of Standards,* (Miscellaneous publications, No. 46), Washington, Government Printing Office, 1921, pp. 299.
Work of Bureau, on airplane engine fuels, lubrication of aircraft engines; general and special investigations of natural gas.

Francis Xavier Busch, *Enemies of the State,* Indianapolis, Bobbs-Merrill Co., 1954, pp. viii + 299.
Includes report and discussion of Teapot Dome cases, involving 2 civil and 6 criminal trials, with aftermath review.

James L. Butler, *Petroleum, Earth, Mineral or Rock Oils,* New York, John W. Amerman, 1862, pp. 5.
Reprint from Annual Report New York Chamber of Commerce, May, 1862. Brief review of oil industry and its place in commerce.

California State Council of Defense, *Report of the Committee on Petroleum,* Sacramento, State Printing Office, 1917, pp. 191.
California oil fields, production, storage, transportation, refining, utilization maintenance, increase of production conservation, naval petroleum reserves conclusions, recommendations. Competent report on California oil industry during First World War.

Worrall Reed Carter, *Beans, Bullets, and Black Oil,* Washington, Government Printing Office, 1953, pp. xix + 482.
Detailed story, for each campaign, of distribution of United States Navy in Pacific; description of fleet tankers and fueling ships.

Chesebrough Manufacturing Company, *Petroleum: Its Origin, Uses, and Future Development,* London, the Company, (c. 1882), pp. 16.
History and uses of Vaseline, a pioneer petroleum specialty product.

James A. Clark and Michel T. Halbouty, *Spindletop,* New York, Random House, 1952, pp. xvi + 306.
History of the 1901 discovery at Spindletop, events leading up to it, and boom days which followed; significance of the field in launching a new era of the oil industry.

J. Stanley Clark, *The Oil Century, From Drake Well to Conservation Era,* Norman, Okla., University of Oklahoma Press, 1958, pp. xxii + 280.
History of oil during past century, with emphasis on technological advances and evolution of production techniques.

Andrew Cone and Walter R. Johns, *Petrolia: A Brief History of the Pennsylvania Petroleum Region,* New York, D. Appleton & Co., 1870, pp. 652.
Describes early history of petroleum, nature and extent of development, drilling and pumping methods, transportation, description of each farm and locality where developments took place. Contains reprint of Silliman Report of 1855. Cone described as "storehouse of facts and figures pertaining to oil," while Johns issued first newspaper devoted especially to petroleum industry. A standard reference for historians interested in early oil industry.

. R. Crum and A. S. Dungan, *Romance of American Petroleum and Gas*, New York, Romance of American Petroleum and Gas Company, 1911 and 1921, 2 vols., pp. 786.

Vol. I deals with discovery and developments, men and events in Appalachian field, during first 50 years of petroleum industry. Planned as 3-volume set. Crum died after Vol. I published, but associates completed and published Vol. II, which deals with later developments in Appalachian field and also with history and progress of fields elsewhere in United States, Mexico, and other foreign areas; contains many biographical sketches and company histories not to be found elsewhere.

. Thomas Curtin, *Men, Oil and War*, Chicago, Petroleum Industry Committee for District No. 2, 1946, pp. 360.

Wartime operations of petroleum industry in 15 Middle Western states comprising District No. 2 of Petroleum Administration for War.

ildegarde Dolson, *The Great Oildorado*, New York, Random House, 1959, pp. xi + 300.

A lively account of Drake's discovery well and of men and events during oil-boom decades, 1860–1880.

atrick Doyle, *Petroleum: Its History, Origin and Use, etc.*, Brisbane, Australia, F. T. F. Keogh, 1880, pp. 28.

Series of articles prompted by Mineral Oils Act; discussion of petroleum distillation and testing, dangers associated with oil use, which author states have been exaggerated.

ubreuil Oil Works Co., *History of Petroleum, Ancient and Modern*, Baltimore, the Company, 1868, pp. 33.

Early uses of petroleum, quality of oils sold domestically for lighting, lubricating, cleaning.

. J. M. Eaton, *Petroleum: A History of the Oil Region of Venango County, Pennsylvania*, Philadelphia, J. P. Skelly & Co., 1866, pp. 299, map.

Author pastor of Presbyterian Church, Franklin, Penna. Oil region, early history of petroleum operations, manner of boring oil wells, bringing oil to surface, and preparing it for use.

S. J. M. Eaton, *Venango County: Centennial Discourse*, Franklin, Penna., *Venango Spectator*, 1876, pp. 48.

Reprint of Fourth of July address.

Henri Erni, *Coal Oil and Petroleum: Their Origin, History, Geology and Chemistry, etc.*, Philadelphia, Henry Carey Baird, 1865, pp. viii + 196.

Author was Chief Chemist to Dept. of Agriculture; articles originally written for Washington, D.C., newspaper.

Ethyl Corporation, *The Road From Hanover*, New York, the Company, 1953, pp. 43.

Start of petroleum technology with scientific examination of crude oil at Dartmouth College in 1853.

Guy W. Finney, *The Great Los Angeles Bubble, etc.*, Los Angeles, Milton Forbes Co., 1929, pp. 203.

Financial speculation in area 1920–1927; mainly of organization and promotion of Julian Petroleum Corporation.

Henry C. Folger, Jr., *Petroleum: Its Production and Products*. Section B. Annual Report of Bureau of Industrial Statistics, Harrisburg, Penna., 1893. Also published as Ch. XXXI, Vol. I of *One Hundred Years of American Commerce*, New York, D. O. Haynes & Co., 1895, 2 vols.

Short summary of history and statistics of American petroleum industry. Author was executive of old Standard Oil Co.

Gerald Forbes, *Flush Production. The Epic of Oil in the Gulf-Southwest*, Norman, Okla., University of Oklahoma Press, 1942, pp. 253.

Development of oil and gas in Gulf-Southwest; histories of selected major fields; oil field lore.

R. J. Forbes, *Bitumen and Petroleum in Antiquity*, Leiden, Netherlands, E. J. Brill, 1936, pp. viii + 109. (Reprinted in Vol. I, author's *Studies in Ancient Technology*, Leiden, E. J. Brill, 1955.)

Authoritative work on oil and its uses from ancient times to end of Middle Ages, by distinguished scholar.

R. J. Forbes, *Studies in Early Petroleum*

History, Leiden, Netherlands, E. J. Brill, 1957, pp. ix + 199.
(See next listing for description.)

R. J. Forbes, *More Studies in Early Petroleum History,* Leiden, Netherlands, E. J. Brill, 1959, pp. 199.
Petroleum and its usage in the ancient world, Middle Ages, and up to Drake well; early Galician, Rumanian, and Russian production and refining, with statistics. A series of separate papers by a distinguished petroleum scholar.

John W. Frey and H. Chandler Ide, Eds., *A History of the Petroleum Administration for War, 1941–45,* Washington, Government Printing Office, 1946, pp. xviii + 463.
Operations of Petroleum Administration for War and its predecessor agencies. Authoritative account written at time by major participants. Important statistics not found elsewhere.

Eugene Marie Friedwald, *Oil and the War,* trans. from French by Lawrence Wolfe, London, William Heinemann, 1941, pp. 88.
Oil situation in Axis countries, their sources of supply; Great Britain, the Empire, and other countries from which oil supplies are derived; conclusions.

Thomas A. Gale, *The Wonder of the Nineteenth Century: Rock Oil in Pennsylvania and Elsewhere,* Erie, Penna., Sloan & Griffith, 1860, pp. 80.
This first book about petroleum following the Drake well was written to satisfy public desire for more information about rock oil, its origin, geology, production, costs, uses, history, prospects; invaluable eyewitness descriptions of early oil wells.

Galena Oil Works, *A Brief History of Petroleum,* the Company, 1876, pp. 16. 2nd Ed. Bradford, Penna., 1883, pp. 35.
Issued as advertising booklet in connection with Philadelphia Centennial Exposition. Probable author: John J. McLaurin.

Paul H. Giddens, *The Birth of the Oil Industry,* New York, Macmillan Co., 1938, pp. xxxix + 216.
The classic account of the beginnings of the Pennsylvania oil industry, 1859–

1870, by a qualified academic historian working from original sources. Invaluable and reliable source material for any writer on oil history. Introduction by Ida M. Tarbell.

Paul H. Giddens, *The Beginnings of the Petroleum Industry. Sources and Bibliography,* Harrisburg, Pennsylvania Historical Commission, 1941, pp. 195.
First part consists of letters, dated during 1854 and 1855, regarding Pennsylvania Rock Oil Co. of New York and other material collected; second part is bibliography of early history of oil industry, with particular attention to newspaper and periodical articles.

Paul H. Giddens, *Early Days of Oil,* Princeton, N.J., Princeton University Press, 1948, pp. viii + 149. (Reissued 1959 under original date.)
Excellent pictorial history of early Pennsylvania industry, based largely upon the photographs of John A. Mather, a contemporary photographer of the oil regions. Readable and accurate running commentary and captions.

Paul H. Giddens, Ed., *Pennsylvania Petroleum 1750–1872; A Documentary History,* Titusville, Penna., Pennsylvania Historical and Museum Commission, 1947, pp. xv + 420.
Literatim copies of all important early documents relating to petroleum and to start of Pennsylvania oil industry, 1750–1872, with connecting commentary explaining significance and noting sources. Originals of most of this material in Drake Well Memorial Park Museum, Titusville, of which Giddens was curator at the time. Invaluable to any historian wishing to examine original accounts himself.

Paul H. Giddens, *Drake Well Memorial Park,* privately printed by the author, 1950.
An album of ten pictures relating to Drake Well Memorial Park.

Paul H. Giddens, *Family History of Colonel Edwin Laurentine Drake,* privately printed by the author, 1950.

Paul H. Giddens, *The American Petroleum Industry—Its Beginnings in Pennsylva-*

nial, n.p., American Newcomen Society, 1959.
Delivered as a Newcomen Society address.

. B. Glasscock, *Then Came Oil,* Indianapolis, Bobbs-Merrill Co., 1938, pp. 349.
Settlement of Indian Territory, discovery of oil, conflicts with cattle industry, statehood, new fields and communities, and development of oil industry, carrying history of Oklahoma oil through Oklahoma City development, with much lore of country and industry.

Charles M. Goodsell, *Manual of Petroleum,* New York, Financial News Assn., 1883, pp. 40.
History, production, and transportation of petroleum, with annual statistics, 1878–1883, and account of oil exchanges.

Llewellyn Graham, *The Romance of Texas Oil,* Fort Worth, Tariff Publishing Co., 1935, pp. 126.
Principal oil discoveries in Texas, beginning with Oil Springs, Nacogdoches County, in winter of 1866–67, to discovery of East Texas oil field 1930.

Stephen Graham, *Liquid Victory,* London, Hutchinson & Co., 1942, pp. 96.
Oil supplies of world; accessibility to belligerents; importance of petroleum in modern warfare.

Great Britain, Admiralty, *Descriptive Illustrated Account of the Admiralty Oil Fuel Pipe Line Connecting the Firths of Clyde and Forth,* London, His Majesty's Stationery Office, 1919, pp. 17.
Account of laying 35 miles of 8-inch pipe line, from west coast of Scotland to base of British Fleet, near Edinburgh, to reduce hazards of mine fields and submarines. Pipe line crew recruited in United States.

Great Britain, Ministry of Fuel and Power, *Report on the Petroleum and Synthetic Oil Industry of Germany,* London, His Majesty's Stationery Office, 1947, pp. v + 134.
Report covering carbonization and gasification of coal, hydrogenation; crude oil production, refining, lubricating oil; testing and evaluation.

Horace Greeley, *The Great Industries of the United States,* Hartford, J. B. Burr & Hyde, 1872, pp. 1304.
Petroleum section probably written by J. B. Lyman; historical and descriptive. Illuminating gas section refers to introduction of natural gas and use of petroleum for gas enrichment.

A. E. Gunther, *Oil Fields Investigations, The German Crude Oil Industry, 1939–45* (British Intelligence Objectives Sub-Committee Report No. 1010–1017, Item No. 30), London, His Majesty's Stationery Office, 1946, var. pag.
Four parts. Investigation to provide technical bases for future development, and to guide Control Commission.

Curtis G. Hamill, *We Drilled Spindletop,* Houston, the author, 1957, pp. 39.
Author, last living person connected with drilling of Spindletop, recorded his recollections of event, along with description of equipment and methods employed.

Proctor W. Hansl, *Years of Plunder: A Financial Chronicle of Our Times,* New York, Harrison Smith and Robert Haas, 1935, pp. 312.
Chapters on John D. Rockefeller, Standard Oil Company, leasing of Elk Hills, and Teapot Dome naval petroleum reserves.

H. Heinlein, *Petroleum Report for 1865,* New York, n.pub., 1866, pages unnumbered.
Covers production, distribution, exports, stocks, and prices, with comments concerning trade. Refers to prior report.

James Dodds Henry, *History and Romance of the Petroleum Industry,* London, Bradbury, Agnew & Co., 1914, pp. xxiv + 319.
Authoritative and well-written history by a competent British journalist, centered around drilling of Drake Well, later life of Colonel Drake and those associated with him; later material. Original plan contemplated additional volumes dealing with industrial and engineering developments, hence book marked Vol. I. Contains insert, "Oil

Fuel and Petrol Supplies," dealing with relationship of continental oil sources to war, written at time of declaration of war against Germany by Great Britain.

J. T. Henry, *The Early and Later History of Petroleum,* Philadelphia, Jas. B. Rodgers Co., 1873, pp. 607.
Valuable, well-written early history based upon on-the-spot investigation while all early participants were still living and could be interviewed. In addition to authoritative account of Drake Well, Henry gives detailed histories of many early producing properties, companies, and individual oilmen. Statistics, tables, and photographic illustrations. Author was Titusville newspaperman.

John P. Herrick, *Empire Oil: the Story of Oil in New York State,* New York, Dodd, Mead & Co., 1949, pp. xx + 474.
History of oil and gas industry of New York; description of early pools and wells, early discoveries, pipe line transportation, refining.

Pattillo Higgins, *Prospectus; The True History of the Beaumont Oil Fields,* Beaumont, Tex., Higgins Standard Oil Co., Ltd., 1902, pp. 71.
History of Spindletop by its original promoter, who subsequently leased to Capt. Anthony F. Lucas, operator of the successful discovery well. Maps, geological sections, well-logs; views of Beaumont during oil boom; account of Higgins' real estate company, the Gladys City Oil, Gas & Mfg. Co.

Harold L. Ickes, *Fightin' Oil,* New York, Alfred A. Knopf, 1943, pp. x + 174.
Work, problems, experiences of Petroleum Administration for War.

F. Tennyson Jesse, *The Saga of San Demetrio,* New York, Alfred A. Knopf, 1943, pp. 84.
Eagle Oil tanker attacked in Atlantic by enemy raider, set afire, abandoned, reboarded next day. Although still burning, crew kept ship afloat and brought it into port.

Willard Rouse Jillson, *The Old American Oil Well,* Frankfort, Roberts Printing Co., 1947, pp. 24.
History of the great gusher of 1829 in Cumberland County, Kentucky.

Willard Rouse Jillson, *First American Gusher,* Frankfort, Roberts Printing Co., 1950, pp. 60.
Notes on history, geology, and production of Stockton well, drilled in Cumberland County, Kentucky, 1829, regarded "not only as the first oil well of commercial importance in America, but one of the largest ever produced in Kentucky."

Willard Rouse Jillson, *The First Oil Well in Kentucky,* Frankfort, Roberts Printing Co., 1952, pp. 51.
Notes history, geology, production, and present status of Beatty oil well, drilled in Wayne, now McCreary, County, Kentucky, 1818, with spring pole rig. Produced heavy black oil, sold locally for medicinal uses.

George R. Kelley, *Oil and Gas in Texas,* Fort Worth, Texas Publicity Royalties, 1920, pp. 22.
History of Texas oil fields, production, refineries, description of operations. Author was oil editor, Ft. Worth *Star-Telegram.*

Joseph C. G. Kennedy, *Preliminary Report on the Eighth Census,* Washington, Government Printing Office, 1862.
Oil development, transition from coal-oil distillation to refining crude oil, status of oil industry in United States. "There appears to be no assignable limit to the flow or to the localities which may be found to yield it, whenever an augmented demand shall warrant farther search of increased production."

Ruth Sheldon Knowles, *The Greatest Gamblers,* New York, McGraw-Hill Book Co., 1959, pp. xii + 346.
Brief biographies of prominent oil finders, from Drake to present, lone wildcatters to large corporations, with emphasis on the Southwest; much new material not previously gathered.

Albert A. Lawrence, *Petroleum Comes of Age,* Tulsa, Scott-Rice Co., 1938, pp. x + 227.
History of early oil regions of New York and Pennsylvania; technological advances in oil industry up to about 1880. Commentary on early oil books and writings.

Charles C. Leonard, *Pithole: Its History,* Venango County, Penna., Morton, Longwell & Co., 1867, pp. 106. Reprinted, Baltimore, Md., West Penn Oil Co., 1945, Ernest C. Miller, Ed., adding photographs and xvii pp. text, gazetteer, biographical notes.
Described as "a collection of facts, fancies, and figures, connected with the history of Pithole," which became first oil boom town and first ghost town, 1865–1867.

J. P. Lesley (Peter Lesley, Jr.), *Coal Oil,* Washington, 1862, pp. 429–447. (Report of Commissioner of Agriculture for 1862. House of Rep. Exec. Document No. 78, 37th Congress, 3rd Session.)
Composition and qualities of coal oil, origin, manufacture and use, statistics.

David D. Leven, *77 Years of Petroleum,* New York, Don-Golden, 1936, pp. 860.

B. Orchard Lisle, *Static Defense of Strategic Oil Installations,* New York, Charles Scribner's Sons, 1942, pp. 12.

Look Magazine, Ed., *Oil for Victory, The Story of Petroleum in War and Peace,* New York, McGraw-Hill Book Co., 1946, pp. 287.
Organization for petroleum supply during World War II; production, transportation, refining, manufacture of special products; illustrated.

W. E. Lucas, *Eagle Fleet, The Story of a Tanker Fleet in Peace and War,* London, Weidenfeld & Nicolson, 1955, pp. 117.
Development of tanker fleet of Eagle Oil Transport Co.; includes accounts of attacks at sea during two wars, postwar developments, accounts of actions at sea, specific attacks by enemy.

John A. Mather, *Mather's Historic Oil Regions of Western Pennsylvania,* Mather's Historical Photographs, Titusville, Penna., 1895.
Contains 12 photographs and descriptive text of early Pennsylvania oil fields, including Drake Well. Mather set up photographic studio in Titusville in 1860.

Lioy May, *Misplaced Glory. The Lost Soldiers of 1847–1865 in the Pennsylvania* Oil Region, Philadelphia, the author, 1946, pp. 353.
Early oil development in Pennsylvania and role of Civil War soldiers in its origin and growth.

John James McLaurin, *Sketches in Crude-Oil,* Harrisburg, 1896, pp. x + 406. 2nd Ed. 1898, pp. xii + 452. 3rd Ed. Franklin, Penna., 1902, pp. xii + 470. All published by author.
Pennsylvania oil business and men responsible for its growth. Romanticized and unreliable in many respects, but a source of much primary information not found elsewhere.

Ernest C. Miller, *North America's First Oil Well,* Warren, Penna., The Western Pennsylvania Historical Magazine, 1959, pp. 16.
Examination of question whose answer still eludes oil historians.

Ernest C. Miller, *Oil Mania, etc.,* Philadelphia, Dorrance & Co., 1941, pp. 140.
Early days of oil development in Pennsylvania.

Ernest C. Miller, *Pennsylvania's Oil Industry,* Gettysburg, Penna., Pennsylvania Historical Association (Pennsylvania History Studies, No. 4), 1954, pp. i + 54; 2nd Ed., 1959, pp. iii + 58.
Discovery of oil in Pennsylvania, with special attention to early history.

T. H. Vail Motter, *The Middle East Theater. The Persian Corridor and Aid to Russia,* Washington, Government Printing Office, 1952, pp. xvii + 545.
Chapter on pipe line projects, increasing refinery capacity in Middle East, building container plants, supplying gasoline to Russia, oil needs within Command.

Silas W. Munn, *Useful Information for Oil Men,* Mannington, W. Va., The Enterprise, 1900, pp. 190.
Records of various wells, tools and equipment used in drilling, and general oil country data. Special attention to fishing tools.

David Murray, *Petroleum, Its History and Properties,* Albany, N.Y., Albany Institute, 1862. Read before meeting of Albany Institute Dec. 16, 1862, and published as Art. VIII, pp. 149–166, Vol. IV. *Transactions* of Albany Institute.

Geographical distribution and geological position of petroleum, discovery of oil in America, oil wells, petroleum products, illuminating power, and explosive qualities.

Oil and Gas Journal, *50 Years of Oil in the Southwest,* Tulsa, Petroleum Publishing Co., 1951, var. pag.

Golden Anniversary Number, supplement to *Oil and Gas Journal,* May 31, 1951. Petroleum industry of the Southwest, beginning with Spindletop well in 1901.

Oil and Gas Journal, *The Petroleum Industry, 1859–1934,* Tulsa, Petroleum Publishing Co., and Oil City, Penna., Oil City Derrick, 1934, pp. 268.

Special historical supplement to *Oil and Gas Journal,* August 27, 1934.

Oil and Gas Journal, *Petroleum Panorama,* Tulsa, Okla., Petroleum Publishing Co., 1959, pp. 652.

Special historical issue commemorating first 100 years of oil in United States. Good source material on technological advances in exploration, drilling, production, transportation, refining, and petroleum-based chemicals.

Oil City Derrick, *The Derrick's Hand-Book of Petroleum,* Oil City, Penna., Derrick Publishing Co., 1884, pp. 110.

Covers 1859 through 1883; data of all important events in history of petroleum region, daily market quotations, daily average production, and tables of field development, runs, shipments, exports, and stocks.

Oil City Derrick, *The Derrick's Hand-Book of Petroleum,* Oil City, Penna., Derrick Publishing Co., 4 vols., 1898 through 1920, pp. 1843.

Vol. I: Extremely detailed chronological and statistical review of petroleum developments from 1859 to 1898, with daily market quotations, tables of runs, shipments, and stocks, oil exports, field operations and other subjects of interest and importance to oil trade; biographical sketches of, and memoirs written by many notable persons engaged in early oil business. Indispens-

able sourcebook for any historian interested in early oil industry.

Vol. II: Bradford Field Chronology 1861–1883; also 72 sketches of "Men Who Have Made Oil History."

Vol. III: Summary of important events 1900–1915 inclusive; market quotations production by states, field reports, or exports.

Vol. IV: Brief summary of important events, 1916–1919; market quotation. and production by states.

Beginning in 1920, Derrick Publishing Co. began publishing:

The Derrick's Annual Review of Oil Fields, with Market Quotations for the Year, 1920, pp. 12; 1921, pp. 44.

The Derrick's Annual Review of Oil Fields of United States, Mexico, and Canada, with Complete Statistical Review, 1922, pp. 55; 1923, pp. 22; 1924 pp. 22; 1925, pp. 13; 1926, pp. 21.

The *Oil City Derrick,* daily paper with authoritative coverage of oil news, was started Sept. 13, 1871.

Oil City Derrick, *The Domain of Oil and Gas,* Oil City, Penna., Oil City Derrick, 1917, pp. 212. (Supplement to *Oil City Derrick,* December 15, 1917.)

Supplement to newspaper that concen trated on oil coverage.

Oil City Derrick, *"50 Years of Progress," A Prospectus of the Pennsylvania Grade Oil Regions,* Oil City, Penna. Derrick Publishing Co., 1935, pp. 36.

History of *Derrick* and Pennsylvania Grade Crude Oil Association.

S. F. Peckham, *Report on the Production Technology, and Uses of Petroleum and Its Products,* Washington, Superintend ent of Documents, 1882, pp. viii + 319

History of petroleum, production, trans portation, sale, statistics of production technology of petroleum and uses. Ex tensive bibliography. A pioneer docu ment.

James Martin Peebles, *The Practical of Spiritualism. Biographical Sketch of Abraham James, Historic Description of his Oil-Well Discoveries in Pleasant ville, Pa., through Spirit Direction,* Chi cago, Horton & Leonard, 1868, pp. 85

James visited Pleasantville site Oct. 31 1866; was seized with trance and desig nated place for drilling of well which was completed, Dec., 1867, as Harmonial Oil-Well No. 1. Contains numerous excerpts from current writings on history and use of oil. Talent for oil finding described. Interesting as a curiosity.

Petroleum Administration for War, *Petroleum in War and Peace,* Washington, 1945, var. pag.
Papers presented by Petroleum Administration before Special Senate Committee to Investigate Petroleum Resources, Nov. 28–30, 1945. Contains 12 statements on major aspects of wartime experience in oil.

Petroleum Times, *Petroleum at War, Etc.,* London, *Petroleum Times,* 1945, pp. 72.
Reprint of articles published by *Petroleum Times;* British oil distribution in wartime; evolution, history, procedure, problems of Petroleum Board.

Philadelphia Board of Trade, *Petroleum, Its Production, Distribution and Its Purchasing Power,* Philadelphia, the Board, 1866, pp. 35.
From the Report of Philadelphia Board of Trade for 1865. Statistical tables on crude oil production, export of crude oil and refined products, well performance, future supply.

Joseph E. Pogue, *Prices of Petroleum and Its Products During the War,* Washington, Government Printing Office, 1919, pp. 55. (Published as Exhibit A, pp. 273–303, to *Report of the General Director of the Oil Division,* also as Part 36, Price Section, Bureau of Planning and Statistics, War Industries Board.)
Price factors peculiar to petroleum; commercial history; price data for war years; relationships of price and value in oil industry.

Reginald Watson Ragland, *A History of the Naval Petroleum Reserves and of the Development of the Present National Policy Respecting Them,* Los Angeles, n. pub., 1944, pp. 180.
Background of naval petroleum reserves and historical development of present national policy regarding them.

Marcus Eli Ravage, *The Story of Teapot Dome,* New York, Republic Publishing Co., 1924, pp. v + 198.

Establishment of naval petroleum reserves and actions involved in their leasing and associated activities.

Lionel V. Redpath, *Petroleum in California,* Los Angeles, the author, 1900, pp. 158.
California oil industry at close of 19th century; biographical sketches of California oilmen; illustrations. Regarded as authoritative.

Mark L. Requa, *Report of the General Director of the Oil Division,* Washington, Government Printing Office, 1921, (*Final Report of the United States Fuel Administration, 1917–19,* pp. 261–272.)
Policy, organization, activities, orders, rules and regulations, control, mobilization of petroleum industry in time of war, future of petroleum industry in light of growing demands.

Erna Risch, *Fuels for Global Conflict,* Washington, Government Printing Office, 1952, pp. xvi + 147. (Quartermaster Corps Historical Studies No. 9, Rev. Ed.)
Requirements and procedures for determination, purchasing for Army in zones and theaters, distribution, technical development, research, inspection, development of containers and equipment, planning for petroleum activities. Originally published 1945, covering period from outbreak of war in 1939 to June, 1944. Subsequent supplement from June, 1944, to end of war.

Carl Coke Rister, *Oil! Titan of the Southwest,* Norman, Okla., University of Oklahoma Press, 1949, pp. xxiii + 467.
History of Mid-Continent, Southwest, and Gulf Coast oil industry—fields, people, and companies—based on extended research and interviews. Considered authoritative.

P. Schweitzer, *A Lecture on Petroleum,* Columbia, Mo., Statesman Book and Job Print, 1879, pp. 64.
Lecture delivered early in 1879, before Missouri House of Representatives, Jefferson City, and followed by enactment of coal-oil bill. Historical review, industrial aspect, chemical composition, refining and testing; statistics; draft of proposed legislation. Contains early petroleum bibliography.

Shell War Achievements Series
  W. E. Stanton Hope, *Tanker Fleet,* London, Anglo-Saxon Petroleum Co., 1948, pp. xiii + 124. Record of Shell tankers, and men who manned them during 1939–45 war period.
  George P. Kerr, *Time's Forelock,* London, Shell Petroleum Co., 1948, pp. xviii + 82. Shell's role in development of commercial aviation and its importance to military aviation in World War II.
  J. W. Fabricius, *East Indies Episode,* London, Shell Petroleum Co., 1949, pp. 142. Japanese attack on Dutch East Indies; work of Royal Dutch-Shell demolition engineers in denying important oil assets to enemy.
  Harold Nockolds, *The Engineers,* London, Shell Petroleum Co., 1949, pp. xi + 108. Wartime accomplishments of Shell engineering staffs in all parts of Allied world in World War II.

Shell Oil Company, *Shell. Soldier and Civilian,* New York, the Company, 1946, pages unnumbered.
Company activities in United States during World War II; research and production of aviation fuels, toluene, chemicals, medicines, and other products of petroleum for military or essential civilian use.

Benjamin Silliman, Jr., *Report on the Rock Oil, or Petroleum, from Venango County, Pennsylvania,* New Haven, 1855, pp. 20. (Reprinted later in works of Cone & Johns, Newton, J. T. Henry, Ida Tarbell, and others, and in *American Chemist,* July, 1871. Facsimiles published in 1949 by Paul H. Giddens, Meadville, Pa., and in 1955 by Ethyl Corp., New York.)
The famous report that helped launch the oil industry. Eveleth, Bissell, & Reed, promoters of Pennsylvania Rock Oil Co., engaged Benjamin Silliman, Jr., professor of chemistry at Yale, one of the leading scientific men of his day, to examine samples of their rock oil to determine its commercial value. Report covered properties of petroleum, products possible to manufacture from it, comparisons of petroleum illuminating oil with common illuminants of the day.

Alfred Wilson Smiley, *A Few Scraps, Oily and Otherwise.* Oil City, Penna., Derrick Press, 1907, pp. 220.

Personal experiences and observations in oil fields of Pennsylvania beginning with Drake well. Author arrived in Titusville in spring of 1860 and knew Colonel Drake.

George Otis Smith, *The Strategy of Minerals, etc.,* New York, D. Appleton & Co., 1919, pp. xix + 371.
Part played by minerals in First World War; their position in reconstruction; discussion of petroleum. Appendix contains control and relief Acts pertaining to minerals. Author headed United States Geological Survey.

P. G. A. Smith, *The Shell That Hit Germany Hardest,* London, Shell Marketing Co., 1919, pp. 77.
Achievements of Royal Dutch-Shell Group of companies during World War I.

Walter Stalder, *A Contribution to California Oil and Gas History,* Los Angeles, *California Oil World,* 1941 (Part II of issue of Nov. 12, 1941), pp. 31–72.
Authoritative work based on diaries, scrapbooks, and files; contains maps, prints, and photographs; important source data on early California oil developments. Author was long-time consulting geologist, and son of pioneer California oilman.

Standard Oil Company (New Jersey), *Ships of the Esso Fleet in World War II,* New York, the Company, 1946, pp. 530.
Jersey Company tankers in all theaters of Allied operations, details of each ship, performance, enemy attacks, tales of heroism, etc. Profusely illustrated.

Alvin P. Stauffer, *The Quartermaster Corps: Operation in the War Against Japan,* Washington, Government Printing Office, 1956, pp. xv + 358.
Petroleum supply problems in Southwest Pacific.

Mark Sullivan, *Our Times: The United States, 1900–1925,* New York, Charles Scribner's Sons, Vols. II and VI, 1927 and 1935, pp. xxxvii + 1342.
Vol. II: History of petroleum, activities of Rockefeller, Standard Oil Company, dissolution of Standard Oil Trust.
Vol. VI: The Twenties, reviews leasing of Teapot Dome and Elk Hills naval pe-

troleum reserves and legal actions which followed. Probably best account extant of Teapot Dome Scandal.

Sunset Petroleum Company, *The History of Petroleum. The Most Entrancing Story Ever Told,* Oklahoma City, the Company, 1918, pp. 48.
Promotional brochure.

Steve S. Szalewicz, *Oil Moon Over Pithole. A Story of a Phenomenon in an Oil Town,* Oil City, Penna., the author, 1958, pp. 92.
Pithole, the career of a fantastic boom-and-bust oil town.

Samuel W. Tait, Jr., *The Wildcatters, An Informal History of Oil-Hunting in America,* Princeton, N.J., Princeton University Press, 1946, pp. xvi + 218.
Scattered accounts of oil exploration history in substantially all major oil producing areas of the United States, and early Canadian industry. While not a comprehensive survey, each vignette is carefully done and contains good material not found elsewhere.

Frederick Arthur Ambrose Talbot, *The Oil Conquest of the World,* London, William Heinemann, 1914, pp. x + 310.
Oil industry during early period of First World War.

James C. Tennent, *The Oil Scouts: Reminiscences of the Night Riders of the Hemlocks,* Oil City, Penna., Derrick Publishing Co., 1915, pp. 87, 2nd Ed., Philadelphia, Tiona Petroleum Co., 1931.
Early oil scouting.

Henry H. Townsend, *New Haven and the First Oil Well,* New Haven, Conn., Yale University Press, privately printed by author, 1934, pp. 40.
Author writes of his uncle, James M. Townsend, one of incorporators of Pennsylvania Rock Oil Co. and chief backer of Seneca Oil Co., which drilled Drake well. Based on family papers, some reproduced.

United States Army, Corps of Engineers, *Airfield and Base Development,* Washington, Government Printing Office, 1951, pp. xii + 559. (In *Engineers of the Southwest Pacific, 1941–45,* Vol. VI.)

Corps of Engineers in Southwest Pacific during war; petroleum faciilties in various theaters of operations; bulk storage, pipe lines, underwater loading lines, drum cleaning and filling plants, construction criteria. Operational stages of oil supply from supply on landing through erection of bulk storage facilities ashore.

United States Navy, Bureau of Naval Personnel, *Petroleum Logistics,* Washington, Government Printing Office, 1955, pp. iii + 190.
Supplying petroleum products for military needs; functions of military and civilian agencies; determination of requirements, purchasing, distribution; fuel depot operations and ocean transportations; petroleum resources, naval petroleum and shale oil reserves.

United States Navy, Bureau of Naval Personnel, *Fundamentals of Petroleum,* Washington, Government Printing Office, 1953, pp. vi + 190.
For petroleum logistics officers. Covers petroleum production, properties of crude oil, refining and testing, military petroleum products, quality surveillance, measuring and sampling, safety, storage, transportation, tanker operations.

United States Strategic Bombing Survey, *Final Report, Oil Division,* Washington, Government Printing Office, 1945. 2nd Ed. 1947, pp. iv + 152.
Wartime integration of German oil, chemical, rubber, and explosives industries; strategic air attacks; effectiveness of bombing techniques and weapons, war history of typical refinery and synthetic oil plants. *Appendices* (Report No. 110) include strategic air attack on German lubricating oil industry and air raid protective measures.

United States Strategic Bombing Survey, *The German Oil Industry,* Washington, Government Printing Office, 1945. 2nd Ed. 1947, pp. xiii + 89, plus 54 Figures.
Eleven other reports cover specific oil refineries and synthetic oil plants. German oil industry before war; performance of oil industry to time of concentrated air attacks; target for strategic bombing, combined bomber offensive; Germany's oil position, influence on

military plans; Allied intelligence concerning Germany's oil position.

United States Strategic Bombing Survey, Oil and Chemical Division, *Oil in Japan's War,* San Francisco, Schwabacher-Frey Co., 1946, pp. 283.
Oil and chemical industries in Japan and East Indies, their part in war effort, inspection of damage caused by bombing of refineries; oil synthetic plants, chemical installations. Industry before Pearl Harbor, war story of Japan's industry, oil statistics 1931–45. Japanese oil industry 1931 to end of war, dependence on Borneo, Java, Sumatra, impact of tanker sinkings; detailed reports on 11 refineries and 2 synthetic oil plants, assessment of bombing damage.

United States Tariff Commission, *Petroleum* (No. 17 of *War Changes in Industry*), Washington, Government Printing Office, 1946, pp. iv + 152.
Postwar prospects and problems; disposal of government-owned facilities; demand and supply conditions in United States before and during war; tariff history on oil; world industry, American interests abroad; review of oil industry in individual foreign countries.

C. A. Warner, *Texas Oil and Gas Since 1543,* Houston, Gulf Publishing Co., 1939, pp. vii + 487.
Authoritative history of Texas oil and gas up to 1939; discovery and development of individual fields, with statistics by years. Contains much material not found elsewhere. Date refers to survivors of De Soto expedition who, in 1543, used pitchlike substance to repair vessels.

M. R. Werner and John Starr, *Teapot Dome,* New York, Viking Press, 1959, pp. x + 306.
Journalistic account of Teapot Dome and Elk Hills scandals of the 1920's.

Franc Bangs Wilkie, *Petrolia; Or, the Oil Regions of the United States,* Chicago, John R. Walsh & Co., 1865, pp. 82.
Guide book to Oil Regions of Pennsylvania, Ohio, and West Virginia; includes six letters written by author between Feb. 22, 1865, and March 6, 1865, from various Oil Region communities; drilling, travel routes, costs, hotels; discussion of "reliable" companies.

Harold F. Williamson and Arnold R. Daum, *The American Petroleum Industry, The Age of Illumination, 1859–1899,* Evanston, Ill., Northwestern University Press, 1959, pp. xvi + 864.
Vol. I of authoritative history of American oil industry, prepared under grant from American Petroleum Institute. Brings together in one place results of all prior research. Excellent for researchers and students seeking definitive information in a single volume.

Leon Wolff, *Low Level Mission,* New York, Doubleday, 1957, pp. 240.
Account of air raid on oil refineries at Ploesti, Rumania; elimination of Ploesti as source of oil products for Axis.

2. STANDARD OIL AND ROCKEFELLER

William Harvey Allen, *Rockefeller; Giant, Dwarf, Symbol,* New York, Institute for Public Service, 1930, pp. xviii + 619.
Review and appraisal; comments concerning others who wrote about Rockefeller.

Sarah Knowles Bolton, *Famous Givers and Their Gifts,* New York, Thomas Y. Crowell & Co., 1896, pp. 383.
Includes account of Rockefeller's life, with special attention to the establishment of Chicago University.

John H. Bonham, *A Brief History of the Standard Oil Trust: Its Methods and Influence,* n.p., n. pub. 1888, pp. 23.
Harsh commentary against Standard Oil Trust; examples of how small refiners were harmed.

Marcus M. Brown, *A Study of John D. Rockefeller, the Wealthiest Man in the World; With His Name Left Out, the History of Education and Religion Could Not Be Written,* Cleveland, the author, 1905, pp. 150.
Title illustrates author's belief that Mr. Rockefeller "is a good man."

George H. Burgess and Miles C. Kennedy, *Centennial History of The Pennsylvania*

Railroad Company, 1846–1946, Philadelphia, the Company, 1949, pp. xxvi + 835.
Origins and development of company; references to early oil tariffs, conflict with Standard Oil in late 1870's.

Joseph I. C. Clarke, *My Life and Memories,* New York, Dodd, Mead & Co., 1925, pp. xv + 404.
Two chapters cover period (c. 1906–1913), when Clarke did publicity for Standard Oil Company.

William Wilson Cook, *Trusts. The Recent Combinations in Trade, etc.,* New York, L. K. Strouse & Co., 1888, pp. 63. 2nd Ed. 1888, pp. 113.
Purposes, organization, liabilities and legality of trusts. 2nd Ed. contains appendices giving results of investigation in 1888 by New York Senate, summary of findings on Standard Oil Trust; Standard Oil Trust Agreement and By-Laws of its Trustees; list of corporations in which stocks were wholly or partially held by Standard Oil Trust.

John Roscoe Day, *The Raid on Prosperity,* New York, D. Appleton & Co., 1907, pp. 352.
Three chapters deal with Standard Oil Company and its defense. Author was Chancellor of Syracuse University.

S. C. T. Dodd, *Combinations: Their Uses and Abuses, with a History of the Standard Oil Trust,* New York, George F. Nesbitt & Co., 1888, pp. 46.
Dodd, solicitor of Standard Oil Trust, drew trust agreement of 1882, and is generally credited with inventing the holding company. A lawyer of rare ability and integrity, he wrote this pamphlet as a public examination of the trust device.

S. C. T. Dodd, *Trusts,* New York, the author, 1900, pp. 132.
Addresses by Mr. Dodd; includes history of Standard Oil Company, ten years of Standard Oil Trust.

(S. C. T. Dodd), *Memoirs of S. C. T. Dodd, Written for His Children and Friends, 1837–1907,* New York, Robert Grier Cooke, 1907.
Account of early contacts with oil business in Pennsylvania and with Standard

Oil Company, including formation of Trust.

Curt E. Engelbrecht and Carl John Bostelmann, *Neighbor John. Intimate Glimpses of John D. Rockefeller,* New York and Harrisburg, The Telegraph Press, 1936, pp. 216.
Record of picture-making and interviews to reveal "the human side of John D. Rockefeller" during his last years.

John Thomas Flynn, *God's Gold; The Story of Rockefeller and His Times,* New York, Harcourt, Brace & Co., 1932, pp. ix + 520.
Author aimed for an impartial examination of Rockefeller's life; related his character and achievements to the times in which he lived.

(Henry C. Folger), *Henry C. Folger, 18 June 1857–11 June 1930,* New Haven, Conn., 1931, pp. 114.
Memorial volume recording life of Henry Clay Folger, early Standard Oil executive.

Joseph Benson Foraker, *Notes of a Busy Life,* 1915, 2 vols., pp. xxi + 1096. 2nd Ed. 1916. 3rd Ed. Cincinnati, Stewart & Kidd, 1917. Footnotes added in 3rd edition, no changes in text.
Includes "The Hearst-Standard Oil Letters" which involved unsustained charges by Mr. Hearst as to payments to and employment of Mr. Foraker in matters involving Standard Oil Company while latter was member of United States Senate.

Frederick Taylor Gates, *The Truth About Mr. Rockefeller and the Merritts,* New York, Knickerbocker Press, n.d. (c. 1911), pp. 32.
Rockefeller's contacts, early 1890's, with Leonidas and Alfred Merritt in connection with iron mining properties in Minnesota, panic of 1893, and subsequent suits. Author was financial adviser to Rockefeller.

F. B. Gowen, *Argument of Franklin Benjamin Gowen, Esq., in the cases of George Rice vs. the Railroad Companies, known as the Standard Oil Monopoly Cases,* Marietta, Ohio, published by George Rice, 1888, pp. 40, with appendix.

Discrimination in rates granted by railroads on petroleum products transported in tank cars by Standard Oil Company and in barrels on freight cars by George Rice.

W. H. Gray, *The Rule of Reason in Texas,* Houston, the author, 1912, pp. 79.
History of Standard Oil Company operations in Texas and Southwest.

Alonzo Hepburn, Chairman, *Report of the Special Committee on Railroads Appointed under a Resolution of the Assembly, Feb. 28, 1879, to Investigate Alleged Abuses in Management of Railroads Chartered by State of New York,* Albany, 1880, pp. 97. (State of New York Assembly Document No. 38.)
Report of the Minority of the Special Committee on Railroads, Submitted to the Assembly, Feb. 17, 1880, Albany, Weed Parsons & Co., 1880, pp. 47. (Assembly Document No. 61.)
Beginnings of famous Hepburn Committee, investigating railroad rate abuses particularly as they applied to Standard Oil Company.

Alonzo Hepburn, Chairman, *Proceedings of the Special Committee on Railroads, Appointed under a Resolution of Assembly to Investigate Alleged Abuses in Management of Railroads Chartered by State of New York,* New York, Evening Post Steam Presses, 1879, 5 vols., pp. 4371, plus Sub-Committee hearing, pp. 168, exhibits, pp. 643, index, pp. 13.
Text of Hepburn Committee hearings.

W. Trevor Holliday, *John D. Rockefeller (1839–1937). Industrial Pioneer and Man,* New York, Newcomen Society, 1948, pp. 32.
Newcomen address based on personal contacts with Rockefeller and association with second generation of Standard Oil men. Author was president of Standard Oil Company (Ohio).

Harold J. Howland, *Standard Oil,* reprinted from *The Outlook,* Oct., 1907, pp. 20.
Author's visits to various properties and plants of company, views of employees interviewed.

Elbert Hubbard, *The Standard Oil Company,* East Aurora, N.Y. Roycrofters, 1910, pp. 24.

Reprint of editorial in *The Fra* magazine, defends Company.

Silas Hubbard, *John D. Rockefeller and His Career,* New York, the author, 1904, pp. 192.
Rockefeller's career as an example of the origin and growth of monopoly.

James F. Hudson, *The Railways and the Republic,* New York, Harper & Bros., 1886, pp. 489.
Railroad domination and discrimination; Standard Oil Company and its relationship to railroads and other modes of transportation; its position in oil business; other references to Company.

Arthur Menzies Johnson, *The Development of American Petroleum Pipelines: A Study in Private Enterprise and Public Policy, 1862–1906,* Ithaca, N.Y., Cornell University Press, 1956, pp. xiii + 307.
Pipe lines as competitive weapons, Standard Oil Co., antitrust legislation, place of pipe lines in oil transportation and public policy, intra-industry controversy, attack on Standard Oil Co., pipe line amendment to Hepburn Act.

Emanuel Mann Josephson, *Rockefeller, Internationalist: The Man Who Misrules the World,* New York, Chedney Press, 1952, pp. 448.
Author's interpretations of various events concerned with oil industry, Rockefeller family, institutes, foundations.

Matthew Josephson, *The Robber Barons. The Great American Capitalists, 1861–1901,* New York, Harcourt, Brace & Co., 1934, pp. viii + 474.
Numerous references to John D. Rockefeller, Standard Oil Company, and Standard Oil Trust.

State of Kansas, Attorney General, *Eighteenth Biennial Report of Attorney General of Kansas, 1911–12,* Topeka, State Printing Office, 1912.
Contains report of L. W. Keplinger, Commissioner of Supreme Court of Kansas, filed June 11, 1912, presenting findings in State of Kansas vs. Standard Oil Company, et al., reviewing operations of company.

Henry H. Klein, *Standard Oil or the People. The End of Corporate Control in America,* New York, the author 1914, pp. 134.
Author contended hardship then existing due to control of government by corporations and that Standard Oil had been chief factor in affairs of nation.

Henry H. Klein, *Dynastic America and Those Who Own It,* New York, the author, 1921, pp. 173.
Lists estates related to Standard Oil; growth of Company; how oil and other industries are controlled.

Henry H. Klein, *My Last 50 Years. An Autobiographical History of "Inside" New York,* New York, the author, 1935, pp. 460.
Account of writing *Standard Oil or The People* and *Dynastic America and Those Who Own It,* includes background, editorial comment, etc.

Henry H. Klein, *Rockefeller or God. Who Will Rule?,* New York, the author, 1938, pp. 77.
Rockefeller-Standard Oil world oil holdings; calendar of dates citing news accounts of Standard Oil activities abroad, financial aides, dividend record of Standard Oil.

Earl Latham, Ed., *John D. Rockefeller. Robber Baron or Industrial Statesman?,* Boston, D. C. Heath & Co., 1949, pp. xii + 115. (Problems in American Civilization No. 7)
Contains readings selected by Department of American Studies, Amherst College, from writings of John T. Flynn, Ida M. Tarbell, Matthew Josephson, John D. Rockefeller, Allan Nevins, Henry Demarest Lloyd, etc., with introduction by Latham and additional comments by Nevins.

Thomas W. Lawson, *Frenzied Finance,* New York, Ridgway-Thayer Co., 1906, pp. xix + 559.
Landmark in "muckraking" works aimed at Standard Oil; author was financier and market operator, and for this reason his exposé carried extra weight.

John Brooks Leavitt, *Memorial of Samuel C. T. Dodd,* New York, 1908, pp. 15.

Memorial prepared and read by John Brooks Leavitt, at request of Executive Committee, before Association of the Bar of the City of New York at meeting held January 14, 1908.

Henry Demarest Lloyd, *Wealth Against Commonwealth,* New York, Harper & Bros., 1894, pp. iv + 563. Reprinted 1903, Summarized edition 1936, National Home Library Foundation, Washington, pp. 366.
Primarily on Standard Oil Trust; original records; first book to bring together mass of information and opinions from court proceedings, investigating committees, current publications, etc. Famous among "muckraking" works on Standard Oil.

Sidney Walter Martin, *Florida's Flagler,* Athens, Ga., University of Georgia Press, 1949, pp. xi + 280.
Henry M. Flagler, John D. Rockefeller, and the Standard Oil Company.

Ernest C. Miller, *Ida Tarbell's Second Look at Standard Oil,* reprinted from *Western Pennsylvania Historical Magazine,* Vol. 39, No. 4, Winter, 1956.
Initial chapter of what was to have been Miss Tarbell's 3rd volume of History of Standard Oil Company, together with historical commentary.

Gilbert Holland Montague, *The Rise and Progress of the Standard Oil Company,* New York, Harper & Bros., 1903, pp. v + 142. 2nd Ed. 1904.
Defense of Standard Oil by friendly author.

John Moody, *The Truth About the Trusts. A Description and Analysis of the American Trust Movement,* New York, Moody Publishing Co., 1904, pp. xxii + 514.
"Oil Trust" described and discussed.

Austin Leigh Moore, *John D. Archbold and the Early Development of Standard Oil,* New York, Macmillan, n.d., pp. 349.
Archbold was leading figure with Standard Oil for half a century.

F. F. Murray, *The Middle Ten,* Titusville, Penna., World Publishing Co., 1895, pp. 119.
Account of formation of fictional com-

pany to combat Standard Oil, and monopolies in general. Title from author's assertion that middle group of people, not upper or lower, is really important.

Allan Nevins, *John D. Rockefeller; The Heroic Age of American Enterprise,* New York, Charles Scribner's Sons, 1940, 2 vols., pp. 1430.
Definitive biography by competent scholar; much detail on Standard Oil companies.

Allan Nevins, *Study in Power; John D. Rockefeller, Industrialist and Philanthropist,* New York, Charles Scribner's Sons, 1953, 2 vols., pp. 941.
Complete rewrite of 1940 volumes, containing much new information, sharper characterization of Rockefeller.
A one-volume abridgment by William Greenleaf was published, 1953, by Charles Scribner's Sons.

State of New York, Senate, *Report of the Senate Committee on General Laws on Investigation Relative to Trusts,* Albany, 1888, pp. 692. (Senate Document No. 50.)
Investigation into matters relating to trusts; testimony of Rockefeller and others; documents and statistics.

State of Ohio vs. The Buckeye Pipe Line Co., et al., Columbus, Supreme Court of Ohio, 1899, pp. vi + 754.
History and status of cases against subsidiaries of Standard Oil Company; testimony; exhibits; depositions.

State of Ohio, Attorney General, *The State of Ohio ex. rel. The Attorney General vs. The Standard Oil Company, Proceedings in Contempt,* Columbus, Supreme Court of Ohio, 1899, 2 parts, pp. 524.
Ohio case against Standard Oil; history; pleadings.

Oil City Derrick, *Pure Oil Trust vs. Standard Oil Company,* Oil City, Penna., Derrick Publishing Co., 1901, pp. lxxvi + 606.
History of legislation leading to formation of Industrial Commission, background of witnesses, appearances, portions of testimony deleted from official report. Historical background of oil

industry presented in testimony of Patrick C. Boyle.

Petroleum Producers' Association, *Report of the Committee on Organization of the Petroleum Producers' Association,* Adopted by the General Council of the Petroleum Producers' Union, Titusville, Penna., the Association, 1878, pp. 15.
Association organized to oppose Standard Oil and the railroads.

Petroleum Producers' Association, *Petroleum Producers' Union, A History of the Organization,* Titusville, Penna., the Association, 1880, pp. 50.
History of lawsuits and investigations in producers' battle with Standard Oil Company and railroads.

Petroleum Producers' Union, *A History of the Rise and Fall of the South Improvement Company,* Oil City, Penna., the Union, 1873, pp. 126.
Testimony presented before subcommittee of House of Representatives Committee on Commerce (1872), to investigate railroad monopolies and combinations. Important document in literature of producers' fight with Standard Oil.

T. W. Phillips, *Crimes of the Standard Oil Trust,* New Castle, Penna., the author, 1907, pp. 22.
Author was vice-chairman, and acting chairman during investigation by United States Industrial Commission, and also successful independent oil producer in western Pennsylvania. Presents extracts of testimony which he regards as "summary of these great commercial crimes of the Standard Oil conspirators."

Charles Sterling Popple, *Standard Oil Company (New Jersey) in World War II,* New York, the Company, 1952, pp. 340.
Company's activities during World War II (1939–1945).

(J. D. Potts), *A Brief History of the Standard Oil Company,* Oil City, Penna., General Council of Petroleum Producers' Union, 1878, pp. 19.
Published anonymously, but reportedly written by Joseph D. Potts, president of Empire Transportation Company, a subsidiary of the Pennsylvania R.R.,

at the time unfriendly to Standard Oil. Urges organization of independent oil producers to combat Standard Oil Company, reviews history and activities of Company, acquisition of refineries and arrangements for rail transportation.

Mark L. Requa, *Alfred Cotton Bedford,* New York, American Petroleum Institute, 1926.
Bedford was identified with Standard Oil Company, from 1881; served as Chairman of National Petroleum War Service Committee in World War I. Address describes price plan adopted and postwar establishment of American Petroleum Institute.

George Rice, *The Standard Oil Company; Its Dishonest Tricks Exposed,* New York, the author, 1881, pp. 16.
Black Death, Marietta, O., the author, 1881, pp. 19.
Railway Discriminations! As Given to the Standard Oil Trust, Marietta, O., the author, pp. 31.
Present Violations by Railroads of Interstate Commerce Act concerning One Commodity, Oil, Marietta, O., the author, 1890, pp. 12.
The Standard Oil Company, 1872–1892, Marietta, O., the author, 1892, pp. 230. Reprinted, with appendix, pp. 36, 1897.
The Proposed Testimony of George Rice to be Given before Industrial Commission at Washington, D.C., Particularly Relating to Standard Oil Trust, etc., n.p., the author, 1899, pp. 77.
Above pamphlets associated with strenuous and extended controversy waged by Mr. Rice against Standard Oil Company and Standard Oil Trust.

John D. Rockefeller, *Random Reminiscences of Men and Events,* New York, Doubleday, Page & Co., 1909, pp. 188. Republished 1913 under title, *The Difficult Art of Getting.* Other editions 1933 and 1937.
Rockefeller's views on "several much-discussed happenings" which he was convinced had "not been fully understood."

(John D. Rockefeller), *A Visit to Mr. John D. Rockefeller by Neighbors and Friends at Forest Hill, Cleveland, Ohio,* Cleveland, Sept. 26, 1905, 35 unnumbered leaves, printed one side only.

(John D. Rockefeller), *John Davison Rockefeller, 1839–1937, A Memorial,* New York, privately printed for Rockefeller Institute for Medical Research, General Education Board, and Rockefeller Foundation, 1937, pp. 110.
Joint Resolution passed by trustees of Rockefeller Institute for Medical Research, General Education Board, and Rockefeller Foundation upon death of Rockefeller; statement of benefactions, representative expressions of respect and sympathy, with names of others who sent messages.

William Ryan, *The Derrick,* Jersey City, N.J., 1911, pp. 28.
Summary of oil operations, emphasis on refining; commends accomplishments of Standard Oil Company. Author employed by Standard Oil for 35 years.

Scofield, Shurmer & Teagle, *Circular Letter Regarding Freight Rates on Oil and Past and Present Discriminations in Favor of the Standard Oil Trust,* Cleveland, the Company, 1888, pp. 13.
Reviews alleged discriminating favors granted Standard Oil by railroads, compared with independent shippers; criticizes administration under Interstate Commerce Commission Act. Company was competitor of Standard Oil, later sold to that Company; Walter Teagle headed Standard Oil (New Jersey) during 1920's.

(Joseph Seep), *This Is My Birthday,* brochure prepared in commemoration of 70th birthday of Joseph Seep, no date or publisher, but probably 1908 in Oil City, pp. 108.
Brief biography, with addresses and messages from oil industry leaders, presented at a reception, Titusville, Penna., May 7, 1908. Seep was famous oil purchaser for Old Standard Oil Trust; was popular and highly respected throughout Oil regions.

Standard Oil Company, *An Inside View of Trusts, Testimony of members of the Standard Oil Company taken by Industrial Commission,* n.p., the Company, 1899, pp. vi + 392.
Testimony of John D. Archbold occupies larger part of book. Published to show accomplishments over 30 years of company in creating and maintaining

market for American oil and employment for American industry.

Standard Oil Company: Employees, *From the Employees of the Standard Oil Company to Its Directors and Stockholders,* New York, the Employees, 1907, pp. 20.
Follows pattern and form of pamphlet from directors, generally supporting government; presents editorial comment directed against company and its actions.

Standard Oil Company (Indiana), *From the Directors of the Standard Oil Company to Its Employees and Stockholders,* New York, the Company, 1907, pp. 32.
Pamphlet states position of company following decision in Chicago & Alton Railroad case, alleges campaign of defamation; public statement of James A. Moffett; reprints editorial comment supporting company.

Standard Oil Company (New Jersey), *The Directors of Standard Oil Company To Its Shareholders,* New York, the Company, 1906, pp. 10.
Communication of May 16, 1906, from C. M. Pratt, Secretary, to shareholders; refutes charges against Standard Oil Company in report by Bureau of Corporations.

Ida M. Tarbell, *The History of the Standard Oil Company,* New York, Macmillan Co., 1904, 2 vols., pp. 815. London, Heinemann, 1905. Reissued, 1925; 2 vols. in one, 1933. Photo-offset republication, New York, Peter Smith, 1950.
Most widely known of all books on Standard Oil Company. Undoubtedly contributed greatly in shaping public opinion on eve of legal action which dissolved Company and did much to influence future reputation of Standard companies. Characterized as one of first thorough histories of a business corporation.

State of Texas, House of Representatives, *Proceedings and Reports of the Bailey Investigation Committee,* Austin, Von Boeckmann-Jones, 1907, pp. 1091.
Proceedings of investigating committee of Texas House of Representatives. Concerned with actions of Joseph Weldon Bailey, while serving as United States Senator from Texas, including his connections with Standard Oil Company, Waters-Pierce Oil Company, and other

interests in oil. Exonerated of all charges.

Truth's Investigator, *The Great Oil Octopus,* London, F. Fisher Unwin, 1911, pp. 255.
Based on articles on many aspects of Standard Oil investigations which appeared in *Truth,* British magazine.

H. H. Tucker, Jr., *Standard Against Uncle Sam, Machinery of Injustice Lubricated by Standard Oil,* Kansas City, Kan., the author, 1907, pp. 600.
Attacks Standard Oil Company; contains numerous photographs of early oil operations in Kansas, biographical sketches, etc. Author was general manager of Uncle Sam Oil Company.

Uncle Sam Oil Company, *The Uncle Sam Oil Company. Memorial of the Uncle Sam Oil Company Relating to Its Business Transactions with Standard Oil Company and the Post Office and Interior Departments,* Kansas City, Kan., the Company, 1913, pp. 135.
Memorial to Congress outlining difficulties encountered by Company in relation to Standard Oil Company and in negotiations for oil and gas lease on Osage Indian Reservation.

United States, Department of Justice, *United States of America v. Standard Oil Company of New Jersey, et. al.* In the United States Circuit Court for the Eastern District of Missouri, St. Louis, Mo., *General Allegation of Conspiracy; Definition of Periods.* Filed Nov. 15, 1906, Washington, Government Printing Office, 1906, pp. 276. *Hearings,* 1908–09, 21 vols., var. pag., with 1044 exhibits.
Important suit against Standard. First phase ended with decision of District Court, Nov. 20, 1909. Record presented to United States Supreme Court, on appeal, included printed testimony and exhibits from hearings during 1907 to 1909 before Special Examiner in New York, Washington, Chicago, and other cities. Testimony of John D. Rockefeller, beginning p. 3053, Nov. 18–24, 1908. Vol. 22. Transcript of record, State of Ohio v. The Standard Oil Company. Resulted in liquidation of Trust Agreement of 1879. Testimony of John D. Rockefeller before Special Master in New York, Oct. 11–12, 1898.

United States Commissioner of Corporations, *Transportation and Freight Rates in Connection with the Oil Industry,* Washington, Government Printing Office (Senate Document No. 428, 59th Congress, 1st Session), 1906, pp. 49.

Railway transportation and freight rates; report found "existence of numerous and flagrant discriminations by railroads in behalf of Standard Oil Co., and its affiliated corporations."

United States Commissioner of Corporations, *Report of the Commissioner of Corporations on the Transportation of Petroleum,* Washington, Government Printing Office (House of Representatives Document No. 812, 59th Congress, 1st Session), 1906, pp. xxvii + 512.

Oil transportation, including shipments by water, advantageous location of Standard Oil refineries, secret railroad rates, etc.

United States Commissioner of Corporations, *Report of the Commissioner of Corporations on the Petroleum Industry,* Washington, Government Printing Office, 1907 and 1909, 3 parts, pp. lxvi + 2077.

Part I: Position of the Standard Oil Company in the Petroleum Industry. Part II: Prices and Profits. Part III: Foreign Trade. Although printed and partially distributed, this volume withdrawn and held confidential, reportedly because of some data received on company-confidential basis. Copy in Archives, Washington, available for examination.

United States Commissioner of Corporations, *Statement of Commissioner of Corporations in Answer to the Allegations of Standard Oil Company Concerning Its Conviction at Chicago for Accepting Concessions on Shipments over the Chicago & Alton Railroad,* Washington, Superintendent of Documents, 1907, pp. 11.

Prepared at the request of Secretary of Commerce and Labor who stated Bureau of Corporations originally discovered rate involved in case and took part in preparation and trial.

United States House of Representatives, *The Standard Oil Trust, Hearings before the Committee on Manufactures, United States House of Representatives, April 6, 1888, 50th Congress, 1st Session,* Washington, Government Printing Office, 1888, (Report No. 3112, Vol. 9, pp. 180–956).

Committee inquired into methods and extent of business done or controlled by Standard Oil Trust. Testimony covers Standard Oil Trust Agreement and arrangements made with Oil Producers' Association in 1887, extensive testimony on rail shipments and railroad traffic in oil. Rockefeller among witnesses.

United States Industrial Commission, *Standard Oil Combination, Hearings before United States Industrial Commission, May 11, 1899, 56th Congress, 1st Session,* Washington, Government Printing Office, 1900, pp. 1325, (House of Representatives Document No. 476, Vol. I, Part I.)

Preliminary report on *Trusts and Industrial Combinations,* together with testimony, review of evidence, charts showing effects on prices, and topical digest, authorized by Act of Congress, June 18, 1898. Standard Oil references in review of evidence; section on Standard Oil combinations in digest of evidence; testimony on Standard Oil and petroleum.

Albert H. Walker, *The "Unreasonable" Obiter Dicta of Chief Justice White in the Standard Oil Case. A Critical Review,* New York, the author, 1911, pp. 21.

Discusses middle 5,000 words included in 12,000 word opinion of Chief Justice White, May 15, 1911, in Standard Oil case, dealing with question whether word "unreasonable" should be implied in Sherman Law, and position of counsel in case.

Charles Austin Whiteshot, *The Oil-Well Driller; A Historical Story of America's Richest Enterprise, The Oil Industry.* Weston, W. Va., the author, 1902, pp. 127. 2nd Ed. subtitle: *A History of the World's Greatest Enterprise, The Oil Industry,* Mannington, W. Va., the author, 1905, pp. 895.

Large part of 2nd Ed. covers *The Beginning and Rise of the Standard Oil Company.* Author was publisher of *The Oil Region News,* est. 1900.

Charles F. Wilner, *J. W. Van Dyke. The Story of a Man and an Industry,* Philadelphia, Atlantic Refining Co., 1936, pp. 11. (Correlated with *A Short History of The Atlantic Refining Company, 1870–1936.*)
Life of John Wesley Van Dyke, a leading innovator in refining technology during years when Atlantic Refining was part of old Standard Oil Company.

B. F. Winkelman, *John D. Rockefeller: The Authentic and Dramatic Story of the World's Greatest Money Maker and Money Giver,* Chicago and Philadelphia, John C. Winston Co., 1937, pp. viii + 310.
Reviews life, oil and philanthropic activities; appraises work and influence on national affairs.

John Kennedy Winkler, *John D.: A Portrait in Oil,* New York, Vanguard Press, 1929, pp. ix + 256. Also, Blue Ribbon Books, New York.
Endeavor to shed light on "a rare and astonishing personality."

B. COMPANY HISTORIES

Amerada Petroleum Corporation, *The First Quarter Century of Amerada Petroleum Corporation, 1919–1944,* New York, the Company, 1945, 44 unnumbered pages.
History and highlights of earlier years, special mention of work in geophysics.

Anglo-American Oil Company, Ltd., *Jubilee, 1888–1938, Five Decades of Progress,* London, the Company, 1938, pp. 15.
Summary of 50 years through series of drawings, divided into decades, and text.

Anglo-Iranian Oil Company, *Fifty Years of Oil. A Survey of the World-Wide Activities of the Anglo-Iranian Oil Company,* London, the Company, 1952.
History of company in Iran, 1901–1951, world-wide interests of company, in production, refining, transportation, marketing.

Anglo-Iranian Oil Company, *The Anglo-Iranian Oil Company and Iran, etc.,* London, the Company, 1951, pp. 20.
History of Company's operations in Iran, benefits to Iran, housing problem, fight against disease; training and education, sport and recreation, food and clothing.

Arabian American Oil Company, *Arabian Oil and World Oil Needs,* New York, the Company, 1948, pp. 48. Rev. Ed.: *Arabian Oil and World Oil Shortage,* 1948, pp. 47.
History of company in Arabia; operations and facilities for production, refining, housing, transportation.

F. Lawrence Babcock, *The First Fifty, 1889–1939,* Chicago, Standard Oil Company (Indiana), 1939, pp. 57.
Account of process developed by Herman Frasch for removing sulphur from crude oil which made possible refining of Lima, Ohio, crude oil; refinery at Whiting, Indiana; development of cracking process; expansion of company in marketing, crude oil production, transportation.

Kendall Beaton, *Enterprise in Oil. A History of Shell in the United States,* New York, Appleton-Century-Crofts, 1957, pp. xiii + 815.
Authoritative history of Shell in United States, 1912–1955; tables of operating and financial data, lists of officers, chronology.

Paul G. Blazer, *E Pluribus Unum! "One Out of Many."* An Oil Company Grows Through Acquisitions, n.p., American Newcomen Society, 1956, pp. 28.
History and growth of Ashland Oil & Refining Company, delivered as Newcomen Society address.

British Petroleum Company, Ltd., *BP Tanker Company,* London, the Company, 1958, pp. 24.
Formation and growth of Company, operations during two World Wars, postwar advancement, sections on tanker layout, operation, crew.

British Petroleum Company, Limited, *BP, Fifty Years in Pictures,* London, the Company, 1959, pp. 159.
Picture history of B.P. operations, with captions and small amount of text. (Company formerly called Anglo-Iranian Oil Co.)

Frances M. Buente, *Autobiography of an Oil Company,* New York, privately printed by Tide Water Oil Co., 1923, pp. 81. Originally published in *Tide Water Topics,* Nov.–Dec. 1923.
Commemorates 45th anniversary of company which began Nov., 1878 as Tide-Water Pipe Company Ltd.; account of laying first pipe line across Alleghenies; manufacture of barrels, their use in oil transportation.

Charles M. Coleman, *P. G. and E. of California, The Centennial Story of Pacific Gas and Electric Company, 1852–1952,* New York, McGraw-Hill Book Co., 1952, pp. x + 385.
Includes chapter on discovery, development, introduction, and distribution of natural gas in California and pipe line connections with outside sources.

Continental Oil Company, *We're Breaking Ground for Another Seventy Five Years,* Houston, the Company, 1950, pp. 48.
Account of events associated with company from its establishment in 1875 to 1950. Illustrated.

Granville Cubage, *Oil: A Handbook for Reference. A Study of the Lloyd Oil Corporation of Ft. Worth, Texas,* Fort Worth, Tex., the author, pp. 98.
Career of Adelbert Durham Lloyd; his theory on origin of petroleum and geological examination of East Texas area for C. M. "Dad" Joiner; reproduction of map showing recommended well location. Discusses Lloyd Oil Corporation.

Charles S. Dennison, *Around the World With Texaco,* New York, the Company, 1925, pp. 165.
Eighteen articles, each covering a Far Eastern country.

Devonian Oil Company, *A History of the Devonian Oil Company, 1891–1941,* Tulsa, the Company, 1941, pp. 32.
Short history of company that had role

in Oklahoma oil boom in "Indian Territory" days.

Fayette B. Dow, *The National Petroleum Association, 1902–1952,* Washington, the Association, 1952, pp. 174.
History of first 25 years published for Silver Anniversary; of second 25 years by Donald C. O'Hara for Golden Anniversary.

Ralph C. Epstein, *GATX: A History of the General American Transportation Corporation, 1898–1948,* New York, North River Press, 1948, pp. x + 198.
History of leading tank car transportation company.

Erie City Iron Works, *The First Hundred Years, 1840–1940,* Erie, Penna., 1940, pp. 41.
History of company which made boiler and other equipment for Drake well.

Leonard M. Fanning, *The Story of the American Petroleum Institute (A Study and Report with Personal Reminiscences),* New York, World Petroleum Policies, 1959, pp. 168.
History of leading oil trade organization by prominent author and editor who served as first API director of information in 1920's.

R. J. Forbes and D. R. O'Beirne, *The Technical Development of the Royal Dutch-Shell, 1890–1940,* Leiden, Netherlands, E. J. Brill, 1957, pp. 670.
History of technical development of one of world's largest oil organizations, against larger background of general technical history of oil business. Development of refining, exploration, production, transport and storage techniques; history of changes in petroleum products; research, development of petroleum-based chemicals.

F. C. Gerretson, *History of the Royal Dutch,* Leiden, Netherlands, E. J. Brill, 1953, Vol. I, pp. 287, 1955, Vol. II, pp. 355, 1957, Vol. III, pp. 307, and Vol. IV, pp. 362. (English translation of *Geschiedenis der "Koninklijke,"* Haarlem, Joh. Enschedé en Zonen, 1932–1941.)
Monumental presentation of history of Royal Dutch Petroleum Company, 1890 through 1914; developments in Netherlands East Indies and elsewhere in

world. History also treats of general oil industry; competition with American companies; etc. Appendices include reproduction of significant documents.

J. Paul Getty, *History of the Oil Business of George F. and J. Paul Getty, 1903–1939,* n.p., the author, 1941, pp. 501.
Company's start in Mid-Continent, growth, investments in Tidewater-Associated Oil Company, work of George Franklin Getty; Paul Getty diaries.

George Sweet Gibb and Evelyn H. Knowlton, *The Resurgent Years, 1911–1927,* New York, Harper & Bros., 1956, pp. xxix + 754.
Second volume of authoritative history of Standard Oil Company (New Jersey); covers 1911–1927, reconstruction and expansion following dissolution decree of 1911. Vol. I by Hidys, *q.v.*

Paul H. Giddens, *Standard Oil Company (Indiana). Oil Pioneer of the Middle West,* New York, Appleton-Century-Crofts, 1955, pp. xviii + 741.
History of company from beginning in 1889 through 1951, account of growth, operations, policies, practices; Stewart-Rockefeller controversy, Company's connection with trial at Madison in detail.

Gilbert & Barker Manufacturing Company, *The Gilbarco Story,* West Springfield, Mass., the Company, 1953, 20 unnumbered pages.
Story of firm started April, 1865, to build gas machine; expansion, development of other equipment, gasoline pumps, oil burners. Subsidiary of Standard Oil Company (New Jersey).

William Henry Gray, *National Association of Independent Oil Producers, Its Work and Policies,* Tulsa, the author, 1924, pp. 209.
Account of Association, devoting attention to oil conditions in Mid-Continent and advocating tariff on oil.

J. Evetts Haley, *Story of the Shamrock,* Amarillo, Tex., the Company, 1954, pp. 78.
First 25 years (1929–1954) of Shamrock Oil and Gas Corporation; oil development in Texas Panhandle.

Eugene I. Harrington, *The Story of General Petroleum Corporation, 1910–1938,* n.p., the Company, n.d., pp. 27.
Life and activities of Capt. John Barneson; supervised laying pipe line from Coalinga to tidewater; sections on purchase of company by Standard Oil Company of New York, brief biographical sketches of leading company officials.

Ralph W. Hidy and Muriel E. Hidy, *History of Standard Oil Company (New Jersey), Pioneering in Big Business 1882–1911,* New York, Harper & Bros. 1955, pp. xxx + 839.
Scholarly study of the policies and practices followed by executives of the Standard Oil combination during the years of its ascendancy. First part covers early years, through 1899; second part 1900 through 1911. Covers entire range of Standard Oil operations; sources outlined in extensive notes. Vol. II by Gibb and Knowlton, *q.v.*

Frank A. Howard, *Buna Rubber,* New York, D. Van Nostrand, 1947, pp. xii + 307.
Story of patent relationships between Standard Oil Company (New Jersey) and I. G. Farben, with particular emphasis on synthetic rubber.

Independent Oil Men's Association *I.O.M.A. Blue Book, 1918–1919,* Chicago, the Association, c. 1920, pp. 354.
History of Association; reviews petroleum work of Bureau of Mines; war organization of petroleum industry; National Petroleum War Service Committee; plan to stabilize prices and maintain uninterrupted flow of crude oil.

Marquis James, *The Texaco Story. The First 50 Years, 1902–1952,* New York, the Company, 1953, pp. 118.
Anniversary history of Texas Company

W. Alton Jones, *The Cities Service Story. A Case History of American Enterprise* n.p., American Newcomen Society 1955, pp. 32.
History of company; special attention to work and accomplishments of Henry L. Doherty, founder of Cities Service Delivered as Newcomen Society address

John O. King, *The Early History of the Houston Oil Company of Texas, 1901–1908,* Houston, Texas Gulf Coast His-

torical Association, 1959, pp. v + 100.
Origin of Houston Oil Company, its
early association with Kirby Lumber
Company, and its subsequent development as petroleum producer in Texas.

**Henrietta M. Larson and Kenneth Wiggins
Porter,** *History of Humble Oil and Refining Company,* New York, Harper
& Bros., 1959, pp. xxiv + 769.
Definitive scholarly history of Humble;
under the auspices of the Business History Foundation.

Roy Lebkicher, *Aramco and World Oil,*
1950, pp. viii + 112. Rev. Ed. New
York, Russell F. Moore Co., 1952.
History of Arabian American Oil Co.,
covering entry of Aramco into Saudi
Arabia, early exploration, wartime operations, postwar expansion, relations
between Saudi Arabian Government
and company.

Henry Longhurst, *Adventure in Oil, The
Story of British Petroleum,* London,
Sidgwick & Jackson, 1959, pp. 286.
Popular-style history of British Petro-
leum Co., Ltd. (formerly Anglo-Persian
Oil Co., Ltd., 1909–35; Anglo-Iranian
Oil Co., Ltd., 1935–54). Account of
Company's founding and growth
through first half century.

John L. Loos, *Oil on Stream, A History of
Interstate Oil Pipe Line Company,
1909–1959,* Baton Rouge, Louisiana
State University Press, 1959, pp. xvi +
411.
History of construction and operation
of Interstate's pipe lines in nine states.

**Massachusetts Institute of Technology, Cen-
ter for International Studies,** *Stanvac in
Indonesia,* Washington, National Planning Association, 1957, pp. xi + 118.
Sixth case study in series on *United
States Business Performance Abroad.*
Reviews activities of subsidiaries of
Standard-Vacuum Oil Company, in Indonesia; early history, prewar experiences, Japanese occupation, postwar developments, relationships with employees and government.

Douglas G. McPhee, *The Story of Shell,*
n. pub., n.p., n.d., pp. 24. Reprinted
from *California Oil World and Petroleum Industry,* May 5, 1937.

Brief historical sketch similar to following title.

Douglas G. McPhee, *The Story of Standard
Oil Company of California,* San Francisco, the Company, 1937, pp. 31.
Establishment and growth of Company,
1875 to 1937, principal accomplishments, brief biographies of principal
officers. Reprint from series in *California Oil World* (Vol. 30, No. 3–7,
Feb. 5–April 5, 1937.)

C. Stuart Morgan, *Notes On Iraq Petroleum
Company, Ltd., and Affiliated Companies,* the Company, 1944, var. pag.
Origin and history of Turkish Petroleum
Company, later Iraq Petroleum Company, Ltd., Red Line area, significant
documents, operations, refineries, marketing, relations with Iraq Government,
future outlook for Middle East oil.

National Resources Commission, *General
Information of Chinese Petroleum Corporation,* Taipeh, Formosa, the Commission, 1951, pp. 51.
Chinese oil production and refining,
emphasis on Formosa, data through
1950.

National Supply Company, *The Story of the
National Supply Company,* Pittsburgh,
the Company, 1948, 42 unnumbered
pages.
History and growth of company, beginning with H. S. Spang & Son in 1828;
joining with John W. Chalfant in 1856
to form Spang-Chalfant, which made
first iron pipe west of Alleghenies, and
"likely" made short lengths of pipe used
by Drake as casing; growth of company.

Harvey O'Connor, *History of Oil Workers
International Union, C.I.O.,* Denver, the
Union, 1950, pp. xiv + 442.
Account of organizing efforts, and ac-
complishments of union.

Ohio Oil Company, *Five Eventful Decades.
A History of the Ohio Oil Company,
1887–1937,* Findlay, O., the Company,
1937, pp. 55.
Growth of Ohio Oil Company, sketches
of people associated with it; reprint of
first report of company.

Ohio Oil Company, *Sixty Years of Progress,
1887–1947. A History of the Ohio Oil*

Company, Findlay, O., the Company, 1947, pp. 47.
Origin of company, expansion to 1911; independent to 1927, period of consolidation and integration.

Oil Well Supply Company, *The "Oilwell" Story. 90 Years of Progress, 1862–1952*, Dallas, the Company, 1952. Reprint of pp. 89–173 of *Oil and Gas Journal*, May 26, 1952.
History of firm, beginning 1862 at Oil City, Pa., when John Eaton started oil well supply business and began five years later to produce equipment specifically for oil industry, made according to specifications and standardized. Company growth in conjunction with oil industry; now a division of United States Steel Corporation.

Oil Well Supply Company, *75 Years of Oil Progress, 1859–1934*, Oil City, Penna., the Company, 1934, pp. 15.
Account of Drake well; history of Company.

Pure Oil Company, *Behind the Pure Seal*, Chicago, the Company, 1957, pp. 34.
History of Company; map, illustrations.

Arnold M. Ross, *Oil is Where You Find It, The Story of Bishop Oil Company, 1920–1953*, San Francisco, the Company, 1953, pp. 47.
Organization, in 1920, of Company as independent crude oil producer in California; growth and expansion into other areas.

Royal Dutch Petroleum Company, *The Royal Dutch Petroleum Company (N. V. Koninklijke Nederlandsche Petroleum Maatschappij) 1890—16 June—1950, Diamond Jubilee Book*, The Hague, the Company, 1950, pp. 204.
Brief history of Royal Dutch-Shell group of companies; technical development of various departments of the business. Translation of identical book published in Dutch.

Richard Sasuly, *I. G. Farben*, New York, Boni & Gaer, 1947, pp. x + 312.
Development work of German chemical trust based on analysis of captured company files. Company held process patents important to oil industry.

P. C. Spencer, *Oil—And Independence! The Story of the Sinclair Oil Corporation*, n.p., American Newcomen Society, 1957, pp. 28.
Activities and accomplishments of Harry F. Sinclair, growth of Sinclair Oil Corporation, leasing of Teapot Dome, resulting developments. Delivered as Newcomen Society address.

Standard Oil Company of California, *Standard Oil Spirit*, San Francisco, the Company, 1923, pp. 62.
Relationship between personnel and management, types of work, employment, advancement, working conditions.

Standard Oil Company (New Jersey), *A Generation of Industrial Peace*, New York, the Company, 1946, pp. 63.
Working conditions, employee-management relations from Bayonne, N.J. strike in 1915 to date, based on contacts and interviews.

Standard Oil Company (New Jersey), *An Introduction to Standard Oil Company (New Jersey)*, New York, the Company, Rev. Ed. 1954, pp. 20.
Reviews beginning of Standard Oil, the Trust Agreement, dissolution decree, evolution and growth to present status.

Standard Oil Company (New Jersey), *The Jersey Standard Story*, New York, the Company, 1955, pp. 74.
Scope and activities, affiliates, subsidiaries.

Standard-Vacuum Petroleum Maatschappij *S.V.P.M. Forty Years of Progress 1912–1952*, Djakarta, Indonesia, the Company, 1953, pp. 48.
Reviews 40 years in which Stanvac engaged in oil exploration, development refining, distribution in Indonesia; chart cover operations back to 1912; community and employee relationships.

Swan-Finch Oil Corporation, *90 Years of Industrial Pioneering, 1853–1943, A History of the Swan-Finch Oil Corporation*, 2nd Ed. New York, the Company, 1943, pp. 37.

Swan-Finch Oil Corporation, *Oil Pioneer for 100 Years, 1853–1953. A Century of Lubrication Pioneering by Swan-Finch*

Oil Corporation, New York, the Company, 1953, pp. 24.
Company supplied fish and tanner's oils and lubricants from whale oil before making lubricating oils and greases from petroleum. Standard Oil Company of New Jersey bought control in 1891 and retained it until dissolution in 1911. Covers early types of lubricants; discusses petroleum lubrication.

Sidney A. Swensrud, *"Gulf Oil" The First Fifty Years, 1901–1951,* n.p., American Newcomen Society, 1951, pp. 32.
History of company; policies and objectives. Delivered as Newcomen Society address.

Frank J. Taylor and Earl M. Welty, *Black Bonanza. How an Oil Hunt Grew Into the Union Oil Company,* New York, McGraw-Hill Book Co., 1950, pp. 280. Rev. Ed.: *Black Bonanza,* 1956, pp. viii + 243.
Story of founding of Union Oil Company of California by Lyman Stewart and Wallace Hardison; journalistic in style.

Wayne C. Taylor and John Lindeman, *The Creole Petroleum Corporation in Venezuela,* Washington, National Planning Association, 1955, pp. x + 105.
Fourth case study in series on United States Business Performance Abroad. Outline and appraisal of activities of company against background of history and economy of Venezuela.

The Texas Company, *Texaco—A Picture Story,* New York, the Company, 1931, pp. 124.
Text and pictures: producing, pipe line transportation, refining, marine, worldwide distribution activities.

Texas Eastern Transmission Corporation, *The Story of Texas Eastern,* Shreveport, La., the Company, 1954, pp. 32.
Big and Little Inch pipe lines during World War II, postwar purchase of lines, conversion to natural gas transportation by Company. Organization, expansion, additional facilities, including underground storage.

Craig Thompson, *Since Spindletop. A Human Story of Gulf's First Half-Century,* Pittsburgh, the Company, 1951, pp. 110.
Growth of Company to integrated worldwide organization; anniversary history.

United Refining Company, *United Refining Company, A Story of Progress,* Warren, Penna., the Company, 1952, pp. 48.
Fifty years of growth of Pennsylvania refiner; reference to Bradford field and water-flooding operations.

C. BIOGRAPHIES OF INDIVIDUALS

(For Rockefeller and others connected with Standard Oil—See Standard Oil.)

Mary Lesley Ames, *Life and Letters of Peter and Susan Lesley,* New York, G. P. Putnam's Sons, 1909, 2 vols., pp. 1088.
Lesley was employed on 1st Geological Survey of Pennsylvania and was Director of 2nd Survey. Wrote on coal oil, Department of Agriculture report, 1862. Biographical notice by his nephew, Benjamin Smith Lyman, gives full account of his work.

Samuel Gamble Bayne, *Derricks of Destiny; An Autobiography,* New York, Brentano's, 1924, pp. xv + 259.
Bayne came from Ireland in 1869; became interested in oil production, established oil well supply firm; drilled over 400 wells; sold equipment for over 20,000 wells; organized Seaboard National Bank.

A. C. Bedford, *Edward L. Drake, Pioneer,* New York, 1923, pp. 21.
Address at Titusville, Penna., Aug. 27, 1923, in observance of Drake Day. (First name of Drake incorrectly given.)

Edwin C. Bell, *History of Petroleum; Life of Col. Edwin L. Drake,* Titusville, Penna., *The Bugle,* 1900, pp. vi + 171.
Life of Col. Drake and drilling of well; written for and published in Titusville "Bugle." Author reached oil country 1866 and became an authority on history of Pennsylvania oil region.

Norman Bridge, *The Marching Years,* New York, Duffield & Co., 1920, pp. 292.
Dr. Bridge, physician associated with E. L. Doheny in his Mexican oil developments, mentions development of Mexican Petroleum Co.

Howard Brunson, *The Oilman Who Didn't Want to Become a Millionaire, His Own Story,* New York, Exposition Press, 1955, pp. 83.
Author spent 27 years in oil fields, starting 1907 at Kern River and then Mid-Continent, before becoming independent drilling contractor and producer.

(William M. Burton), *William Meriam Burton. A Pioneer in Modern Petroleum Technology,* Cambridge, Mass., University Press, 1952, pp. 97.
A record of his accomplishments with Standard Oil Co. of Indiana as pioneer in oil cracking and awards bestowed upon him.

James A. Clark, *Three Stars for the Colonel, The Biography of Ernest O. Thompson,* New York, Random House, 1954, pp. 265.
Story of "colorful, controversial and competent" Gen. Ernest O. Thompson, "father of effective petroleum conservation."

W. L. Connelly, *The Oil Business As I Saw It. Half a Century with Sinclair,* Norman, Okla., University of Oklahoma Press, 1954, pp. xiv + 177.
Connelly began as roustabout at Bradford, late 1880's; describes oil developments and association with H. F. Sinclair; refers to Teapot Dome, Baku, and Venezuela.

Robert Crawford Cotner, *James Stephen Hogg: A Biography,* Austin, University of Texas Press, 1959, pp. xxvi + 617.
Biography of James Stephen Hogg, 1851–1906, Attorney-General and Governor of Texas. Includes account of suit filed against Waters-Pierce Oil Company and Standard Oil Company for alleged violation of Texas antitrust laws. Chap. XIX, pp. 518–555, deals with Hogg-Swayne Syndicate and Texas Company and early oil developments.

Wallace Davis, *Corduroy Road: The Story of Glenn Herbert McCarthy,* Houston, Anson Jones Press, 1951, pp. 282.

Life of man hailed as "King of the Wildcatters."

Sir Henri Deterding and Stanley Naylor, *An International Oilman,* London, Ivor Nicholson & Watson, and New York, Harper & Bros., 1934, pp. 126.
Autobiography of chief builder of Royal Dutch-Shell group of companies; appeared originally in *Saturday Evening Post.*

Leonard M. Fanning, *Edwin L. Drake Father of the Petroleum Industry,* New York, Mercer Publishing Co., 1954, pp. 10. ("Father of Industries" Series)
Circumstances leading to and following drilling of Drake well; work and fortunes of Drake.

Guy Woodward Finney, *Mericos H. Whittier. His Career. The Story of a California Oil Pioneer, Civic Leader and Humanitarian Whose Note-worthy Career Won Him Honor Among Men,* Los Angeles, Stationers Corp., 1940, pp. xiv + 115.

Nathaniel S. Fleischer, *The Flaming Ben Hogan, Pugilist, Pirate, Gambler, Civil War Spy, Oil Magnate, Evangelist,* New York, C. J. O'Brien, 1941, pp. 32.
Early gambling king of Pennsylvania oilfields, called "wickedest man in the world."

Valentin R. Garfias, *Garf from Mexico,* Mexico, D. F., Editorial Jus, 1950, pp. 261.
Author worked in California oil fields; was first professor of petroleum engineering at Stanford; worked as geologist in many foreign countries; trained many to look for oil.

Winalee Gentry, *One More River to Cross,* Philadelphia, Westminster Press, 1955, pp. 237.
Experiences in the field by a wife who helped her oilman husband, Dux Gentry, Jackson, Michigan.

Lucille Glasscock, *A Texas Wildcatter; A Fascinating Saga of Oil,* San Antonio, Naylor Co., 1952, pp. 126.
Oil operations of Gus Glasscock, from his first attempt in Ranger, 1919, through developments in Texas, and concluding with offshore drilling by

means of specially designed and constructed barge. Written by his wife.

Ralph Hewins, *Mr. Five Per Cent; The Story of Calouste Gulbenkian,* New York, Rinehart & Co., 1958, pp. x + 261.
Life story, based in part on typewritten "Memoirs" of Gulbenkian; deals also with foundation of Iraq Petroleum Company and other oil developments in Middle East.

Edward W. Kelman and Theon Wright, *Hugh Roy Cullen: A Story of American Opportunity,* New York, Prentice-Hall, 1954, pp. 376.
Cullen went into oil business in 1917, drilled discovery well at Pierce Junction, 1921. In 1926, after production exhausted, he reassembled leases and drilled deeper to discover prolific production. Was one of wealthiest Texas producers at his death.

Alfred Richard Knight, *Now Justice Comes to Washington,* n.p., Business Methods Publishing Co., 1944, pp. 226.
Author's experiences selling asphalt, early 20th century; employment by oil companies; activities in connection with legal actions on tax matters of one oil company.

John Lodwick, *Gulbenkian; An Interpretation of the Richest Man in the World,* New York, Doubleday & Co., 1958; pp. vii + 289.
Life of Calouste Gulbenkian, based on recollections of David H. Young, who served for 2 decades as private secretary to Gulbenkian.

Sam T. Mallison, *The Great Wildcatter, The Story of Mike Benedum,* Charleston, W. Va., Education Foundation of West Virginia, 1953, pp. 528.
"The story of finding oil as told in the adventures of the man who has found more of it than anyone in history."

John Joseph Matthews, *Life and Death of an Oilman. The Career of E. W. Marland,* Norman, Okla., University of Oklahoma Press, 1951, pp. 259.
Story of "one of the nation's greatest plungers in oil." Author knew Ernest Marland, who was founder of present Continental Oil Company, later Congressman from Oklahoma and governor of the state, and founder of Interstate Oil Compact Commission.

Reid Sayers McBeth, *Pioneering the Gulf Coast; A Story of the Life and Accomplishments of Capt. Anthony F. Lucas,* New York, the author, 1918, pp. 80.
Life of Capt. Lucas; discovery and development of Spindletop oilfield, salt and sulphur exploration and production; use of rotary drill at Spindletop, development and use of valve to check back-pressure and addition of mud to drilling fluid.

William Larimer Mellon and Boyden Sparkes, *Judge Mellon's Sons,* Pittsburgh, privately printed, 1948, pp. 570.
Story of 5 sons of Judge Thomas Mellon; pipe line and refinery activity in Pennsylvania; participation in Spindletop development; establishment and development of Gulf Oil Corp.

Joseph Millard, *The Wickedest Man,* New York, Fawcett Publications, 1954, pp. 187. ("Gold Medal" paperback book) Life of Ben Hogan (Benedict Hagan), described as "wickedest man in the world." He arrived in Pithole during excitement of oil discovery in 1865, remained through rise and drop in production; moved to other oil centers before becoming evangelist.

Ernest C. Miller, *John Wilkes Booth, Oilman,* New York, The Exposition Press, 1947, pp. 78.
Pennsylvania oil activities of President Lincoln's assassin.

Nettie Elizabeth Mills, *The Lady Driller, The Autobiography,* New York, Exposition Press, 1955, pp. 176.
Account of experiences of author as drilling contractor in Oklahoma and Texas.

Isador Molk, *The Making of An Oilman,* New York, Citadel Press, 1958, pp. 252.
Autobiography of pioneer in oil fields of Midwest.

Harvey O'Connor, *Mellon's Millions, The Biography of a Fortune: The Life and Times of Andrew W. Mellon,* New York,

John Day Co., 1933, pp. xv + 443.
Oil plays prominent part in this account, including formation of Gulf Oil Corp., operations abroad, etc.

Mary Logan Orcutt, *Memorabilia of William Warren Orcutt, 1869–1942,* Los Angeles, Fred S. Lang Press, 1945, pp. xxi + 93.
Orcutt was early practitioner applying geology in field of oil exploration; was famous head of geological department of Union Oil Company of California.

Robert L. Owen, *Remarkable Experiences of H. F. Sinclair with his Government,* Tulsa, n. pub., 1929, pp. 46.
Author, first United States Senator from Oklahoma, reviews record in Congress and in courts concerning leasing of Teapot Dome and ensuing actions.

Glyn Roberts, *The Most Powerful Man in the World: The Life of Sir Henri Deterding,* New York, Covici-Friede, 1938, pp. 448.
Alleged activities of head of Royal Dutch–Shell Group; written by staff member of London *Daily Worker.*

(Henry R. Rouse), *Biography of Henry R. Rouse and History of the Rouse Estate,* Warren, Penna., Commissioners of Rouse Estate, 1907, pp. 35.
Rouse participated in drilling second oil well in Pennsylvania; perished, 1861, in first great oil fire.

Melodia B. Rowe, *Captain Jones—The Biography of a Builder,* Hamilton, O., Hill-Brown Printing Co., 1942, pp. 262.
Life of Joseph Thomas Jones, who entered Pennsylvania oil fields in 1865 and was known as "Dry Hole" Jones because his first 12 drilling attempts were failures. Employed James C. Tennent as oil scout. Tennent wrote *The Oil Scouts, Reminiscences of the Night Riders of the Hemlocks.* Jones moved to Sisterville, West Virginia, 1891, became leading producer; later founded and helped develop Gulfport, Mississippi.

John Rowland, *Lord Cadman, Ambassador for Oil,* London, Herbert Jenkins, 1960.
Cadman was pioneer in oil technology and instruction; Chairman of Anglo–Persian Oil Co.; participated in negotia-

tions affecting British oil interests in Middle East and elsewhere.

John A. Spender, *Weetman Pearson, First Viscount Cowdray, 1856–1927,* London Cassell & Co., 1930, pp. xi + 315.
Cowdray founded famous Mexican Eagle Company, one of largest Mexican oil companies.

John Washington Steele, *Coal Oil Johnny Story of His Career as Told by Himself,* Franklin, Penna., the author, 1902, pp 211.
Author, who acquired reputation of profligate spender, had inherited rich oil-producing property at an early age his name became synonymous with foolish spending. Settled down to respectable career in later life.

(John Washington Steele), *Life of Coal Oi Johnny,* by Coal Oil Johnny, New York Bell and Bogart Soap Co., 1901, pp. 13 See above.

Festus Paul Summers, *Johnson Newlon Camden, A Study in Individualism,* G P. Putnam's Sons, 1937, pp. xi + 605 Camden built oil refinery at Parkersburg 1867; transferred plant to Standard Oil Company, 1875; bought or leased many oil refineries; elected to United States Senate in 1881.

George Francis Trainer, *The Life and Adventures of Ben Hogan, the Wickedest Man in the World,* New York, n. pub., 1878, pp. 276.
Hogan, in collaboration with Trainer, outlined his early career in Pennsylvania oil regions, and described his conversion.

Robert Watchorn, *The Autobiography of Robert Watchorn,* Herbert Faulkner West, Ed., Oklahoma City, Robert Watchorn Charities, Ltd., 1958. pp. xix + 218.
Colorful career of Derbyshire coal miner who was successively first secretary of United Mine Workers of America, U. S. Commissioner of Immigration, treasurer of Union Oil Co. of California, and Oklahoma oil producer. Text written in 1931, published with emendations on centennial of Watchorn's birth.

Caspar Whitney, *Charles Adelbert Canfield*, Boston, The Merrymount Press, 1930, pp. viii + 217.

Partner of famous California firm Canfield & Chanslor; important pioneer in California oil production, 1890–1915; best remembered for his leading role in opening up Mexican oil fields.

Ruth Keech Whittier, *Reminiscences of Other Days*, Los Angeles, Times-Mirror Press, 1925, pp. 218.

Contains *A Short Sketch of the M. H. Whittier Family*, by Mericos H. Whittier, which includes account of his activities in California oil development. Includes Whittier's work as oil driller and producer in Los Angeles and San Joaquin Valley, association with early California oilmen, and development of Kern River field.

W. E. Youle, *Sixty Three Years in the Oil Fields*, Taft, Cal., Midway Driller Publishing Co., 1926, pp. 61, plus 61 unnumbered pages with 28 biographies and portraits. Memorial Edition printed by Fuller Printing Co. 1st Ed. 1926, pp. 81, with 13 portraits.

Author's work and experiences in Pennsylvania oil fields, 1863–76; move to California, where for 50 years he was one of state's most famous drillers and discoverer of several of California's earliest oil fields. California oil history is that prior to 1900.

XV.

Reference Works, Dictionaries, Directories, Bibliographies

A. REFERENCE WORKS, INCLUDING TECHNICAL

American Institute of Mining and Metallurgical Engineers, *General Index to Petroleum Publications* (*1921–1952*) of *the Institute,* Dallas, Petroleum Branch, the Institute, 1954, pp. v + 149.
Institute Transactions, Mining and Metallurgy, Journal of Petroleum Technology; special papers, contributions, technical publications; Elements of the Petroleum Industry; Antitrust Laws et. al., v. Unit Operation of Oil and Gas Pools; Conservation.

Stephen Osgood Andros, *The Petroleum Handbook,* Chicago, Shaw Publishing Co., 1919, pp. 206.
Fundamentals of oil industry, from oil wells to distribution of refined products.

Anglo-Iranian Oil Company (now British Petroleum Co.), *Our Industry,* London, the Company, 1947, pp. 304. 2nd Ed. 1949, pp. 368. 3rd Ed. 1958, pp. 472.
General description of oil industry from initial search for new fields to disposal of finished products, prepared for Company personnel. Includes summary of Company history.

Raymond Foss Bacon and William A. Hamor, *The American Petroleum Industry,* New York, McGraw-Hill Book Co., 1916, 2 vols., pp. xvi + 963.
A classic reference book, representing comprehensive survey of American petroleum industry as of publication date. History, finding, drilling, production and refining of oil, with section on shale oil.

Max W. Ball, *This Fascinating Oil Business,* Indianapolis, Bobbs-Merrill Co., 1940, pp. 444.

Comprehensive, authoritative and highly readable description of oil business in all its branches. Slightly outdated, but simple style still commends it to students.

William Theodore Brannt, *Petroleum: Its History, etc.,* Philadelphia, Henry Carey Baird & Co., 1895, pp. xxvii + 715.
An omnium gatherum based mainly on German writings of Hans Höfer and Alexander Veith.

Benjamin Johnson Crew, *A Practical Treatise on Petroleum: Its Origin, Geology, Geographical Distribution, etc.,* Philadelphia, Henry Carey Baird & Co., 1887, pp. xxiv + 508.
Author connected with petroleum refining, from early days; died before manuscript complete. Work completed by brother, J. Lewis Crew, and others.

David T. Day, *A Handbook of the Petroleum Industry,* New York, John Wiley & Sons, 1922, 2 vols., pp. xvi + 1970.
Classic reference book covering occurrence of petroleum, petroleum geology, oil field development and production, transportation, characteristics, and methods of testing, refining, engineering, plant and apparatus design, processes, oil usage, internal combustion engines, pipe lines, with tables and glossary.

A. E. Dunstan, A. W. Nash, Benjamin T. Brooks, Sir Henry Tizard, Eds., *The Science of Petroleum,* London, Oxford University Press, 1938, 4 vols., pp. 3192.
Vol. V (Benjamin T. Brooks and A. E. Dunstan, Eds.) Part I (Crude Oils:

Chemical and Physical Properties), 1950, pp. viii + 200; Part II (Synthetic Products of Petroleum), 1953, pp. x + 328; Part III (Refinery Products), 1955, pp. viii + 397. Vol. IV (V. C. Illing, Ed.), Part I (The World's Oilfields—Eastern Hemisphere), 1953, pp. vi + 174.

Definitive work by authoritative authors of all nationalities on all aspects of petroleum technology; Vols. I–IV published as and indexed as a unit. Succeeding volumes bring particular subjects up to date.

eonard M. Fanning, *World Petroleum Policies,* New York, Mona Palmer Publishing Corp., 1957, loose-leaf.
Chronological sourcebook of quotations, bearing on all important aspects of oil industry public issues.

irgil B. Guthrie, Ed., *Petroleum Products Handbook,* McGraw-Hill Book Co., 1960, pp. xviii, var. pag.
Practical information and data for efficient storage, handling, and utilization of petroleum products.

obert E. Hardwicke, *The Oilman's Barrel,* Norman, Okla., University of Okla. Press, 1958, pp. xi + 122.
History of 42-gallon oil barrel.

istitute of Petroleum, *Modern Petroleum Technology,* London, the Institute, 1946, pp. viii + 466. 2nd Ed. 1954, pp. viii + 702.
Articles on exploration, drilling, production, refining, utilization, distribution, measurements, tests, and economics.

istitute of Petroleum, *Review of Petroleum Technology,* London, the Institute of Petroleum (formerly Institution of Petroleum Technologists), 1935–54, 14 vols.
Technical papers on exploration, production, refining, and related matters.

istitution of Petroleum Technologists, *Petroleum: Twenty-Five Years Retrospect, 1910–1935,* London, the Institution, 1935, pp. xix + 219.
Twenty-one articles dealing with advances in petroleum science and technology.

G. P. Koch, *Oil—From The Ground Up,* San Francisco, Shell Oil Co., pp. 544. Privately published in loose-leaf form, 1936, 1938, 1940; New York, 1948.
Textbook for company salesmen's training course conducted by author.

G. P. Koch, *Oil-Text,* San Francisco, Shell Oil Co., 1941, pp. ix + 298 + xxvi.
Textbook for staff instruction in fundamentals of manufacturing and marketing oil products.

David D. Leven, *Done in Oil,* New York, Ranger Press, 1941, pp. xxxii + 1084. 2nd Ed.: *Petroleum Encyclopedia, Done in Oil,* New York, Ranger Press, 1942, pp. xxxii + 1084.
Extremely comprehensive coverage of oil industry, including economics, supply, oil fields, reserves, conservation, proration, expropriation, transportation, refining, marketing, finance, royalties, plus glossary and extensive statistical tables.

Albert Lidgett, *Petroleum,* London, Sir Isaac Pitman & Sons, 1919, pp. vii + 168. 3rd Ed. 1928, pp. xii + 160.
Chief phases of oil industry, petroleum in British Empire, in First World War, etc.; Scottish shale oil industry; principal companies.

Ernest Raymond Lilley, *The Oil Industry,* New York, D. Van Nostrand Co., 1925, pp. x + 548.
Summary and guide.

Henry Neuberger and Henri Noalhat, *Technology of Petroleum,* trans. from French by John Geddes McIntosh, London, Scott, Greenwood & Co., 1901, pp. 666.
Origin of petroleum, detailed description, including legislation, history, and statistics, of world's oil fields; hand excavation and digging of wells; methods of boring; accidents, explosive; storage and transport; management.

Richard Maxwell Pearl, *Guide to Geologic Literature,* New York, McGraw-Hill Book Co., 1951, pp. xi + 239.
Reference book on problems of geologic literature; library facilities and services; types of geologic literature including periodicals, abstracts, theses, maps, etc.

G. A. Purdy, *Petroleum: Prehistoric to Petrochemicals,* Toronto, Copp Clark

Publishing Co., 1957, pp. 492. New York, McGraw-Hill Book Co., 1958. Comprehensive reference book containing review of Canadian oil industry, discussion of petroleum refining and products, including petrochemicals.

Sir Boverton Redwood, *Petroleum: Its Production and Use,* New York, D. Van Nostrand, 1887, pp. 210. (Van Nostrand's Science Series No. 92.) Abridgment of Canton Lectures, 1886, before Society of Arts, London.

Sir Boverton Redwood, *Petroleum: A Treatise* (commonly called *A Treatise on Petroleum*), London, Charles Griffin & Co., and Philadelphia, J. B. Lippincott, 1896, 2 vols., pp. 900. 2nd Ed. 1906, 2 vols., pp. xxxi + 1064. 3rd Ed. 1913, 3 vols., pp. xxxii + 1167. 4th Ed. 1922, 3 vols., pp. xxx + 1353. 5th Ed. 1926, Reprint of 4th Ed.
One of the landmark oil reference books by a distinguished British petroleum consultant and chemist. Author knew his subject from firsthand information acquired through a lifetime of travel and consulting work. 3rd, 4th, and 5th editions contain extensive bibliography. Detailed history of oil by countries; maps; manufacturing processes; pipe line and tanker transport, with drawings and diagrams.

Sir Boverton Redwood and Arthur Eastlake, *Petroleum Technologist's Pocket-Book* London, Charles Griffin & Co., 1915 pp. 454. 2nd Ed. 1923, pp. xxiv + 546 Reference work on petroleum geology physical and chemical properties of oil oil production, refining, transport storage, and testing, uses, weights and measures. Maps.

Shell (formerly Asiatic) Petroleum Company, *A Petroleum Handbook,* London the Company, 1933, pp. 362. 2nd Ed 1938, pp. 473. 3rd Ed. 1948, pp. 658 4th Ed. 1959, pp. ix + 678.
Royal Dutch-Shell Group informational text for staff members. Reviews all aspects of oil industry, with chapter on Company history.

S. G. Symons, *The Waverly Handbook* Pittsburgh, Waverly Oil Works Co. 1949, 11th Ed. pp. 866. (6th Ed. 1914 1915, pp. 320; 7th Ed. 1918; 8th Ed 1922, pp. 1040; 9th Ed. 1937, pp. 902. Tables useful to oil production men text on secondary recovery methods standards, other data.

The Texas Company, *Petroleum Products* New York, the Company, 1933, pp. 80 2nd Ed. 1939, pp. 87. 3rd Ed. 1944, pp. 154.
Oil finding, production, refining, transportation and use, with flow charts.

B. DICTIONARIES AND GLOSSARIES

American Chemical Society, *Joint Symposium on the Nomenclature of Hydrocarbons,* Washington, the Society, 1949, pp. 132.
Seven papers with names, structural codes, and ciphers applied to hydrocarbons.

American Geological Institute, *Glossary of Geology and Related Sciences,* Washington, the Institute, 1957, pp. x + 325.
Original or earliest definition of each term; current and variant usages and spellings; synonyms and equivalent foreign language terms; selected list of glossaries and dictionaries.

American Petroleum Institute, *Glossary of Terms Used in Petroleum Refining,* New

York, the Institute, 1953, pp. iv + 188 Terms selected from published source which constitute their authority.

Lalia Phipps Boone, *The Petroleum Dictionary,* Norman, Okla., University of Oklahoma Press, 1952, pp. xiii + 338 Origin, development, characteristics of oil field language; dictionary of word and terms includes about 6,000 entries Author principally interested in picturesque speech and dialect of oil producing; very little on other aspects of business.

Oscar P. Irizarry, *Glossary of the Petroleum Industry,* Tulsa, Petroleum Publishing Co., 1947, pp. ix + 316.
In two parts, English-Spanish and

Spanish-English; more than 12,000 technical terms and expressions.

rthur T. King, *Oil Refinery Terms in Oklahoma,* Greensboro, N.C., American Dialect Society, Woman's College of the University of North Carolina, 1948, pp. 3–64, Publication No. 9.
Words and definitions collected by author at refineries in Tulsa and Oklahoma City; author's main interest was dialect and picturesque speech.

arcel Mitzakis, *The Oil Encyclopaedia,* London, Chapman & Hall, 1922, pp. xvi + 557.
Alphabetical listing and description, dictionary style, of oil industry terms, specifications, tests, process patents, petroleum hydrocarbons, products, oil fields, leading oil producing areas, commercial terms, argot, tankers, statistics of main operations, etc. Highly useful reference work as of date of compilation.

H. Molyn, *Dictionary. Dutch-English, English-Dutch. Petroleum Prospecting, Drilling, Production, Refining, Laboratories, Transportation, Applications,* New York, printed for Oceanic Exchange Co., 1946, pp. 352.
Oil technical terms turned into Dutch and vice versa.

n American Petroleum and Transport Company, *Petroleum Glossary,* New York, the Company, 1922, pp. 52.
Published as supplement to *Mexican Petroleum.*
Oil terms with emphasis on those current in exploration and production at date of publication.

itz Persch, *English-German Oil Dictionary,* Berlin, Rudolph Schmidt, 1955, pp. 416.
Bilingual list of terms used in geology, geophysics, drilling, production, storage, transportation of oil.

itz Persch, *Oil Dictionary. German, English, French, and Spanish,* Berlin, Industrieverlag von Hernhaussen, 1944, pp. 528.
Oil terms in four languages.

itz Persch, *German-English Drilling Engineering Ditctionary,* Berlin, Rudolph Schmidt, 1953, pp. 147.

Technical oil terms in German and English.

Petroleum Educational Institute, *Illustrated Petroleum Dictionary and Products Manual,* Los Angeles, the Institute, 1952, pp. 502.
Terms commonly used in petroleum and allied industries; information, fully illustrated, on petroleum, petroleum products, equipment using products. Probably most complete and most useful of various petroleum dictionaries.

Hollis Paine Porter, *Petroleum Dictionary for Office, Field, and Factory,* Houston, Gulf Publishing Co., 1930, pp. 234. 2nd Ed. 1936, pp. 253. 3rd Ed. 1941, pp. 263. 4th Ed. 1948, pp. 326.
Words and terms used in exploration and production; prepared for students of production engineering. Excellent for material covered, but few terms from other ends of business.

Jerome B. Robertson, *Oil Slanguage. An Explanation of Terms and Slang of Oil Fields from Pennsylvania to California, Texas to Montana—and Around the World,* Evansville, Ind., Petroleum Publishers, 1954, pp. 181.
Words and phrases used in industry; comments and anecdotes.
Considered interesting but not authoritative.

Ronald K. Ross, *A Dictionary of Petroleum Terms,* Sydney, Australia, New Century Press, 1948, pp. 119.
Words and terms in industry; brief German-English; French-English glossary.

Shell Petroleum Company, *Glossary of Selected Petroleum Terms,* London, the Company, 1943, pp. 71.
Glossary of technical terms common to oil products trade, with equivalent words in French, German, and Spanish. Conversion tables.

Howard Russell Williams and Charles J. Meyers, *Oil and Gas Terms: Annotated Manual of Legal, Engineering, Tax Words and Phrases,* Albany, Banks & Co., and Matthew Bender & Co., 1957, pp. vi + 282.
Defines words and phrases commonly encountered in oil and gas law, land leasing, tax filing; with case citations.

Manuel J. Zevada and Eleuterio Martinez, *Glossary of the Petroleum Industry and Spanish-English and English-Spanish Vocabulary of Technical Terms Used in This Industry,* Mexico, D. F., Government of Mexico, 1930, pp. 363.

Vocabulary with appendices coveri nomenclature of drilling rigs and equ ment; citations. Prepared by Vocabula Commission of Petroleum Bure Government of Mexico.

C. DIRECTORIES

Ernest C. Brown, *Brown's Directory of American Gas Companies, 1960 Edition,* New York, Moore Publishing Co., 1959, pp. xxiv + 507. 1st Ed. 1887. Ernest C. Brown, original author; compiled by publisher in more recent years. List of city-gas public utilities for United States and Canada, transmission companies, by states and communities; operating data for each; holding, operating, service companies; commissions, associations, public regulatory officials.

R. W. Byram & Company, *Oil Directory of Texas, 1959,* Austin, the Company, 1959, pp. 355.
Oil and gas producers, oil and gas purchasing and transporting companies, refineries, gasoline, carbon black, cycling, and repressuring plants in Texas.

Geophysical Directory, *The Geophysical Directory, 1959,* Houston, the Geophysical Directory, 14th Ed., 1959, pp. 413. Latest in a series published annually since 1946.
Companies and individuals connected with, or engaged in geophysical exploration for petroleum in United States or abroad; includes those who have used geophysical service, 1942–59.

Gulf Publishing Company, *Composite Catalog of Oil Field Equipment and Services,* 23rd Revision, Houston, The Company, 1958, 3 vols., pp. 5384.
Catalogs of manufacturers of oil field equipment and service concerns.

The Refinery Catalog; A Composite Catalog File of Equipment, Materials, and Services for Refining, Petrochemicals, Natural Gasoline, 26th Revision, Houston, Gulf Publishing Co., 1959, pp. 980. Title varies since 1934.
Specifications and other data on oil refining, natural gasoline, and petro-

chemical equipment and services, fil by 300 manufacturers and suppliers.

J. V. Howell and A. I. Levorsen, *Direct of Geological Material in North Am ica,* 2nd Ed., Washington, Americ Geological Institute, 1957, pp. vi + 2 (1st Ed. published 1946 as Part 2, B letin, Vol. 30, No. 8, pp. 1321–14 American Association of Petrole Geologists, Tulsa.)
Sources of geological information with each province or state, including oil a gas trade journals.

R. C. Megargel & Co., *Megargel's Man of South American Oil Companies, 19 Edition,* New York, the Company, 19 pp. 133. 1927 Ed. pp. 187.
Comments on principal established a prospective oil fields in South Ameri information on organization, properti finances, personnel for 37 companies 1926 edition; 56 companies in 19 edition.

Midwest Oil Register Publications, Tul C. L. Cooper.
Midwest Oil Register. Published an ally since 1945.
Directory of Producers and Drill Contractors: Texas, 1959, pp. 6 *Oklahoma, 1959,* pp. 318; *Californ 1959,* pp. 194; *Kansas, 1959,* pp. 1 *Michigan, Indiana, Illinois, Kentuc 1959,* pp. 214; *Louisiana, Mississip Arkansas, Florida, Georgia, 1959,* 170; *Rocky Mountain Region, Willis Basin, Four Corners, New Mexico, 19* pp. 232.
Directory of Oil Refineries, Constr tion, Petrochemical, and Natural (Processing Plants, 1959, 1959, pp. 4 *Directory of Pipe Line Companies a Pipe Line Contractors, 1959,* 1959, 339.
Oil Directory of Canada, 1959, 1959, 409.

Oil Directory of Foreign Companies Outside the U.S.A. and Canada, 1959, 1959, pp. 292.
Directory of Geophysical and Oil Companies Who Use Geophysical Service, 1959, 1959, pp. 487.
Directory of Oil Well Drilling Contractors, 1958, pp. 531.
Water-Flooding and Offshore Companies.
Directory of Oil Well Supply Companies.

E. Murray & Co., *Oil Trade Blue Book. Directory and Dictionary of the Mineral Oil Industry,* Chicago, F. E. Murray & Co., 1920, pp. 272. In 1923–1924, published by Murray-Duff Corp., Chicago, as Quarterly Directory and Buyers' Guide of the Mineral Oil Industry.
Covers producing, refining, compounding, natural gasoline manufacturers, jobbers, marketing, traffic, manufacturing companies.

il Men's Association of America, *Texas Oil Directory,* Dallas, (Hank Seale Oil Directories.) *Supplemental Listings, 1958,* pp. 184.
Initiated in 1957 with *Continental Oil Directory.* Texas Oil Directory is basic copy, with Supplemental Listings includes information on important changes in oil industry during year.

enry Ozanne, *The Canada Oil Record, 1958,* Washington, Petroleum Industry Projects, 1958, pp. iv + 456.
Operating and financial data on Dominion-chartered oil companies in Canada; Canadian activities of American oil companies.

enry Ozanne, *The Gas Record,* Washington, Petroleum Industry Projects, 1953, pp. 430. 1954 Ed., pp. 425. No editions since.
Information similar to *Oil Record* on public utility gas companies and natural gas pipe line companies in United States.

enry Ozanne, *The Oil Record, 1958,* Washington, Petroleum Industry Projects, 1958, pp. vii + 1183. Published annually, initial edition, 1950.
Detailed operating and financial data on some 200 oil companies, chiefly United States.

L. Parsons, *The Oil Bradstreet. Official Oil Book of California,* Los Angeles, Parsons & Ellis, 1909, pp. 48. Name later changed to *Oil Bradstreet and Mining Director,* Los Angeles, Financial News Publishing Co. Published through 31 editions, concluding with 1939.
Oil companies in California, with financial and operating data as it appears on state tax rolls.

Petroleum Publishing Company, *Plant and Personnel Directory. Crude-Oil Refineries, Field-Processing Plants, Petrochemical Plants, 1957–58,* Tulsa, the Company, 1957, pp. 154.
Statistical summary, North American operating refineries, field processing plants, refinery personnel in United States and Canada, field processing plant and petrochemical plant personnel. Compiled by staff of *Oil & Gas Journal.*

Petroleum Register, *Petroleum Register* (now titled *International Petroleum Register*), New York, 1919, annually to date. Publisher, 1919–1925, *Oil Trade Journal;* 1926–1927, Holland S. Reavis; 1928–1929, Chilton Class Journal Co.; 1930–1932, not published; 1933–1938, Petroleum Register Co.; 1939, Russell Palmer (title: *World Petroleum Register*); 1940–1949, Palmer Publications (under original title); 1950 to date, Palmer Publications (title: *International Petroleum Register.*)
Listing of oil companies, domestic and foreign, together with brief description of company's business and list of elected officers. Information (particularly in volumes for 1940's) sometimes outdated.

J. Alfred Powell, *Powell's Oil and Gas Directory. The Oil Business in a Nutshell,* Bartlesville, Okla., the author, 1918, pp. 146. Subsequent editions for 1919, 1920, 1921.
Oil and gas companies in Kansas, Oklahoma, Texas, Louisiana; oil well supply houses; refineries; pipe lines; casinghead plants; general oil statistics.

Hank Seale, *Hank Seale Oil Directories, Louisiana, Texas Gulf Coast, East Texas, Arkansas, and Mississippi, 1959,* Dallas, Oil Men's Association of America, 1959, pp. 132.
Lists oil producers, operators, drilling

contractors, landmen, company and independent geologists, production superintendents, petroleum engineers, lease brokers.

Walter E. Skinner, *Skinner's Oil and Petroleum Year Book, 1959,* London, Walter E. Skinner, 1959, pp. 795, 50th Edition. Contains operational and financial data on 1100 companies actively producing oil or engaged in refining, transporting, and marketing oil, and financing oil development. Established by Walter Robert Skinner. First edition, *The Oil, Petroleum, and Bitumen Manual, and*

Kindred Companies for 1910, Lond the Capitalist, 1910, pp. 128. Publish annually in successive years, except 1941, when premises of the printer we destroyed by enemy action. Valual for tracing details of company na changes, stockholdings, annual earnin etc.

Herbert S. Stoneham & Co., *Oil and Ki dred Companies,* London, the Compan 3rd Ed., 1911, pp. cxlvi + 177. Extracts from publications in Unit States on oil companies.

D. BIBLIOGRAPHIES

Alberta Society of Petroleum Geologists, *Annotated Bibliography of Geology of Sedimentary Basin of Alberta and of Adjacent Parts of British Columbia and Northwest Territories, 1845–1955,* Calgary, the Society, 1958, pp. xv + 499.
Sources of geologic information on Alberta.

Anne Laura Baden, *The Petroleum Industry. A Selected List of Recent References,* Washington, Division of Bibliography, Library of Congress, 1942, pp. 60.
Four hundred ninety-two items, of thenrecent publication, items 1–284 being books, with Library of Congress catalogue numbers noted, and items 285–492 covering then-recent articles published in periodicals.

E. DeGolyer and Harold Vance, *Bibliography on the Petroleum Industry,* College Station, Tex., Agricultural and Mechanical College of Texas, 1944, pp. xxxii + 730. (Bulletin, 4th Series, Vol. 15, No. 11.)
Combines about 12000 items in personal bibliography of DeGolyer with that of Petroleum Engineering Department at Texas A. & M. and that of S. F. Shaw on air and gas lift, mostly periodical references to items in oil journals, bulletins, proceedings.

Robert E. Hardwicke, *Petroleum and Natural Gas Bibliography,* Austin, University of Texas, 1937, pp. xii + 167.

Significant initial compilation of abo 1400 books and pamphlets on oil i dustry; references to legal works i cluded. Considered definitive and a curate as of date of compilation: Ja 1, 1937.

Institute of Petroleum, London, *Libra Catalogue,* 1956, pp. vii + 87.
Books in library of Institute.

Interstate Oil Compact Commission, *Inde to Publications of the Interstate O Compact Commission, 1935–56,* Okl homa City, the Commission, 1957, p 245. *Supplement,* pp. 34.
Provides general index of proceedings meetings since 1942 and all separat pamphlets and reports of Commissio Supplement covers reports of meeting held 1935 to 1942 for which transcript were published only in mimeographe form.

Arthur McAnally and Duane Henry Du Bose Roller, *A Check List of the E DeGolyer Collection in the History o Science and Technology, as of Aug. 1 1954,* Norman, Okla., University o Oklahoma Press, 1951. 2nd Ed. 1953 pp. 52. 3rd Ed. 1954, pp. vi + 127.
Collection established at University o Oklahoma in 1949. First check list con tained about 600 entries; second abou 1200; third about 3000, representin about 5000 volumes.

D. F. McNeill, *A Selected Bibliography o the History of the Canadian Oil In* *dustry,* Ottawa, Department of Mines and Technical Services, 1957, pp. 13. References to Canadian oil history, Alberta, Saskatchewan, Manitoba, Ontario, Quebec, New Brunswick.

Mark White Pangborn, Jr., *The Earth for the Layman,* Washington, American Geological Institute, 1950, pp. 50. 2nd Ed. 1957, pp. 68.
"Nearly 1400 good books and pamphlets of popular interest on geology, mining, oil, maps, and related subjects." With brief description of each.

Sir Boverton Redwood, *A Treatise on Petroleum,* London, Charles Griffin & Co., 1922, 3 vols. (See listing under Technical Reference Works.)
Vol. 3 contains bibliography of more than 8000 items.

Walter Rundell, Jr., *Centennial Bibliography,* Boston, Harvard University Graduate School of Business Administration, 1959, pp. 17. (Reprint, pp. 430–447, *Business History Review,* Vol. xxxiii, No. 3, Autumn, 1959.)

Short descriptive bibliography of recent economic and history books on petroleum industry in United States; 130 items.

Curtis Stevens, *Petroleum Sourcebook, 1958, A Regional Bibliography of Petroleum Information,* Amarillo, Tex., National Petroleum Bibliography, 1958, pp. iv + 179.
First of annual series designed to present in single volume location of petroleum literature and data most often sought. References compiled from issues of *National Petroleum Bibliography* covering 1957; divided according to regions, states, and foreign areas.

Lester Charles Uren, *A Decimal Classification for the Filing of Data Pertaining to the Petroleum and Related Industries,* Cleveland, O., National Petroleum Publishing Co., 1928, pp. 78. 2nd Ed.: *Decimal System for Classifying Data Pertaining to the Petroleum Industry,* Dallas, Petroleum Engineer, 1940, pp. 53. 3rd Ed., Berkeley, Cal., University of California Press, 1953, pp. 94.

XVI.

General Books on Oil
and Gas

A. POPULAR BOOKS ON OIL INDUSTRY

American Petroleum Institute, *Oil,* New York, the Institute, 1930, pp. 188. Revised and enlarged edition: *Petroleum, The Story of An American Industry,* 1935, pp. 95. 2nd Ed. 1949, pp. 118.
History and development of oil industry.

American Petroleum Institute, Department of Information Staff, *2,347 Products— Plus,* New York, the Institute, 1955, pp. 7.
Background Information Bulletin. Discusses the many products from petroleum.

Angier Chemical Co., *Petroleum: Its Mission,* Boston, Angier Chemical Co., 1890, pp. 32.
Petroleum emulsions in treatment of certain ailments.

Association of Scientific Workers, *Report on Petroleum,* London, the Association, 1950, pp. 23.
Discussion of British petroleum policy and suggestions.

G. W. Auxier, *The Story of Oil,* Calgary, Western Canada Petroleum Assn., 1951, pp. 68.
General description of fundamentals of oil industry.

Florus R. Baxter, *Petroleum: A Class Room Talk,* Rochester, N.Y., Vacuum Oil Co., 1905, pp. 46.
History, geography, geology, origin, chemistry, composition, and production of petroleum and manufacture of petroleum products as of 1905.

Ned Baylis, *The Story of Oil,* London, Burke Publishing Co., 1947, pp 95.
History of oil and its operations in all branches, with discussion of British interests in world oil production.

Ray Bethers, *The Magic of Oil,* New York Aladdin Books, 1949, pp. 47.
Brief history of operations and uses of oil.

Charles E. Bowles, *The Petroleum Industry* Kansas City, Mo., Schooley Stationery & Printing Co., 1921, pp. xv + 189.
History, description of oil fields, methods, and oil finance.

R. Nelson Boyd, *Petroleum: Its Development and Use,* London, Whittaker & Co 1895, pp. 85.
Brief general survey of oil.

British Industries Series, *Oil,* London, Cassell & Co., 1953, pp. 120.
British Industries Series. Growth of oil industry, operational aspects, and social and economic effects.

Christopher T. Brunner, *The Problem of Oil,* London, Ernest Benn, 1930, pp. 231
Uses of oil, distribution, and organization of industry.

Ella Lane Carl, *Letters of a Texas Oil Driller's Wife,* New York, Comet Press 1959, pp. 222.
Letters written 1927–1931 describing oil field life in Borger and Pampa fields of Texas.

Keith Clevenger, *The Petroleum Industry,* Boston, Bellman Publishing Co., 1941, pp. 28. (No. 35 of Vocational and Professional Monographs)
Origin of petroleum, exploration and production methods, functional division of industry, petroleum in the chemical laboratory, legal and economic considerations.

Lester Byron Colby, *The Wizardry of Oil,* Houston, C. A. Bryan, 1917, pp. 19.
Financial gains from oil investments, stories of successful oilmen.

James Gerald Crowther, *About Petroleum,* New York, Oxford University Press, 1938, pp. xiv + 181.
Origin, characteristics, finding, drilling, production, transportation, refining, and use of petroleum.

Russell Walters Cumley and Helen M. Strong, *America's Oil,* Evanston, Ill., Row, Peterson & Co., 1942, pp. 48. (Basic Social Education Series) Text.
Oil discovery, development, distribution, use, refining, conservation.

Russell Walters Cumley, *Roughneck, The Way of Life in the Oil Fields,* Evanston, Ill., Row, Peterson & Co., 1941, pp. 64.
Work of exploration, leasing, drilling, production field men against historical background.

Frederick E. Dean, *The True Book About Oil,* London, Frederick Muller, 1957, pp. 142.
Quick summary of oil exploration, drilling, offshore operations, transportation, refining, product use; oil developments in British Commonwealth.

Gustav Egloff, *Earth Oil,* Baltimore, Williams & Wilkins Co., 1933, pp. xi + 158. (Listed as *The Story of Oil* in Century of Progress Series)
History, exploration and drilling for oil, properties, refining, uses; future oil resources.

Harold Fleming, *The American Oil Industry, A Forty-Odd Thousand Company Enterprise,* New York, American Petroleum Institute, 1953, pp. 10.
Background Information Bulletin. Story of the competitive enterprises making up oil industry.

John Joseph Floherty, *Flowing Gold. The Romance of Oil,* Philadelphia, J. B. Lippincott Co., 1945, pp. 255. 2nd Ed. 1957, pp. 223.
Description of oil industry in all phases, accounts of personal contacts and interviews depicting "romance" of industry. Revised edition discusses relationship between oil and atomic energy.

Great Britain, Imperial Institute, *Petroleum,* London, John Murray, 1921, pp. x + 110.
Properties, occurrence, production, refining, and uses of petroleum; sources of supply in British Empire and dependencies.

Godfrey Harrison, *The Story of Oil,* London, Sir Isaac Pitman & Sons, 1955, pp. ix + 70.
Tells origin of oil, how found, produced, transported, and refined; growth of oil industry; supply and demand; Britain's part in oil.

Thomas Hollyman, *The Oilmen,* New York, Rinehart & Co., 1952, pages unnumbered.
Some 200 photographs of Shell Oil employees at work in oil fields, pipe lines, refineries, service stations. Printed in gravure.

Institute of Petroleum, Ed., *Oil—The Task Ahead,* London, the Institute, 1952.
First postwar summer meeting of Institute of Petroleum, held at Hastings, June 27–29, 1952, with three addresses on subject.

Isaac F. Marcosson, *The Black Golconda, The Romance of Petroleum,* New York, Harper & Bros., 1924, pp. 369.
"Pot boiler" by a writer of industrial biographies.

Reid Sayers McBeth, *Oil, The New Monarch of Motion,* New York, Markets Publishing Corp., 1919, pp. 210.
General description of oil industry.

Herbert McKay, *Oil,* London, Oxford University Press, 1943, pp. 71.
Empire at Work Series. Production, transportation, refining, etc.

Sydney H. North, *Petroleum: Its Power and Uses,* London, Walter Scott Publishing Co., 1904, pp. 132.

Useful Red Series. General description of oil industry.

James E. Payne, *The Wonderful Wizards of Oil,* New York, American Petroleum Institute, 1953, pages unnumbered.
Background Information Bulletin. Oil production, modern refining, and products resulting therefrom.

Petroleum Information Bureau, *Oil: 100 Facts on Oil,* London, Naldrett Press, 1949, pp. 32. (Smatterbook No. 28)
Facts about oil history and industry.

William B. Plummer, Samuel Orrick Rice, and Douglas Campbell, *The Story of Petroleum,* Chicago, Encyclopedia Britannica, 1940, pp. 95.
History of crude oil and products, survey of oil industry, its occupations and opportunities.

Oscar Halvorsen Reinholt, *Oildom, Its Treasures and Tragedies,* 1924, Part I, pp. 384 + index. Part II, 1927, and provisional supplement, dated 1930. Published in final form, Philadelphia, David McKay Co., 1930.
Information on all aspects of oil industry, based on author's contacts and experiences.

W. J. Roberts, *The Story of Oil,* London, Lloyd Cole, 1943, pp. 56.
The petroleum industry from oil well to consumer.

Jerry Robertson, *ABC's of Oil,* Evansville, Ind., Petroleum Publishers, 1953, pp. 86.
How petroleum is explored for, found, produced, sold, paid for, and moved to market.

Victor Ross, *The Evolution of the Oil Industry,* New York, Doubleday, Page & Co., 1920, pp. xvi + 178.
Review of oil industry, exploration, drilling, gathering and transporting, refining, shipping, oil in First World War, and future outlook; recommends diplomatic support of American oil companies.

Stewart Schackne and N. D'Arcy Drake, *Oil for the World,* New York, Harper & Bros., 1950, pp. 128. 2nd Ed. 1955.
Significance of petroleum and its products to human welfare and world economy. How oil is found, wells drilled, crude oil transported, refined, products

distributed and marketed. Published also in German, Spanish, Italian, and Portuguese, each with revisions. Authors associated with Standard Oil Co. (N.J.)

George Sell, Ed., *Essential Factors in the Future Development of the Oil Industry,* London, Institute of Petroleum, 1956, pp. xxxii + 176.
Papers dealing with outlook for world energy, atomic energy, oil demand, oil resources, changing pattern of world oil movements, developments in oil refinery techniques, oil's future as source of chemicals, and oil finance.

Elizabeth Smedley, *Oil and Gas,* Chicago, Albert Whitman & Co., 1944, pp. 48.
Part of Elementary Science Series. Simple general history of petroleum, description of composition, production, refining, transportation, and use. A W.P.A. Writer's Project.

Chester F. Smith, *Air Pollution,* New York, American Petroleum Institute, 1956, pp. 7.
Background Information Bulletin. What oil industry is doing to determine causes of "smog."

C. K. Stillwagon, *Rope Chokers: A Collection of Human Interest Stories,* Houston, Well Equipment Manufacturing Co., 1945, pp. xi + 227. 2nd Ed. Houston, Rein Co., 1955.
Title is nickname by which cable tool drillers are known. Stories are author's experiences in oil fields of Pennsylvania, c. 1915.

William J. Sweeney, *Petroleum and its Products,* College Station, Penna., Pennsylvania State College, 1950, pp. 52 + 96, illustrations and tables.
Occurrence, production, resources, composition and analysis, refining, chemical products from petroleum, and utilization of petroleum products.

Hugh S. Taylor, *The ABC's of Science in Oil Recovery,* New York, American Petroleum Institute, 1927, pp. 16.
Principles associated with increased recovery of oil.

Walter Sheldon Tower, *The Story of Oil,* New York, D. Appleton & Co., 1909, pp. xi + 270. 2nd Ed. 1916.
Oil developments during preceding fifty

years, magnitude and range of operations, and American participation in growth.

Walter Sheldon Tower and John Roberts, *Petroleum. The Motive Power of the Future,* London, Hodder & Stoughton, 1912, pp. viii + 246.
Revised edition of *The Story of Oil.*

Vacuum Oil Co., *Cheating Davy Jones' Locker, The Use of Oil to Protect Life and Property at Sea,* Rochester, N.Y., Vacuum Oil Co., 1914, pp. 32.
Use of oil to calm seas.

George Thompson Walker, *Petroleum, Its History, Occurrence, etc.,* Minneapolis, Van Tilburg Co., 1915, pp. 46.
Summary book.

Edward Ward, *Oil Is Where They Find It,* London, George G. Harrap & Co., 1959, pp. 255.
Popular account by B.B.C. commentator of oil industry in various lands—Venezuela, New Guinea, Ecuador, Nigeria, Holland—based on conversations with staff of Royal Dutch-Shell Group companies.

Robert Bartow Weaver, *Men and Oil,* Chicago, University of Chicago Press, 1938, pp. 39.
Booklet to accompany educational film of same title.

Cyril Webber, *The Story of Petrol; the Spirit of the Age,* London, Thomas Nelson & Sons, 1934, pp. 217.
Summary and review, with mention of gradual displacement of coal by oil in British economy.

B. BOOKS FOR YOUNG PEOPLE

American Petroleum Institute, *Facts About Oil,* New York, the Institute, 1950, pp. 31. 2nd Ed. 1954, pp. 32. 3rd Ed. 1955, pp. 32.
Text. All phases of petroleum industry.

Norman Bate, *Who Fishes for Oil?,* New York, Charles Scribner's Sons, 1955, pages unnumbered.
With text and pictures, portrays offshore oil drilling.

Mody Coggins Boatright, *Gib Morgan, Minstrel of the Oil Fields,* El Paso, Texas Folk-Lore Society, 1945, pp. xi + 104.
Morgan spent many years as gypsy driller, carrying his stories with him.

Walter Buehr, *Oil, Today's Black Magic,* William Morrow & Co., 1957, pp. 96.
One of junior series, dealing with all phases of oil industry.

Bob Duncan, *The Dicky Bird Was Singing: Men, Women and Black Gold,* New York, Rinehart & Co., 1952, pp. 282.
Popular "human interest" account of Southwestern oil fields, events, and people.

W. W. Evans, *Petroleum,* London, Educational Supply Assn., 1955. 2nd Ed. 1957, pp. 90. (How Things Are Obtained Series)
Text. Story of petroleum from oil well to refinery; work of people in oil industry.

Raymond Fawcett, *Oil,* published 1947; revised and enlarged 1949; republished 1952 by P. R. Gawthorn, Ltd., London, pp. 48.
One of "Where Does it Come From" series. Under general heading of *Mystery of a Drop of Oil,* covers all phases of oil business, with special attention to British oil developments in Middle East.

Shepard Henkin, *Opportunities in the Petroleum Industry,* New York, Vocational Guidance Manuals, 1952, pp. 95.
Deals with employment opportunities in petroleum industry, educational requirements, remuneration.

Ann Jackson, *The Wonders of Oil,* New York, Dodd, Mead & Co., 1940, pp. xii + 146.
Covers oil in past ages, oil in America, searching for oil, drilling, producing, refining, etc.

Merritt Mauzey, *Oil Field Boy,* New York, Abelard-Schuman, Ltd., 1957, pp. 80.
By telling story of boy born in oil coun-

try, book gives history of three generations in oil and introduces modern aspects of industry, including offshore drilling.

Josephine and Ernest Norling, *Pogo's Oil Well,* New York, Henry Holt & Co., 1955, pp. 56.
Story of boy and his dog watching successful drilling of oil well in California and visit to refinery.

Elizabeth Olds, *Deep Treasure,* Boston, Mass., Houghton Mifflin Co., 1958, pp. 28.
Story of Drake and Spindletop wells, origin and occurrence of oil, drilling, refining, and transportation.

Josephine Perry, *The Petroleum Industry,* New York, Longmans, Green & Co., 1946, pp. 128.
"America at Work" series, designed to give story of magnitude of oil industry, its history, methods, and development.

Maud and Miska Petersham, *The Story Book of Oil,* Philadelphia, John C. Winston Co., 1935, pp. 35. Republished 1948.
With colored drawings, book tells of formation of oil, its discovery, production, refining, transportation, and uses.

Maud and Miska Petersham, *The Story Book of Earth's Treasures. Gold, Coal, Oil, Iron and Steel,* Philadelphia, John C. Winston Co., 1935.
Includes section on oil, covering origin, discovery, development, refining, storage, transportation, and use.

Eleanor Philips, *About Oil,* Los Angeles, Melmont Publishers, Inc., 1955, pp. 31.
Part of "Look-Read-Learn" series, intended for teaching of children. Presents story of oil finding, various operations, and uses.

Petroleum and Natural Gas. What the Boys and Girls Learned About These Things During a Holiday Excursion, etc. By "A MAN" of the Great Rock Island Route, Chicago, 1887, pp. 79. Copyrighted 1886 by Everitte St. John, probable author.
Regarded as first book on oil written for boys and girls. Third of series of seven on various industries issued by Rock Island Railroad between 1884 and 1890 as Christmas gifts to children.

Standard Oil Co. of California, *The Story of Oil,* San Francisco, Standard Oil Co. of California, n.d., pp. 24. 2nd Ed. 1957, pp. 49, title, *Oil.*
Oil primer for school children.

Clara Tutt, *Petroleum,* Columbus, American Education Press, Inc., 1939, pp. 32.
Broad, general discussion of basic functions of oil industry.

Robert R. Wheeler and Maurine Whited, *Oil—From Prospect to Pipeline,* Houston, Gulf Publishing Co., 1958, pp. ix + 115.
Student guidebook on exploration for, drilling, and producing oil; ownership, value, and financing; oil dictionary and list of abbreviations.

Margaret Veitch Young, *Black Gold, The Story of Petroleum,* Chicago, Young & Phelps, 1936, pp. 31.
History, production, and refining of petroleum, primarily for students in upper grades.

Free School Booklets published by American Petroleum Institute, New York.
Petroleum in Our Age of Science.
The Physics of Petroleum.
The Chemistry of Petroleum.
Petroleum in Our Modern Society.
The Conservation of Petroleum.
What Makes This Nation Go.
There's a Place for You in the Oil Industry.

XVII.

Serials and Periodicals

A. SERIALS

American Gas Association and American Petroleum Institute, *Proved Reserves of Crude Oil, Natural Gas Liquids, and Natural Gas,* New York, published jointly by the Association and the Institute.

Vol. I, through Dec. 31, 1946, 1947.
Vol. II–XII, through Dec. 31, 1957, 1958.

Estimates of proved petroleum reserves in United States, as made by American Petroleum Institute, were included in *American Petroleum Industry, 1935.* Publication in 1937 of similar estimates, including revision of 1935 estimates, initiated annual surveys which have been continued without interruption. Condensate reserves were segregated from crude oil, in 1946, when American Gas Association joined in supplying reserve data on other natural gas liquids and on natural gas. Estimates of proved reserves of crude oil in Western Canada, as provided by Canadian Petroleum Association, were added in Vol. VI, Dec. 31, 1951. Natural gas liquids were added in Vol. VII. Estimates of crude oil and natural gas liquids were extended in Vol. X to include all of Canada, and estimates of natural gas reserves in Canada were added in Vol. XII.

American Petroleum Institute, *Proceedings,* New York, the Institute, 1920 to date. First Annual Meeting of American Petroleum Institute held November 17–19, 1920, with *Proceedings,* 63 pages, published December 10, 1920 as Vol. I, No. 132. *Proceedings* of each of first 8 annual meetings published in single volume. Beginning with 9th annual meeting, December, 1928, *Proceedings* published in Sections (Marketing, Refining, Production, Transportation). First semiannual meeting, Division of Development and Production Engineering, held June, 1928, with *Proceedings* published as D. & P. E. Bulletin No. 202, pp. 165. First midyear meeting held, 1931, Proceedings of which were included in annual *Proceedings* thereafter.

Institute on Mineral Law, *Proceedings,* Baton Rouge, Louisiana State University.
First Annual Institute, 1953, pp. x + 203. Thirteen papers: production and regulation in Louisiana, unitization, conservation, geology and petroleum engineering.
Second Annual Institute, 1954, pp. 177. Ten papers: pooling and unitization.
Third Annual Institute, 1955, pp. 211. Ten papers.
Fourth Annual Institute, 1956, pp. 179. Eight papers: government regulation of gas production, conservation, etc.
Fifth Annual Institute, 1957, pp. ix + 182. Nine papers: Louisiana titles in Gulf of Mexico, well spacing, financing, conservation.
Sixth Annual Institute, 1958, pp. viii + 181. Eight papers: income tax law, voluntary unitization agreements, functions of geologist, conservation in production, review of decisions in mineral law, conservation development.

International Drilling Congress, *Proceedings.*
First International Drilling Congress, Bucharest, Rumania, 1925.
Second International Drilling Congress, Paris, 1929.

International Petroleum Congress
First International Petroleum Congress,

Universal Exhibition, Paris, 1900.
Second International Petroleum Congress, Universal Exhibition, Liége, Belgium, 1905.
Third International Petroleum Congress, Bucharest, Rumania, 1907.

Pennsylvania State College, *Proceedings of the First Petroleum and Natural Gas Conference,* State College, Penna., 1930, pp. 119; 2nd Conference, 1932, pp. 105; *Proceedings of the 3rd Pennsylvania Mineral Industries Conference, Petroleum and Natural Gas Section,* 1933, pp. 174; *4th Conference and Spring Meeting, American Petroleum Institute, Div. of Production, Eastern District,* 1934, pp. 69; *5th Conference,* 1935, pp. 136; *6th Conference,* 1936, pp. 105; *7th Conference,* 1937, pp. 96; *8th Conference,* 1938, pp. 94; *9th Conference,* 1940, pp. 66; *10th Conference,* 1941, pp. 116.
Papers presented devoted to technical matters concerned with production, refining, natural gas, and other aspects of petroleum technology.

Pennsylvania State College, *Proceedings of the Eighth Technical Conference on Petroleum Production,* State College, Penna., Pennsylvania State College, 1944, pages unnumbered. *9th Conference,* 1945, pp. 80; *10th Conference,* 1946, pp. 84; *11th Conference,* 1947, pp. 124; *12th Conference,* 1948, pp. 274; *13th Conference,* 1949, pp. 218; *14th Conference,* 1950, pp. 265; *15th Conference,* 1951, pp. 138; *16th Conference,* 1952, pp. 148; *17th Conference,* 1953, pp. 131; *18th Conference,* 1954, pp. 139; *19th Conference,* 1955, pp. 137.
Papers devoted to technical matters such as reservoir conditions, mechanics of production, water flooding, etc.

Southwestern Legal Foundation, *Proceedings,* Albany, N.Y., Matthew Bender & Co.
First Annual Institute, 1949, pp. x + 623. Eight papers on law of oil and gas; 10 on taxation. Foundation organized for research and legal education in Texas, Louisiana, Arkansas, New Mexico.
Second Annual Institute, 1951, pp. xi + 555. Eight papers: problems in law; 4 papers: tax problems in connection with lease; 4 papers: tax problems in assignment.

Third Annual Institute, 1952, pp. xvii + 489. Eight papers.
Fourth Annual Institute, 1953, pp. xi + 507. Seventeen papers.
Fifth Annual Institute, 1954, pp. xiii + 658. Sixteen papers.
Cumulative Index to Vol. 1–5, 1954, pp. 201. Lists subject matter, cases, statutes. Institute not held 1950.
Sixth Annual Institute, 1955, pp. xiii + 620. Seventeen papers.
Seventh Annual Institute, 1956, pp. xii + 787. Seventeen papers.
Eighth Annual Institute, 1957, pp. xi + 660. Fourteen papers.
Ninth Annual Institute, 1958, pp. xi + 652. Fourteen papers.
Tenth Annual Institute, 1959, pp. ix + 566.

F. M. Van Tuyl, *Review of Petroleum Geology,* Golden, Colo., Colorado School of Mines.
Covers important events of year, advances in petroleum geology and allied subjects, new and improved techniques, production and reserves, world exploration and development, noteworthy discoveries, and trends in petroleum geology and geophysics.
1942, Vol. 38, No. 3 of Quarterly, 1943, pp. 73.
1943, Vol. 39, No. 2 of Quarterly, 1944, pp. 127.
1944, F. M. Van Tuyl and W. S. Levings, Vol. 40, No. 2 of Quarterly, 1945, pp. 136.
1945, Van Tuyl and Levings, Vol. 41, No. 3 of Quarterly, 1946, pp. 203.
1946, Van Tuyl and Levings, Vol. 42, No. 3 of Quarterly, 1947, pp. 316.
1947, Van Tuyl, Levings, and L. W. LeRoy, Vol. 43, No. 3 of Quarterly, 1948, pp. 334.
Review continued in periodical publications of American Association of Petroleum Geologists.

World Petroleum Congress, *Proceedings.*
First World Petroleum Congress, London, 1933.
Second World Petroleum Congress, Paris, 1937.
Third World Petroleum Congress, The Hague, 1951.
Fourth World Petroleum Congress, Rome, 1955.
Fifth World Petroleum Congress, New York, 1959.

B. PERIODICALS

List of Oil Trade Periodicals
and General Newspapers
Carrying Oil Materials
With Indication of Libraries
Having Most Nearly Complete Files

Compiled by Virginia Smyth

Librarian, American Petroleum Institute

AMERICAN PERIODICALS

American Association of Petroleum Geologists Bulletin—Tulsa, Okla.—1917 to date.
Technical and scholarly papers on various geological developments and occurrences. A section devoted to activities of the AAPG.
American Petroleum Institute
Arkansas University
University of Arizona
Los Angeles Public Library
Library of Congress
John Crerar Library
University of Chicago
Indiana University
Oklahoma Agricultural and Mechanical College
University of Oklahoma

American Gas Association Monthly—New York—1919 to date.
Feature articles on current activities in the gas industry with statistics. Section devoted to activities of American Gas Association.
Massachusetts Institute of Technology
American Gas Association

California State Library

American Petroleum Institute Quarterly—New York—1931 to May, 1959.
From 1931 to 1956—a report of API activities (divisional and committee) with occasional historical or economic articles of interest. Change of format in 1957 to timely popular articles of industry scope by well-known industry and national authors.
American Petroleum Institute
California State Library, Sacramento
Los Angeles Public Library
Library of Congress
John Crerar Library
Free Library—Philadelphia

Automotive Industries—(Monthly)—Philadelphia—1895 to date.
Technical and statistical information on the automotive and aircraft industries. Publishes excellent annual statistical issue.
Library of Congress
Free Library—Philadelphia

193

Butane-Propane News—(Monthly)—Los Angeles—1939 to date.
Articles on marketing of liquefied petroleum gases; some statistical information.
Los Angeles Public Library
John Crerar Library
University of Iowa Library
New York Public Library

California Oil World—(Twice Monthly)—Palmer Publications, Los Angeles—1944 to date.
Devoted to news items on production activity in California.
California State Library

Drilling—(Monthly)—Dallas—1939 to date.
Interesting articles and items on current production activity; contains much statistical data on drilling operations.
University of Texas

Fuel Oil and Oil Heat—(Monthly)—New York—1942 to date.
News articles on oil heating industry. Has good statistical section on trends.
Los Angeles Public Library
Library of Congress
U.S. Patent Office
Public Library, Houston
University of Texas

Fuel Oil Journal—1936—see *Oil Trade Journal*.
Cornell University
Library of Congress
Tulsa Public Library
Public Library, Seattle

Fuel Oil News—(Monthly)—Oliver Klinger, Editor and Publisher, Bayonne, N.J.—1933 to date.
Items of interest to fuel oil dealers. Has current price section; also covers air-conditioning industry.
New York Public Library

Gas Age—(Fortnightly)—Moore Publications, New York—1921 to date.
Combined in August, 1921, with *The Gas Record* to form *Gas Age—Record* name changed back to *Gas Age*—Vol. 80, No. 3 (August 5, 1937).
Library of Congress
U.S. Patent Office
Franklin Institute

Gasoline Retailer—(Semi-Monthly)—Newspaper—New York—1930 to date.
News items of service station operation and gasoline marketing. Addressed to service station operators.
Library of Congress
Gasoline Retailer Office—New York

The Independent—(Monthly publication of Independent Petroleum Association of America)—Tulsa, Okla.—1941 to date.
Articles on timely subjects by well-known oil industry names. News items and personnel news, a price index and a Facts and Forecast Section.
Louisiana State University
West Virginia University

International Oilman—(Monthly)—Orchard Lisle, Ft. Worth, Tex., September, 1957—(Formerly *Oil Forum*, q.v.)
Popularly written articles on current subjects by industry and national people.
American Petroleum Institute
Los Angeles Public Library
U.S. Bureau of Mines
Library of Congress
Texas Engineer's Library

Interstate Oil Compact Commission Quarterly—Oklahoma City, Okla.—(See *The Oil and Gas Compact Bulletin*)—1941–1945.
American Petroleum Institute
California State Library
Library of Congress
Public Library, Cleveland
New York State Library
Oklahoma Agricultural and Mechanical College
Tulsa Public Library
Temple University
Free Library—Philadelphia
John Crerar Library

Journal of Petroleum Technology—(Monthly)—Dallas—1949 to date.
Technical papers and notes on petroleum production problems. Contains news of activities of Society of Petroleum Engineers, American Institute of Mining Metallurgical and Petroleum Engineers.
Arkansas University
University of Arizona
Library of Congress
Oklahoma Agricultural and Mechanical College
Tulsa Public Library
Free Library—Philadelphia
Engineering Society Library, New York

Agricultural and Mechanical College of Texas

LP-Gas—(Monthly)—Moore Publications, New York—1941 to date.
Publication addressed to wholesalers and retailers of "bottled gas."

LPGA Times—(Monthly publication of Liquefied Petroleum Gas Association) —1955 to date.
Liquefied Petroleum Gas Association— Chicago
New York Public Library
American Petroleum Institute

National Petroleum News—(Weekly)— founded by Warren C. Platt, well-known oil journalist, Cleveland, 1909, and operated by him until 1953 (April); wide coverage of oil industry, with emphasis on marketing; monthly refining section, which eventually became *Petroleum Processing* (q.v.); purchased 1953 by McGraw-Hill, New York, and converted to monthly addressed to oil marketers. Excellent section on prices (Monthly), New York, April, 1953, to date.
American Petroleum Institute
Library of Congress
John Crerar Library
Public Library, St. Louis
New York Public Library

Natural Gas—October, 1920–February, 1926—(Combined with *Gas Age,* 1937).
(See *Gas Age.*)

NLGI Spokesman—(Monthly)—National Lubricating Grease Institute, Kansas City, Mo.—1937 to date.
Technical articles on lubricating greases, news items; excellent patent section.
National Lubricating Grease Institute
Battelle Memorial Institute Library
Columbia University Library
John Crerar Library
New York Public Library
Carnegie Library of Pittsburgh
Tulsa Public Library

Offshore—(Monthly)—Conroe, Tex.— 1953 to date.
Brief technical and news items on Gulf Coast offshore operations. Good coverage of new equipment used.
(Not in *Union List of Serials.*)

Offshore Drilling—(Monthly)—New Orleans—1954 to July, 1959. Name changed to *The Work Boat* (*q.v.*).
Roughly similar in content to *Offshore,* above.
(Not in *Union List of Serials.*)

Oil—(1945–January 10, 1952, merged with *Petroleum World* January 17, 1952)— Los Angeles.
Weekly newspaper of California oil-producing industry.
American Petroleum Institute

Oil—(Monthly)—New Orleans, La.— 1941 to date.
Drilling and production news; chiefly Louisiana articles.
Library of Congress
New York Public Library
University of Texas

Oil Age—(1910 merged with *Petroleum World* February, 1929)—Los Angeles.
California State Library
University of Illinois
Free Library—Philadelphia
Engineering Societies Library

Oil and Gas Compact Bulletin—Quarterly —Oklahoma City, Okla.—1955 (Formerly *Interstate Oil Compact Commission Quarterly* 1942–1954).
Papers and reports of member states' officials and well-known oilmen on subject of conservation as presented at meetings of Interstate Oil Compact Commission. Excellent reference material on what states are doing in field oil conservation.
American Petroleum Institute
California State Library
Library of Congress
Public Library, Cleveland
New York State Library
Oklahoma A. & M. College
Tulsa Public Library
Temple University
Free Library—Philadelphia
John Crerar Library

Oil and Gas Journal—Founded and operated for many years by Patrick C. Boyle, of Oil City *Derrick* (q. v.)—(Weekly) Tulsa, Okla.—1910 to date.
Complete coverage of all divisions of industry, with emphasis on exploration, production, pipelining, and refining. News sections, plus section of technical

papers, personnel news; leasing and wildcatting news; statistical and price section. Several special issues published during year provide good current summaries of a particular field of interest such as Canadian operations, International operations, Gulf Coast operations, Pipe Lines, Refining, Economic Review and Forecast.
American Petroleum Institute—1920 to date.
Stanford University
University of California
University of Denver
University of Minnesota
Ohio State University
Free Library—Philadelphia

Oil and Gas News (Weekly)—Mount Pleasant, Mich.—1931 to date.
News of drilling and production activities in Michigan.
Library of Congress
Detroit Public Library
University of Michigan

Oil Bulletin—(December, 1914)—Superseded by *Summary of News and Events of California's Oil Industry.*
University of Arizona
University of Southern California
University of Oklahoma
Free Library—Philadelphia

Oil Daily—Chicago, Keith Fanshier, Editor—1951 to date.
Report of current happenings. Daily price section and daily quotations of oil company securities.
(Not in *Union List of Serials.*)

Oil Engineering and Finance—(January, 1922–July, 1926)—name changed to: *Oil Engineering and Technology.*
Massachusetts Institute of Technology
New York Public Library
Engineering Societies Library
Free Library—Philadelphia

Oil Engineering and Technology—July, 1926—September, 1928.
Massachusetts Institute of Technology
New York Public Library
Engineering Societies Library
Free Library—Philadelphia

Oil Forum—(Monthly)—Orchard Lisle, Ft. Worth, Tex.—1946–August, 1957.
Formerly called *Tankers;* published at

New York, moved to Ft. Worth, Texas; rechristened *International Oilman* September, 1957. (See listing.)
American Petroleum Institute
Los Angeles Public Library
U.S. Geological Survey
New York Public Library
Free Library—Philadelphia
Texas Engineers Library

Oil Investors' Journal—St. Louis, 1902; combined with *Oil and Gas Journal,* 1910.
(All those listed for *Oil and Gas Journal,* except API.)

The Oil Marketer—(Fortnightly)—Bayonne, N.J.—1929 to date.
Petroleum Marketing news in tabloid form.
(Not in *Union List of Serials.*)

Oil, Paint, and Drug Reporter—(Weekly)—St. Louis and New York—1871 to date.
News items on petroleum industry happenings, statistics, and price information—particularly in years before 1900 when it was only authoritative American oil trade paper. A "must" for historical research in period 1871–1914.
University of Illinois
Ft. Wayne Public Library
Tulane University
Detroit Public Library
Chemists Club.

Oil Trade Journal—1916—Vol. 1–18, No. 30, 1911–March, 1927, Vol. 1–7, No. 10, 1911–October, 1916, as *Fuel Oil Journal,* Vol. 7, No. 11–Vol. 15, No. 8, November, 1916, August, 1924, *Oil Trade Journal.*
Cornell University
Library of Congress
Tulsa Public Library
Public Library, Seattle

Oil Weekly—Gulf Public Co., Houston—1921–1947, rechristened *World Oil* and converted to monthly June, 1947.
News articles on exploration, drilling, and producing activities. Good statistics.
American Petroleum Institute
U.S. Bureau of Mines
University of Illinois
University of Iowa
Louisiana State University
New York Public Library

Oklahoma A. & M. College
Tulsa University

Oildom—(Daily)—Bayonne, N.J.—1911 —1959.
News items on all phases of industry.
U.S. Dept. of Agriculture
U.S. Geological Survey

Petrochemical Industry — (Monthly) — Conroe, Texas—July, 1958 to date.
Technical and news articles devoted to petrochemicals and their processes.
American Petroleum Institute

Petroleum Age—1881—May, 1888.
U.S. Patent Office
University of Minnesota
University of Pennsylvania

Petroleum Age and Service Station Merchandising—Vol. 1–31, No. 12, December, 1914–December, 1937.

Petroleum Engineer—(Monthly)—Dallas —1929 to date.
News and technical papers covering engineering aspects of exploration, production, and pipelining.
American Petroleum Institute
Los Angeles Public Library
University of Southern California
Colorado School of Mines
Library of Congress
Public Library, St. Louis
New York Public Library
University of Texas

Petroleum Gazette
Library of Congress
New York State Library

Petroleum Marketer—(Monthly) Chicago —1933 to date.
Some API statistics and news items on current industry events; addressed to wholesalers and retailers of petroleum products.
Detroit Public Library

Petroleum Processing—(Originally refining section of *National Petroleum News* q.v.), Cleveland; now McGraw-Hill— (Monthly)—New York—1937 to September, 1957.
Technical and popular articles on refining and manufacture of petroleum-based chemicals.
American Petroleum Institute
California State Library

Library of Congress
Los Angeles Public Library
Bureau of Mines
Georgia Institute of Technology
Engineering Societies Library
Tulsa University
Free Library—Philadelphia
University of Texas
University of Wisconsin
Public Library, Seattle

Petroleum Refiner—(Monthly)—Houston —August, 1942, to date.
Chiefly technical articles on refining and manufacture of petroleum-based chemicals.
American Petroleum Institute
Battelle Memorial Institute Library
University of California
Carnegie Institute of Technology Library
Tulsa Public Library

Petroleum Today—(Quarterly)—American Petroleum Institute, New York—Autumn, 1959.
Popular articles of industry scope by well-known industry and national authors.
American Petroleum Institute

Petroleum Week—(Weekly)—McGraw-Hill, N.Y.—July, 1955, to date.
Broad news coverage of all phases of oil industry; occasional economic studies; good coverage of political developments affecting oil industry.
American Petroleum Institute

Petroleum World and Oil—(Weekly as a newspaper except every fourth week when it appears in a technical magazine; continues *Oil*, Los Angeles (q.v.)— Palmer Publications, Los Angeles— 1915 to May, 1959. Name changed to *Western Oil & Refining*, June, 1959.
Good coverage of current happenings in the domestic petroleum industry; California operations highlighted.
California State Library
Cleveland Public Library
University of California
University of Illinois
John Crerar Library
Los Angeles Public Library
Louisiana State Library
Mellon Institute Library
Texas A. & M. College
Tulsa Public Library

Pipeline Construction—(Monthly)—Houston—June, 1956, to date.
(See *Pipeliner*.)
(Not in *Union List of Serials*.)

Pipeline Industry—(Monthly)—Houston—1954 to date.
Articles and news items on pipeline developments, construction, operations and maintenance.
(Not in *Union List of Serials*.)

Pipe Line News—(Monthly)—Oliver C. Klinger, Editor and Publisher, Bayonne, N.J.—1929 to date.
Articles and news items on pipeline design, operation, and management.
U.S. Bureau of Mines
John Crerar Library
New York Public Library
Engineering Societies Library
Tulsa Public Library

Pipeliner—(Monthly)—Gulf Publishing Co., Houston—1945 to June, 1956.
Articles on new developments in pipelining. Section on planned and approved pipe line construction projects.
(Not in *Union List of Serials*.)

Platt's *Oilgram*—Daily—McGraw-Hill, New York.
A daily news sheet of current happenings. Originally published by Warren C. Platt February 6, 1934, to April, 1953, when McGraw-Hill took over.
(Not in *Union List of Serials*.)

Producers Monthly—Bradford, Pa., 1936 to date.
Technical and news articles on secondary recovery operations. Some statistics.
American Petroleum Institute
Library of Congress

Refiner and Natural Gasoline Manufacture—Houston, September, 1922–July, 1942.
Then *Petroleum Refiner* (q.v.).
American Petroleum Institute
Los Angeles Public Library
U.S. Patent Office
John Crerar Library
Chemists Club
Tulsa Public Library
Public Library—Houston

Rocky Mountain Oil Reporter—(Monthly)—Denver—1944 to date.
News items on the drilling and production activities in the Rocky Mountains area.
Los Angeles Public Library
Denver Public Library
U.S. Bureau of Mines
New York Public Library
Dallas Public Library

Super Service Station—(Monthly)—Chicago—1928 to date.
News articles on developments and events in service station and allied operations.
John Crerar Library
New York Public Library
Free Library—Philadelphia
Detroit Public Library

Tankers—(Monthly)—Orchard Lisle N.Y.
Renamed *Oil Forum*, January, 1947.
(Not in *Union List of Serials*.)

Western Oil & Refining—(Monthly)—Los Angeles—June, 1959 to date.
Technical and news articles on all divisions of the petroleum industry.
California State Library
Cleveland Public Library
University of California
University of Illinois
John Crerar Library
Los Angeles Public Library
Louisiana State Library
Mellon Institute Library
Texas A. & M. College
Tulsa Public Library

Williston Basin Oil Review—(Monthly)—Bismarck, N.D.—1952 to date.
News items on activities in exploration and production in the Williston Basin area.
(Not in *Union List of Serials*.)

The Work Boat—(Monthly, August through June, semi-monthly in July)—New Orleans—August, 1959, to date.
Content same as predecessor—*Offshore Drilling*.
American Petroleum Institute

World Oil—(Monthly)—Gulf Publishing Co., Houston—1947 to date. (Formerly *Oil Weekly*.)
Good coverage of international production operations. Technical and news articles on all phases. Annually publishes Authoritative Review and Forecast Issue in February and an International Issue in August.

American Petroleum Institute
University of Illinois
Louisiana State University
New York Public Library
Tulsa University

World Petroleum—(Monthly)—Palmer
Publications, New York—1930 to date.
Devoted to all phases of international
oil industry; signed articles covering
developments, trends, etc., predominate;
has section of personnel and similar

news; authoritative annual review of
foreign refining.
Los Angeles Public Library
Geological Survey and National Museum
Library of Congress
Dow Chemical Co. (Midland, Mich.)
New York Public Library
Engineering Societies Library
Tulsa Public Library
Public Library, Houston
University of Texas

CANADIAN PERIODICALS

Canadian Oil and Gas Industries—
(Monthly) Quebec—1939 to date.
Hamilton Public Library (Canada)
McGill University (Montreal)
National Research Council (Ottawa)
New York Public Library

Oil in Canada—(Weekly)—Winnipeg—
1937 to date.
Brief news items on oil and gas produc-

tion activities in Canada.
Sun Life Assurance
U.S. Geological Survey
Library of Congress
New York Public Library

Oil Week—(Weekly)—Calgary—1950 to
date.
News items on Canadian activities.
(Not in *Union List of Serials*.)

BRITISH PERIODICALS

Institute of Petroleum Review—(Monthly)
—London, 1947 to date.
Excellent scholarly and historical
articles, plus news items of interest on
industry and Institute of Petroleum
activities.
Los Angeles Public Library
University of California
Library of Congress
U.S. Bureau of Mines
University of Illinois
New York Public Library
Tulsa Public Library
Franklin Institute (Philadelphia)
University of Texas

Journal of the Institute of Petroleum—
(Monthly)—London—1941 to date.
Very good technical articles and a fine
abstract section covering all divisions of
the industry from all types of journals.
American Petroleum Institute
Los Angeles Public Library
Library of Congress
University of Chicago
New York Public Library
Engineering Societies Library

Tulsa Public Library
Public Library, Houston

Petroleum—(London)—(Monthly)—1928
to date.
A current news section; some well-written
technical articles and a report on
new technical developments and patents.
Library of Congress
Tulsa University
University of Texas

Petroleum Press Service—(Monthly, with
weekly price service)—London—1934
to date.
Interesting survey articles on current
industry problems and activities in every
country. Section devoted to company
news and a statistical section including
prices and market quotations and oil
securities. Especially good in fields of
tanker transportation and petroleum
economics. Issued in English, French,
German, Arabic.

Petroleum Review—(Acquired by *Petroleum Times*)—London—1900-1919.

Edited by Dr. Paul M. Dvorkovitz, a Russian petroleum engineer with excellent firsthand knowledge of oil business. Particularly good for historical research on international operations during period of its publication.
New York Public Library
University of Oklahoma
University of Texas

Petroleum Times—(Fortnightly)—London —1899 to date.

Interesting articles on economic, historical, and technical aspects of the industry, with chief emphasis on operations outside U.S.A.
American Petroleum Institute
University of California
U.S. Geological Survey
University of Illinois
New York Public Library
University of Texas

GENERAL NEWSPAPERS OF VALUE IN OIL RESEARCH

Covering early days of Pennsylvania oil industry—On file at Drake Museum, Titusville:
Oil City Register
Petroleum Gazette—1897–May, 1918.
Petroleum Reporter
Pithole Daily Record
The Petroleum Centre Daily Record
Titusville Daily Evening Press
Titusville Gazette and Oil Creek Reporter
The Venango Spectator

Chicago Journal of Commerce—Chicago, 1920–1951, Keith Fanshier, Petroleum Editor, 1925–1951. Absorbed by *The Wall Street Journal*, 1951.

Daily Morning News—(Texas)—1885 to date.

Houston Chronicle—(Texas)—1901 to date.

Los Angeles Times—(California)—1881 to date.

New York Journal of Commerce—1827 to date.
Thorough coverage of petroleum industry, with reliable price section.

Rocky Mountain News—(Denver)—1859 to date. Colorado Historical Society.

The Titusville Morning Herald—Titusville, Pa.—1865 to date.

Tulsa Daily World—Tulsa, Okla.—1906 to date.

Tulsa Tribune—Tulsa, Okla.—1904 to date.

Wichita Beacon—(Kansas)—1872 to date.
Keith Fanshier was oil editor (1922–1924.)

Index